REVISED AND E

NEW HYMNS AND WORSHIP SONGS

A SUPPLEMENTARY COLLECTION

Acknowledgements

The publishers wish to express their gratitude to the copyright holders who have granted permission to include their material in this book.

Every effort has been made to trace the copyright holders of all the songs in this collection and we hope that no copyright has been infringed. Apology is made and pardon sought if the contrary be the case, and a correction will be made in any reprint of this book.

Important Copyright Information

We would like to remind users of this hymnal that the reproduction of any song texts or music without the permission of the copyright holder is illegal. Details of all copyright holders are clearly indicated under each song.

Many of the song *texts* may be covered either by a Christian Copyright Licensing (CCL) licence or a Calamus licence. If you possess a CCL or Calamus licence, it is essential that you check your instruction manual to ensure that the song you wish to use is covered.

If you are *not* a member of CCL or Calamus, or the song you wish to reproduce is not covered by your licence, you must contact the copyright holder direct for their permission.

Christian Copyright Licensing (Europe) Ltd., have also now introduced a *Music Reproduction Licence.* Again, if you hold such a licence it is essential that you check your instruction manual to ensure that the song you wish to reproduce is covered. The reproduction of any music not covered by your licence is both illegal and immoral.

If you are interested in joining CCL or Calamus they can be contacted at the following addresses:

Christian Copyright Licensing (Europe) Ltd. P.O. Box 1339, Eastbourne,
East Sussex. BN 21 1AD.
Tel: 01323 417711, Fax: 01323 417722

Calamus, 30 North Terrace, Mildenhall, Suffolk, IP28 7AB.
Tel: 01638 716579, Fax: 01638 510390.

First published in Great Britain in 2001 by
KEVIN MAYHEW LIMITED
Buxhall, Stowmarket
Suffolk IP14 3BW

The following editions are available.

Words edition Catalogue No.1413181
ISBN No. 1 84003 728 8 ISMN No. M 57004 869 4

Organ/choir Catalogue No. 1413184
ISBN No. 1 84003 727 X ISMN No. M 57004 868 7

Printed and bound in Great Britain

Foreword

Although we hope it will be welcomed as a valuable collection in its own right, *New Hymns and Worship Songs* has a more specific purpose: to update existing Anglican hymnals so that congregations can sing the best and most loved compositions of recent years alongside the traditional hymns found in all books.

Almost 90 per cent of the 440 hymns given here will not be found in either of the two most widely used Anglican hymn books. It is a great pity that congregations should be denied such standard fare as the Taizé chants, the beautiful music of Iona, Graham Kendrick's ever more popular songs or those hymns which, although widely used for many years, are not to be found in other collections, fine pieces such as *O Lord, my God (How great thou art); How lovely on the mountains (Our God reigns)* and *Be still, my soul* set to the majestic tune *Finlandia.*

As well as including hymns and songs composed in recent years, this collection has a small number of rewritten traditional texts. For example, God is working his purpose out, notoriously wayward in its metre, is given in a strictly metrical version which makes it easier to sing and, therefore, more enjoyable for all concerned.

Another editorial consideration had to do with the kind of images sometimes used. There is a growing belief that, in an increasingly violent society, militarism and triumphalism should not be expressed and apparently sanctified in hymnody; the scope for misuse of those themes is frequently demonstrated. However, it must be acknowledged that some such texts have fine tunes which we should not lose, and the solution in certain cases has been to commission new texts, such as *Stand up, stand up for Jesus; God is our strength from days of old and Onward Christian pilgrims,* to fit the original tunes.

The singing of hymns and psalms in worship pre-dates Christianity. It is something that Jesus himself would have been familiar with in the temple, and he certainly sang at the Last Supper - 'After psalms had been sung they left for the Mount of Olives', writes Matthew. What a wonderful tradition we share!

We hope that in this diverse and approachable collection of hymns we have sown some seeds; that is all we can do. It is in the worship of the churches that those seeds must be brought to glorious flower.

THE PUBLISHER

ACKNOWLEDGEMENTS

The publishers wish to express their gratitude to the following for permission to include copyright material in this publication. Details of copyright owners are given above each individual hymn.

The Estate of L.T.J. Arlott, The Old Presbytery, Alderney, Channel Islands, GY9 3TF.

Ascent Music, PO Box 263, Croydon, CR9 5AP. International copyright secured. All rights reserved.

Ateliers et Presses de Taizé, F-71250 Taizé-Communauté, France.

Canon John Bowers, 13 Bathhurst, Orton Goldhay, Peterborough, PE2 5QH.

Canterbury Press, St Mary's Works, St Mary's Plain, Norwich, NR3 3BH.

Continuum International, The Tower Building, 11 York Road, London, SE1 7NX.

CopyCare Ltd, PO Box 77, Hailsham, East Sussex, BN27 3EF, on behalf of Birdwing Music/EMI Christian Music Publishing; Birdwing Music/BMG Songs Inc./Ears to Hear Music/EMI Christian Music Publishing; Body Songs; Paul Booth; Bud John Songs/EMI Christian Music Publishing; Deep Fryed Music/Music Services; HarperCollins Religious; Hope Publishing; Lillenas Publishing Co; Maranatha! Music; House of Mercy Music/Maranatha! Music; Mercy/Vineyard Publishing; Mission Hills Music; People of Destiny Int; The Rodeheaver Co/Word Music Inc; Salvationist Publishing & Supplies; Straightway/Mountain Spring/EMI Christian Music Publishing; Vineyard Songs (UK/Eire); Word Music Inc/Maranatha! Music; Word of God Music; Word's Spirit of Praise Music;

Mrs M Cross, Honeybee House, Brigsteer, Kendal, Cumbria, LA8 8AP.

Daybreak Music Ltd, Silverdale Road, Eastbourne, East Sussex, BN20 7AB. All rights reserved. International copyright secured.

The Rt Rev'd Timothy Dudley-Smith, 9 Ashlands, Ford, Salisbury, Wiltshire, SP4 6DY.

Durham Music, 11 Uxbridge Street, London, W8 7TQ.

Dr Elinor F. Downs, 26 Dinmore Raod, Selkirk, NY 12158, USA.

GIA Publications Inc, 7404 S. Mason Ave, Chicago, IL 60638, USA.

The Grail, c/o Lesley Toll, 23 Carlisle Road, London, NW6 6TL.

Rev'd Mary Hancock, 55 Huntspill Street, London, SW17 0AA.

David Higham Associates, 5-8 Lower John Street, Golden Square, London, W1F 9HA.

Rev Pierre-Marie Hoog, L'Elise St Lgnace, 75006 Paris, France.

Hymns Ancient & Modern Ltd, St Mary's Works, St Mary's Plain, Norwich, NR3 3BH.

IQ Music Ltd, Commercial House, 52 Perrymount Road, Haywards Heath, West Sussex, RH16 3DT.

Jubilate Hymns, Southwick House, 4 Thorne Park Road, Chelston, Torquay, TQ2 6RX.

Kingsway's Thankyou Music, PO Box 75, Eastbourne, East Sussex, BN23 6NW, on behalf of Kingsway's Thankyou Music; Celebration (for Europe and British Commonwealth); Darlene Zschech/Hillsongs (for UK and Europe); Stuart K Hine/SK Hine Trust (Excluding North and South America); Integrity's Hosanna! Music (for UK only); Peter West/Integrity's Hosanna! Music; Kingsway's Thankyou Music; Scripture in Song (for UK only).

Leosong Copyright Service Ltd, 13 Berners Street, London, W1T 3LH.

Make Way Music, PO Box 263, Croydon, CR9 5AP. International copyright secured. All rights reserved.

McCrimmon Publishing Co, 10-12 High Street, Great Wakering, Southen-on-Sea, Essex, SS3 0EQ.

New Dawn Music, 5536 NE Hassalo, Portland, OR 97213, USA.

Novellos & Co, 8/9 Frith Street, London, W1V 5TZ.

OCP Publications, 5536 N E Hassalo, Portland OR 97213, USA.

Oxford University Press, Great Clarendon Street, Oxford, OX2 6DP.

Restoration Music Ltd, PO Box 356, Leighton Buzzard, Beds, LU7 8WP.

Mr Alexander Scott, 4 Anthony Close, Colchester, Essex, CO4 4LD.

Sovereign Lifestyle Music Ltd, PO Box 356, Leighton Buzzard, Beds, LU7 8WP.

Sovereign Music UK, PO Box 356, Leighton Buzzard, Beds, LU7 8WP.

Stainer & Bell Ltd, PO Box 110, Victoria House, 23 Gruneisen Road, London, N3 1DZ.

St Mungo Music, 5 Beech Avenue, Glasgow, G41 5BY.

SPCK, Holy Trinity Church, Marylebone Road, London, NW1 4DU.

Josef Weinberger Ltd, 12-14 Mortimer Street, London, W1N 7RD.

Wild Goose Resource Group, Iona Community, 840 Govan Road, Glasgow, G51 3UU.

1

Dave Bilbrough

Abba, Father, let me be
yours and yours alone.
May my will for ever be
more and more your own.
Never let my heart grow cold,
never let me go.
Abba, Father, let me be
yours and yours alone.

2

Robert Bridges (1844-1930) from J. Heerman (1585-1647)
alt. based on an 11th century Latin meditation

1. Ah, holy Jesu,
how hast thou offended,
that so to judge thee
mortals have pretended?
By foes derided,
by thine own rejected,
O most afflicted.

2. Who was the guilty?
Who brought this upon thee?
Alas, O Lord,
my treason hath undone thee.
'Twas I, Lord Jesu,
I it was denied thee:
I crucified thee.

3. Lo, the good shepherd
for the sheep is offered;
the slave hath sinnèd,
and the Son hath suffered;
for our atonement
Christ himself is pleading,
still interceding.

4. For me, kind Jesu,
was thy incarnation,
thy mortal sorrow,
and thy life's oblation;
thy death of anguish
and thy bitter passion,
for my salvation.

5. Therefore, kind Jesu,
since I cannot pay thee,
I do adore thee,
and will ever pray thee,
think on thy pity
and thy love unswerving,
not my deserving.

3

vs. 1-4 unknown, vs. 5-7 Damian Lundy (1944-1997)

1. Alleluia . . .

2. Jesus is Lord . . .

3. And I love him . . .

4. Christ is risen . . .

Additional verses may be composed to suit the occasion. For example:

5. Send your Spirit . . .

6. Abba, Father . . .

7. Come, Lord Jesus . . .

4

Donald Fishel (b. 1950)

Alleluia, alleluia,
give thanks to the risen Lord,
alleluia, alleluia, give praise to his name.

1. Jesus is Lord of all the earth.
He is the King of creation.

2. Spread the good news o'er all the earth.
Jesus has died and is risen.

3. We have been crucified with Christ.
Now we shall live for ever.

4. God has proclaimed the just reward:
'Life for us all, alleluia!'

5. Come, let us praise the living God,
joyfully sing to our Saviour.

5

Tricia Richards

1. All heav'n declares
   the glory of the risen Lord.
   Who can compare
   with the beauty of the Lord?
   For ever he will be
   the Lamb upon the throne.
   I gladly bow the knee
   and worship him alone.

2. I will proclaim
   the glory of the risen Lord.
   Who once was slain
   to reconcile us all to God.
   For ever you will be
   the Lamb upon the throne.
   I gladly bow the knee
   and worship you alone.

6

Roy Turner

1. All over the world the Spirit is moving,
   all over the world,
   as the prophets said it would be.
   All over the world there's a mighty
   revelation
   of the glory of the Lord,
   as the waters cover the sea.

2. All over this land the Spirit is
   moving . . .

3. All over the Church the Spirit is
   moving . . .

4. All over us all the Spirit is
   moving . . .

5. Deep down in my heart the Spirit
   is moving . . .

7

Sebastian Temple (1928-1997)

1. All that I am, all that I do,
   all that I'll ever have, I offer now to you.
   Take and sanctify these gifts
   for your honour, Lord.
   Knowing that I love and serve you
   is enough reward.
   All that I am, all that I do,
   all that I'll ever have I offer now to you.

2. All that I dream, all that I pray,
   all that I'll ever make I give to you today.
   Take and sanctify these gifts
   for your honour, Lord.
   Knowing that I love and serve you
   is enough reward.
   All that I am, all that I do,
   all that I'll ever have I offer now to you.

8

Michael Cockett (b. 1938)

All the nations of the earth,
praise the Lord who brings to birth
the greatest star, the smallest flow'r.
Alleluia.

1. Let the heavens praise the Lord, alleluia.
   Moon and stars, praise the Lord, alleluia.

2. Snow-capped mountains, praise the
   Lord, alleluia.
   Rolling hills, praise the Lord, alleluia.

3. Deep sea water, praise the Lord, alleluia.
   Gentle rain, praise the Lord, alleluia.

4. Roaring lion, praise the Lord, alleluia.
   Singing birds, praise the Lord, alleluia.

5. Earthly monarchs, praise the Lord,
   alleluia.
   Young and old, praise the Lord, alleluia.

9

Somerset Corry Lowry (1855-1932)

1. A man there lived in Galilee
like none who lived before,
for he alone from first to last
our flesh unsullied wore;
a perfect life of perfect deeds
once to the world was shown,
that people all might mark his steps
and in them plant their own.

2. A man there died on Calvary
above all others brave;
the human race he saved and blessed,
himself he scorned to save.
No thought can gauge the weight
of woe
on him, the sinless, laid;
we only know that with his blood
our ransom price was paid.

3. A man there reigns in glory now,
divine, yet human still;
that human which is all divine
death sought in vain to kill.
All pow'r is his; supreme he rules
the realms of time and space;
yet still our human cares and needs
find in his heart a place.

10

vs. 1-4 John Newton (1725-1807) alt.
v. 5 John Rees (1828-1900)

1. Amazing grace! How sweet the sound
that saved a wretch like me.
I once was lost, but now I'm found;
was blind, but now I see.

2. 'Twas grace that taught my heart to fear,
and grace my fears relieved.
How precious did that grace appear
the hour I first believed.

3. Through many dangers, toils and snares
I have already come.
'Tis grace that brought me safe thus far,
and grace will lead me home.

4. The Lord has promised good to me,
his word my hope secures;
he will my shield and portion be
as long as life endures.

5. When we've been there a thousand years,
bright shining as the sun,
we've no less days to sing God's praise
than when we first begun.

11

John L. Bell (b. 1949) and Graham Maule (b. 1958)

1. Among us and before us,
Lord, you stand
with arms outstretched
and bread and wine at hand.
Confronting those
unworthy of a crumb,
you ask that to your table
we should come.

2. Who dare say No,
when such is your resolve
our worst to witness,
suffer and absolve,
our best to raise in lives
by God forgiv'n,
our souls to fill on earth
with food from heav'n?

3. Who dare say No,
when such is your intent
to love the selves
we famish and resent,
to cradle our
uncertainties and fear,
to kindle hope as
you in faith draw near?

4. Who dare say No,
when such is your request
that each around your table
should be guest,
that here the ancient word
should live as new
'Take, eat and drink –
all this is meant for you.'?

Continued overleaf

5. No more we hesitate
and wonder why;
no more we stand indiff'rent,
scared or shy.
Your invitation leads us
to say 'Yes',
to meet you where you nourish,
heal and bless.

12 Charles Wesley (1707-1788)

1. And can it be that I should gain
an int'rest in the Saviour's blood?
Died he for me, who caused his pain?
For me, who him to death pursued?
Amazing love! How can it be
that thou, my God, shouldst die
for me?

*Amazing love! How can it be
that thou, my God, shouldst die
for me?*

2. 'Tis myst'ry all! th'Immortal dies:
who can explore his strange design?
In vain the first-born seraph tries
to sound the depths of love divine!
'Tis mercy all! Let earth adore,
let angel minds inquire no more.

3. He left his Father's throne above
so free, so infinite his grace;
emptied himself of all but love,
and bled for Adam's helpless race;
'tis mercy all, immense and free;
for, O my God, it found out me.

4. Long my imprisoned spirit lay
fast bound in sin and nature's night;
thine eye diffused a quick'ning ray,
I woke, the dungeon flamed with light;
my chains fell off, my heart was free;
I rose, went forth, and followed thee.

5. No condemnation now I dread;
Jesus, and all in him, is mine!
Alive in him, my living Head,
and clothed in righteousness divine,
bold I approach the eternal throne,
and claim the crown, through Christ
my own.

13

v. 1 unknown, based on John 13:34-35
vs. 2-4 Aniceto Nazareth, based on John 15 and 1 Cor. 13

*A new commandment I give unto you:
that you love one another as I have loved you,
that you love one another as I have loved you.*

1. By this shall all know
that you are my disciples
if you have love one for another. *(Repeat)*

2. You are my friends
if you do what I command you.
Without my help you can do nothing.
(Repeat)

3. I am the true vine,
my Father is the gard'ner.
Abide in me: I will be with you. *(Repeat)*

4. True love is patient,
not arrogant nor boastful;
love bears all things, love is eternal.
(Repeat)

14

Fred Pratt Green (1903-2000)

1. An upper room did our Lord prepare
for those he loved until the end:
and his disciples still gather there,
to celebrate their risen friend.

2. A lasting gift Jesus gave his own:
to share his bread, his loving cup.
Whatever burdens may bow us down,
he by his cross shall lift us up.

3. And after supper he washed their feet
for service, too, is sacrament.
In him our joy shall be made
complete –
sent out to serve, as he was sent.

4. No end there is! We depart in peace,
he loves beyond our uttermost:
in ev'ry room in our Father's house
he will be there, as Lord and host.

15

Peter West, Mary Lou Locke and Mary Kirkbride

Ascribe greatness to our God, the Rock,
his work is perfect and all his ways are
just. *(x2)*
A God of faithfulness
and without injustice,
good and upright is he. *(x2)*

16

18th century

1. As Jacob with travel
was weary one day,
at night on a stone
for a pillow he lay;
he saw in a vision
a ladder so high
that its foot was on earth
and its top in the sky:

Alleluia to Jesus who died on the tree,
and has raised up a ladder of mercy for me,
and has raised up a ladder of mercy for me.

2. This ladder is long,
it is strong and well-made,
has stood hundreds of years
and is not yet decayed;
many millions have climbed it
and reached Zion's hill,
and thousands by faith
are climbing it still:

3. Come let us ascend!
all may climb it who will;
for the angels of Jacob
are guarding it still:
and remember, each step
that by faith we pass o'er,
some prophet or martyr
has trod it before:

4. And when we arrive
at the haven of rest
we shall hear the glad words,
'Come up hither, ye blest,
here are regions of light,
here are mansions of bliss.'
O who would not climb
such a ladder as this?

17

Martin Nystrom, based on Psalm 42:1-2

1. As the deer pants for the water,
so my soul longs after you.
You alone are my heart's desire
and I long to worship you.

You alone are my strength, my shield,
to you alone may my spirit yield.
You alone are my heart's desire
and I long to worship you.

2. I want you more than gold or silver,
only you can satisfy.
You alone are the real joy-giver
and the apple of my eye.

3. You're my friend and you are my brother,
even though you are a king.
I love you more than any other,
so much more than anything.

18

John Daniels

As we are gathered, Jesus is here;
one with each other, Jesus is here;
joined by the Spirit, washed in the blood,
part of the body, the church of God.
As we are gathered, Jesus is here;
one with each other, Jesus is here.

19

Graham Kendrick (b. 1950)

At this time of giving,
gladly now we bring
gifts of goodness and mercy
from a heav'nly King.

1. Earth could not contain the treasures
heaven holds for you,
perfect joy and lasting pleasures,
love so strong and true.

2. May his tender love surround you
at this Christmastime;
may you see his smiling face
that in the darkness shines.

3. But the many gifts he gives
are all poured out from one;
come, receive the greatest gift,
the gift of God's own Son.

Last two refrains and verses:

Lai, lai, lai . . . etc

20

David Fellingham

1. At your feet we fall,
mighty risen Lord,
as we come before your throne
to worship you.
By your Spirit's pow'r
you now draw our hearts,
and we hear your voice
in triumph ringing clear.

I am he that liveth,
that liveth and was dead.
Behold, I am alive for evermore.

2. There we see you stand,
mighty risen Lord,
clothed in garments pure and holy,
shining bright.
Eyes of flashing fire,
feet like burnished bronze,
and the sound of many waters
is your voice.

3. Like the shining sun
in its noonday strength,
we now see the glory
of your wondrous face.
Once that face was marred,
but now you're glorified,
and your words like a two-edged sword
have mighty pow'r.

21

Original text: William James Kirkpatrick (1838-1921)
Alternative text, vs. 2 & 3: Michael Forster (b. 1946)

1. Away in a manger,
no crib for a bed,
the little Lord Jesus
laid down his sweet head.
The stars in the bright sky
looked down where he lay,
the little Lord Jesus,
asleep on the hay.

2. The cattle are lowing,
the baby awakes,
but little Lord Jesus
no crying he makes.
I love thee, Lord Jesus!
Look down from the sky,
and stay by my side
until morning is nigh.

3. Be near me, Lord Jesus;
I ask thee to stay
close by me for ever,
and love me, I pray.
Bless all the dear children
in thy tender care,
and fit us for heaven,
to live with thee there.

An alternative version

1. Away in a manger,
no crib for a bed,
the little Lord Jesus
laid down his sweet head.
The stars in the bright sky
looked down where he lay,
the little Lord Jesus,
asleep on the hay.

2. The cattle are lowing,
they also adore
the little Lord Jesus
who lies in the straw.
I love you, Lord Jesus,
I know you are near
to love and protect me
till morning is here.

3. Be near me, Lord Jesus;
I ask you to stay
close by me for ever,
and love me, I pray.
Bless all the dear children
in your tender care,
prepare us for heaven,
to live with you there.

22

Graham Kendrick (b. 1950)

1. Beauty for brokenness,
hope for despair,
Lord, in the suffering,
this is our prayer.
Bread for the children,
justice, joy, peace,
sunrise to sunset
your kingdom increase.

2. Shelter for fragile lives,
cures for their ills,
work for the craftsmen,
trade for their skills.
Land for the dispossessed,
rights for the weak,
voices to plead the cause
of those who can't speak.

God of the poor,
friend of the weak,
give us compassion, we pray,
melt our cold hearts,
let tears fall like rain.
Come, change our love
from a spark to a flame.

3. Refuge from cruel wars,
havens from fear,
cities for sanctu'ry,
freedoms to share.
Peace to the killing fields,
scorched earth to green,
Christ for the bitterness,
his cross for the pain.

4. Rest for the ravaged earth,
oceans and streams,
plundered and poisoned,
our future, our dreams.
Lord, end our madness,
carelessness, greed;
make us content with
the things that we need.

Refrain

5. Lighten our darkness,
breathe on this flame,
until your justice
burns brightly again;
until the nations
learn of your ways,
seek your salvation
and bring you their praise.

Refrain

23 Elizabeth C. Clephane (1830-1869) alt.

1. Beneath the cross of Jesus
I fain would take my stand,
the shadow of a mighty rock
within a weary land;
a home within a wilderness,
a rest upon the way,
from burning heat at noontide and
the burden of the day.

2. O safe and happy shelter!
O refuge tried and sweet!
O trysting place where heaven's love
and heaven's justice meet!
As to the holy patriarch
that wondrous dream was giv'n,
so seems my Saviour's cross to me
a ladder up to heav'n.

3. There lies, beneath its shadow,
but on the farther side,
the darkness of an awful grave
that gapes both deep and wide;
and there between us stands the cross,
two arms outstretched to save;
a watchman set to guard the way
from that eternal grave.

4. Upon that cross of Jesus
mine eye at times can see
the very dying form of One
who suffered there for me;
and from my stricken heart, with tears,
two wonders I confess –
the wonders of redeeming love,
and my unworthiness.

5. I take, O cross, thy shadow
for my abiding place!
I ask no other sunshine than
the sunshine of his face;
content to let the world go by,
to reckon gain as loss –
my sinful self, my only shame,
my glory all – the cross.

24 Unknown, based on Psalm 46

1. Be still and know that I am God. *(x3)*
2. I am the Lord that healeth thee. *(x3)*
3. In thee, O Lord, I put my trust. *(x3)*

25 David J. Evans

1. Be still, for the presence of the Lord,
the Holy One, is here.
Come, bow before him now,
with reverence and fear.
In him no sin is found,
we stand on holy ground.
Be still, for the presence of the Lord,
the Holy One, is here.

2. Be still, for the glory of the Lord
is shining all around;
he burns with holy fire,
with splendour he is crowned.
How awesome is the sight,
our radiant King of light!
Be still, for the glory of the Lord
is shining all around.

3. Be still, for the power of the Lord
is moving in this place;
he comes to cleanse and heal,
to minister his grace.
No work too hard for him,
in faith receive from him.
Be still, for the power of the Lord
is moving in this place.

26 Katherina von Schlegel (b. 1697)
trans. Jane L. Borthwick, alt.

1. Be still, my soul: the Lord is at your side;
bear patiently the cross of grief and pain;
leave to your God to order and provide;
in ev'ry change he faithful will remain.
Be still, my soul: your best, your
heav'nly friend,
through thorny ways, leads to a joyful end.

2. Be still, my soul: your God will undertake
to guide the future as he has the past.
Your hope, your confidence let nothing
shake,
all now mysterious shall be clear at last.
Be still, my soul: the tempests still obey
his voice, who ruled them once on Galilee.

3. Be still, my soul: the hour is hastening on
when we shall be for ever with the Lord,
when disappointment, grief and fear
are gone,
sorrow forgotten, love's pure joy restored.
Be still, my soul: when change and tears
are past,
all safe and blessèd we shall meet at last.

27

Bob Gillman

Bind us together, Lord,
bind us together with cords
that cannot be broken.
Bind us together, Lord,
bind us together, Lord,
bind us together in love.

1. There is only one God,
there is only one King.
There is only one Body,
that is why we sing:

2. Fit for the glory of God,
purchased by his precious Blood,
born with the right to be free:
Jesus the vict'ry has won.

3. We are the fam'ly of God,
we are his promise divine,
we are his chosen desire,
we are the glorious new wine.

28

Frances Jane van Alstyne (Fanny J. Crosby) (1820-1915)

1. Blessèd assurance, Jesus is mine:
O what a foretaste of glory divine!
Heir of salvation, purchase of God;
born of his Spirit, washed in his blood.

This is my story, this is my song,
praising my Saviour all the day long.
(Repeat)

2. Perfect submission, perfect delight,
visions of rapture burst on my sight;
angels descending, bring from above
echoes of mercy, whispers of love.

3. Perfect submission, all is at rest,
I in my Saviour am happy and blest;
watching and waiting, looking above,
filled with his goodness, lost in his love.

29

Mike Anderson (b. 1956)

Bless the Lord, my soul!
Bless the Lord, my soul!
Let all that is within me praise his name!
(Repeat)

1. Praise the Lord on cymbals,
praise the Lord on drums,
praise the Lord
for all that he has done.

2. Praise the Lord on trumpet,
praise the Lord in song,
praise him all
who stand before his throne.

3. Praise him for his mercy,
praise him for his pow'r,
praise him for
his love which conquers all.

30

Hubert J. Richards (b. 1921)

1. Blest are you, Lord of creation,
you provide the bread we offer,
fruit of your earth and work of our hands.

Blest be the Lord for ever, Amen. (Repeat)

2. Blest are you, Lord of creation,
you provide the wine we offer,
fruit of your earth and work of our hands.

3. Blest are you, Lord of creation,
look with favour on our off'rings,
pour out your Spirit over these gifts.

31

'Lucis Creator Optime' trans. unknown

1. Blest Creator of the light,
making day with radiance bright,
thou didst o'er the forming earth
give the golden light its birth.

2. Thou didst mark the night from day
with the dawn's first piercing ray;
darkness now is drawing nigh;
listen to our humble cry.

3. May we ne'er by guilt depressed
lose the way to endless rest;
nor with idle thoughts and vain
bind our souls to earth again.

4. Rather may we heav'nward rise
where eternal treasure lies;
purified by grace within,
hating ev'ry deed of sin.

5. Holy Father, hear our cry
through thy Son our Lord most high,
whom our thankful hearts adore
with the Spirit evermore.

32

Geoffrey Ainger (b. 1925)

1. Born in the night, Mary's child,
a long way from your home;
coming in need, Mary's child,
born in a borrowed room.

2. Clear shining light, Mary's child,
your face lights up our way;
light of the world, Mary's child,
dawn on our darkened day.

3. Truth of our life, Mary's child,
you tell us God is good;
prove it is true, Mary's child,
go to your cross of wood.

4. Hope of the world, Mary's child,
you're coming soon to reign;
King of the earth, Mary's child,
walk in our streets again.

33

John L. Bell (b. 1949) and Graham Maule (b. 1958)

1. Bread is blessed and broken,
wine is blessed and poured:
take this and remember
Christ the Lord.

2. Share the food of heaven
earth cannot afford.
Here is grace in essence –
Christ the Lord.

3. Know yourself forgiven,
find yourself restored,
meet a friend for ever –
Christ the Lord.

4. God has kept his promise
sealed by sign and word:
here, for those who want him –
Christ the Lord.

34

Janet Lunt

Broken for me, broken for you,
the body of Jesus, broken for you.

1. He offered his body, he poured out his soul;
   Jesus was broken, that we might be whole.
2. Come to my table and with me dine;
   eat of my bread and drink of my wine.
3. This is my body given for you;
   eat it remembering I died for you.
4. This is my blood I shed for you,
   for your forgiveness, making you new.

35

Richard Gillard

1. Brother, sister, let me serve you,
   let me be as Christ to you;
   pray that I may have the grace to
   let you be my servant, too.
2. We are pilgrims on a journey,
   fellow trav'llers on the road;
   we are here to help each other
   walk the mile and bear the load.
3. I will hold the Christlight for you
   in the night-time of your fear;
   I will hold my hand out to you,
   speak the peace you long to hear.
4. I will weep when you are weeping;
   when you laugh, I'll laugh with you.
   I will share your joy and sorrow
   till we've seen this journey through.
5. When we sing to God in heaven,
   we shall find such harmony,
   born of all we've known together
   of Christ's love and agony.
6. Brother, sister, let me serve you,
   let me be as Christ to you;
   pray that I may have the grace to
   let you be my servant, too.

36

Steven Fry

By his grace we are redeemed,
by his blood we are made clean,
and we now can know him face to face.
By his pow'r we have been raised,
hidden now in Christ by faith,
we will praise the glory of his grace.

37

Noel and Tricia Richards

By your side I would stay;
in your arms I would lay.
Jesus, lover of my soul,
nothing from you I withhold.

Lord, I love you, and adore you;
what more can I say?
You cause my love to grow stronger
with every passing day.
(Repeat)

38

Eddie Espinosa, based on Isaiah 64:8

Change my heart, O God,
make it ever true;
change my heart, O God,
may I be like you.
You are the potter, I am the clay;
mould me and make me:
this is what I pray.

39

Mary MacDonald (1817-1890)
trans. Lachlan MacBean (1853-1931)

1. Child in the manger, infant of Mary;
   outcast and stranger, Lord of all;
   child who inherits all our transgressions,
   all our demerits on him fall.
2. Once the most holy child of salvation
   gently and lowly lived below;
   now as our glorious mighty Redeemer,
   see him victorious o'er each foe.

Continued overleaf

3. Prophets foretold him, infant of wonder;
angels behold him on his throne;
worthy our Saviour of all their praises;
happy for ever are his own.

40

John E. Bowers (b. 1923)

Christians, lift up your hearts,
and make this a day of rejoicing;
God is our strength and song;
glory and praise to his name!

1. Praise for the Spirit of God,
who came to the waiting disciples,
there in the wind and the fire
God gave new life to his own:

2. God's mighty pow'r was revealed
when those who once were so fearful
now could be seen by the world,
witnessing bravely for Christ:

3. Praise that his love overflowed
in the hearts of all who received him,
joining together in peace
those once divided by sin:

4. Strengthened by God's mighty pow'r
the disciples went out to all nations,
preaching the gospel of Christ,
laughing at danger and death:

5. Come, Holy Spirit, to us,
who live by your presence within us,
come to direct our course,
give us your life and your pow'r:

6. Spirit of God, send us out
to live to your praise and your glory;
yours is the pow'r and the might,
ours be the courage and faith:

41

Brian Wren (b. 1936)

1. Christ is alive! Let Christians sing.
The cross stands empty to the sky.
Let streets and homes with praises ring.
Love, drowned in death, shall never die.

2. Christ is alive! No longer bound
to distant years in Palestine,
but saving, healing, here and now,
and touching ev'ry place and time.

3. In ev'ry insult, rift and war,
where colour, scorn or wealth divide,
Christ suffers still, yet loves the more,
and lives, where even hope has died.

4. Women and men, in age and youth,
can feel the Spirit, hear the call,
and find the way, the life, the truth,
revealed in Jesus, freed for all.

5. Christ is alive, and comes to bring
good news to this and ev'ry age,
till earth and sky and ocean ring
with joy, with justice, love and praise.

42

John L. Bell (b. 1949) and Graham Maule (b. 1958)

1. Christ's is the world in which we move,
Christ's are the folk we're summoned
to love,
Christ's is the voice which calls us to care,
and Christ is the one who meets us here.

To the lost Christ shows his face;
to the unloved he gives his embrace;
to those who cry in pain or disgrace,
Christ makes with his friends a
touching place.

2. Feel for the people we most avoid,
strange or bereaved or never employed;
feel for the women, and feel for the men
who fear that their living is all in vain.

3. Feel for the parents who've lost their child,
feel for the women whom men
have defiled,
feel for the baby for whom there's
no breast,
and feel for the weary who find no rest.

4. Feel for the lives by life confused,
riddled with doubt, in loving abused;
feel for the lonely heart, conscious of sin,
which longs to be pure but fears to begin.

43

Michael Saward (b. 1932)

1. Christ triumphant, ever reigning,
Saviour, Master, King.
Lord of heav'n, our lives sustaining,
hear us as we sing:

Yours the glory and the crown,
the high renown, th'eternal name.

2. Word incarnate, truth revealing,
Son of Man on earth!
Pow'r and majesty concealing
by your humble birth:

3. Suff'ring servant, scorned, ill-treated,
victim crucified!
Death is through the cross defeated,
sinners justified:

4. Priestly King, enthroned for ever
high in heav'n above!
Sin and death and hell shall never
stifle hymns of love:

5. So, our hearts and voices raising
through the ages long,
ceaselessly upon you gazing,
this shall be our song:

44

John L. Bell (b. 1949) and Graham Maule (b. 1958)

Cloth for the cradle,
cradle for the child,
the child for our ev'ry joy and sorrow;
find him a shawl that's woven by us all
to welcome the Lord
of each tomorrow.

1. Darkness and light
and all that's known by sight,
silence and echo fading,
weave into one a welcome for the Son,
set earth its own maker serenading.

2. Claimant and queen,
wage earners in between,
trader and travelling preacher,
weave into one a welcome for the Son,
whose word brings new life to ev'ry
creature.

3. Hungry and poor,
the sick and the unsure,
wealthy, whose needs are stranger,
weave into one a welcome for the Son,
leave excess and want beneath the
manger.

4. Wrinkled or fair,
carefree or full of care,
searchers of all the ages,
weave into one a welcome for the Son,
the Saviour of shepherds and of sages.

45

Sue McClellan (b. 1951), John Paculabo (b. 1946)
Keith Ryecroft (b. 1949)

1. Colours of day dawn into the mind,
the sun has come up, the night is behind.
Go down in the city, into the street,
and let's give the message
to the people we meet.

Continued overleaf

So light up the fire and let the flame burn,
open the door, let Jesus return,
take seeds of his Spirit, let the fruit grow,
tell the people of Jesus, let his love show.

2. Go through the park, on into the town;
the sun still shines on; it never goes down.
The light of the world is risen again;
the people of darkness
are needing our friend.

3. Open your eyes, look into the sky,
the darkness has come, the sun came to die.
The evening draws on, the sun disappears,
but Jesus is living,
and his Spirit is near.

2. Come and weep, come and mourn
for your sin that pierced him there;
so much deeper
than the wounds of thorn and nail.
All our pride, all our greed,
all our fallenness and shame;
and the Lord has laid
the punishment on him.

3. Man of heaven, born to earth
to restore us to your heaven.
Here we bow in awe
beneath your searching eyes.
From your tears comes our joy,
from your death our life shall spring;
by your resurrection power
we shall rise.

46

Graham Kendrick (b. 1950)

1. Come and see, come and see,
come and see the King of love;
see the purple robe
and crown of thorns he wears.
Soldiers mock, rulers sneer
as he lifts the cruel cross;
lone and friendless now,
he climbs towards the hill.

We worship at your feet,
where wrath and mercy meet,
and a guilty world
is washed by love's pure stream.
For us he was made sin –
oh, help me take it in.
Deep wounds of love
cry out 'Father, forgive.'
I worship, I worship
the Lamb who was slain.

47

Brian Wren (b. 1936)

1. Come, build the church - not heaps of stone
in safe, immobile, measured walls,
but friends of Jesus, Spirit-blown,
and fit to travel where he calls.

2. Come, occupy with glad dissent
where death and evil fence the ground,
and pitch a Resurrection-Tent
where peace is lived, and love is found.

3. Exposed upon the open ground
to screams of war in East and West,
our ears will catch a deeper sound:
the weeping of the world's oppressed.

4. In wearied face, or frightened child,
in all they know, and need to say,
the living Christ shall stand revealed.
Come, let us follow and obey!

48 Unknown, alt.

Come, come, come to the manger,
children, come to the children's King;
sing, sing, chorus of angels,
star of morning o'er Bethlehem sing.

1. He lies 'mid the beasts of the stall,
who is Maker and Lord of us all;
the wintry wind blows cold and dreary,
see, he weeps, the world is weary;
Lord, have pity and mercy on me!

2. He leaves all his glory behind,
to be Saviour of all humankind,
with grateful beasts his cradle chooses,
thankless world his love refuses;
Lord, have pity and mercy on me!

3. To the manger of Bethlehem come,
to the Saviour Emmanuel's home;
the heav'nly hosts above are singing,
set the Christmas bells a-ringing;
Lord, have pity and mercy on me!

49 Michael Forster (b. 1946) based on 1 Corinthians 12: 4-11

1. Come, Holy Spirit, come!
Inflame our souls with love,
transforming ev'ry heart and home
with wisdom from above.
O let us not despise
the humble path Christ trod,
but choose, to shame the worldly-wise,
the foolishness of God.

2. All-knowing Spirit, prove
the poverty of pride,
by knowledge of the Father's love
in Jesus crucified.
And grant us faith to know
the glory of that sign,
and in our very lives to show
the marks of love divine.

3. Come with the gift to heal
the wounds of guilt and fear,
and to oppression's face reveal
the kingdom drawing near.
Where chaos longs to reign,
descend, O holy Dove,
and free us all to work again
the miracle of love.

4. Spirit of truth, arise;
inspire the prophet's voice:
expose to scorn the tyrant's lies,
and bid the poor rejoice.
O Spirit, clear our sight,
all prejudice remove,
and help us to discern the right,
and covet only love.

5. Give us the tongues to speak,
in ev'ry time and place,
to rich and poor, to strong and weak,
the word of love and grace.
Enable us to hear
the words that others bring,
interpreting with open ear
the special song they sing.

6. Come, Holy Spirit, dance
within our hearts today,
our earthbound spirits to entrance,
our mortal fears allay.
And teach us to desire,
all other things above,
that self-consuming holy fire,
the perfect gift of love!

50 George Herbert (1593-1633)

1. Come, my Way, my Truth, my Life:
such a way as gives us breath;
such a truth as ends all strife;
such a life as killeth death.

Continued overleaf

2. Come, my Light, my Feast, my Strength:
such a light as shows a feast;
such a feast as mends in length;
such a strength as makes his guest.

3. Come, my Joy, my Love, my Heart:
such a joy as none can move;
such a love as none can part;
such a heart as joys in love.

51

Brian Doerkson

Come, now is the time to worship.
Come, now is the time to give your heart.
Come, just as you are to worship.
Come, just as you are before your God,
come.

One day every tongue will confess you
are God,
one day every knee will bow.
Still, the greatest treasure remains for
those
who gladly choose you now.

52

Patricia Morgan and Dave Bankhead

Come on and celebrate
his gift of love, we will celebrate
the Son of God who loved us
and gave us life.
We'll shout your praise, O King,
you give us joy nothing else can bring;
we'll give to you our offering
in celebration praise.

Come on and celebrate, celebrate,
celebrate and sing,
celebrate and sing to the King. *(Repeat)*

53

Martin E. Leckebusch (b. 1962)

1. Come, wounded Healer, your
suff'rings reveal –
the scars you accepted, our anguish to
heal.
Your wounds bring such comfort in
body and soul
to all who bear torment and yearn to
be whole.

2. Come, hated Lover, and gather us near,
your welcome, your teaching, your
challenge to hear:
where scorn and abuse cause rejection
and pain,
your loving acceptance makes hope live
again!

3. Come, broken Victor, condemned to a
cross –
how great are the treasures we gain
from your loss!
Your willing agreement to share in our
strife
transforms our despair into fullness of
life.

54

William Sparrow-Simpson (1859-1952)

1. Cross of Jesus, cross of sorrow,
where the blood of Christ was shed,
perfect man on thee was tortured,
perfect God on thee has bled.

2. Here the King of all the ages,
throned in light ere worlds could be,
robed in mortal flesh, is dying,
crucified by sin for me.

3. O, mysterious condescending!
O, abandonment sublime!
Very God himself is bearing
all the sufferings of time!

4. Evermore, for human failure,
by his Passion we can plead;
God has borne all mortal anguish,
surely he will know our need.

5. This - all human thought surpassing -
this is earth's most awful hour,
God has taken mortal weakness!
God has laid aside his pow'r!

6. Once the Lord of brilliant seraphs,
winged with love to do his will,
now the scorn of all his creatures,
and the aim of ev'ry ill.

7. Up in heav'n, sublimest glory
circled round him from the first;
but the earth finds none to serve him,
none to quench his raging thirst.

8. Who shall fathom that descending
from the rainbow-circled throne,
down to earth's most base profaning,
dying desolate, alone.

9. From the 'Holy, Holy, Holy,
we adore thee, O most High',
down to earth's blaspheming voices
and the shout of 'Crucify'.

10. Cross of Jesus, cross of sorrow,
where the blood of Christ was shed,
perfect man on thee was tortured,
perfect God on thee has bled.

55

Michael Forster (b. 1946)

1. Cry 'Freedom!' in the name of God,
and let the cry resound;
proclaim for all that freedom
which in Jesus Christ is found,
for none of us is truly free
while anyone is bound.

Cry 'Freedom!' cry 'Freedom!'
in God's name!
Cry 'Freedom!' cry 'Freedom!'
in God's name!

2. Cry 'Freedom!' for the victims
of the earthquake and the rain:
where wealthy folk find shelter
and the poor must bear the pain;
where weapons claim resources
while the famine strikes again.

3. Cry 'Freedom!' for dictators
in their fortresses confined,
who hide behind their bodyguards
and fear the open mind,
and bid them find true freedom
in the good of humankind.

4. Cry 'Freedom!' in the church when
honest doubts are met with fear;
when vacuum-packed theology
makes questions disappear;
when journeys end before they start
and mystery is clear!

5. Cry 'Freedom!' when we find ourselves
imprisoned in our greed,
to live in free relationship
and meet each other's need.
From self released for others' good
we should be free indeed!

56

John L. Bell (b. 1949) and Graham Maule (b.1958)

Dance and sing, all the earth,
gracious is the hand that tends you:
love and care ev'rywhere,
God on purpose sends you.

1. Shooting star and sunset shape
the drama of creation;
lightning flash and moonbeam share
a common derivation.

2. Deserts stretch and torrents roar
in contrast and confusion;
treetops shake and mountains soar
and nothing is illusion.

Continued overleaf

Dance and sing, all the earth,
gracious is the hand that tends you:
love and care ev'rywhere,
God on purpose sends you.

3. All that flies and swims and crawls
displays an animation;
none can emulate or change
for each has its own station.

4. Brother man and sister woman,
born of dust and passion,
praise the one who calls you friends
and makes you in his fashion.

5. Kiss of life and touch of death
suggest our imperfection:
crib and womb and cross and tomb
cry out for resurrection.

57

Mike Anderson (b. 1956)

Dance in your Spirit,
we dance in your Spirit,
we dance in your Spirit of joy! (Repeat)

1. Jesus, you showed us the way to live,
and your Spirit sets us free,
free now to sing, free to dance and shout,
'Glory, glory' to your name.

2. Jesus, you opened your arms for us,
but we nailed them to a cross;
but you are risen and now we live,
free from, free from ev'ry fear.

3. Your Spirit brings peace and gentleness,
kindness, self-control and love,
patience and goodness and faith and joy,
Spirit, Spirit fill us now.

58

George Ratcliffe Woodward (1848-1934)

1. Ding dong, merrily on high!
In heav'n the bells are ringing;
ding dong, verily the sky
is riv'n with angels singing.

Gloria, hosanna in excelsis!
Gloria, hosanna in excelsis!

2. E'en so here below, below,
let steeple bells be swungen,
and io, io, io,
by priest and people sungen.

3. Pray you, dutifully prime
your matin chime, ye ringers;
may you beautifully rhyme
your evetime song, ye singers.

59

Gerard Markland (b. 1953), based on Isaiah 43:1-4

Do not be afraid, for I have redeemed you.
I have called you by your name;
you are mine.

1. When you walk through the waters,
I'll be with you.
You will never sink beneath the waves.

2. When the fire is burning
all around you,
you will never be consumed by the flames.

3. When the fear of loneliness
is looming,
then remember I am at your side.

4. When you dwell in the exile
of the stranger,
remember you are precious in my eyes.

5. You are mine, O my child,
I am your Father,
and I love you with a perfect love.

60

Phineas Fletcher (1582-1650)

1. Drop, drop, slow tears,
and bathe those beauteous feet,
which brought from heav'n
the news and Prince of peace.

2. Cease not, wet eyes,
his mercies to entreat;
to cry for vengeance
sin doth never cease.

3. In your deep floods
drown all my faults and fears;
nor let his eye
see sin, but through my tears.

61 John Hampden Gurney (1802-1862)

1. Fair waved the golden corn
in Canaan's pleasant land,
when full of joy, some shining morn,
went forth the reaper-band.

2. To God so good and great
their cheerful thanks they pour;
then carry to his temple-gate
the choicest of their store.

3. Like Israel, Lord, we give
our earliest fruits to thee,
and pray that, long as we shall live,
we may thy children be.

4. Thine is our youthful prime,
and life and all its pow'rs;
be with us in our morning time,
and bless our evening hours.

5. In wisdom let us grow,
as years and strength are giv'n,
that we may serve thy Church below,
and join thy saints in heav'n.

62 Chris Bowater

Faithful God, faithful God,
all-sufficient one, I worship you.
Shalom my peace,
my strong deliverer,
I lift you up,
faithful God.

63 Thomas Benson Pollock (1836-1896)

1. Faithful Shepherd, feed me
in the pastures green;
faithful Shepherd, lead me
where thy steps are seen.

2. Hold me fast, and guide me
in the narrow way;
so, with thee beside me,
I shall never stray.

3. Daily bring me nearer
to the heav'nly shore;
may my faith grow clearer,
may I love thee more.

4. Hallow ev'ry pleasure,
ev'ry gift and pain;
be thyself my treasure,
though none else I gain.

5. Day by day prepare me
as thou seest best,
then let angels bear me
to thy promised rest.

64 Graham Kendrick

1. Far and near hear the call,
worship him, Lord of all;
families of nations, come,
celebrate what God has done.

2. Deep and wide is the love
heaven sent from above;
God's own Son, for sinners died,
rose again – he is alive.
Say it loud, say it strong,
tell the world what God has done;
say it loud, praise his name,
let the earth rejoice –
for the Lord reigns.

3. At his name, let praise begin;
oceans roar, nature sing,
for he comes to judge the earth
in righteousness and in his truth.

65

Ian Smale

Father God,
I wonder how I managed to exist
without the knowledge of your parenthood
and your loving care.
But now I am your child,
I am adopted in your family
and I can never be alone,
'cause, Father God, you're there beside me.
I will sing your praises,
I will sing your praises,
I will sing your praises,
for evermore.

66

Graham Kendrick (b. 1950)

1. Father God, we worship you,
make us part of all you do.
As you move among us now,
we worship you.

2. Jesus King, we worship you,
help us listen now to you.
As you move among us now,
we worship you.

3. Spirit pure, we worship you,
with your fire our zeal renew.
As you move among us now,
we worship you.

67

Jenny Hewer (b. 1945)

1. Father, I place into your hands
the things I cannot do.
Father, I place into your hands
the things that I've been through.
Father, I place into your hands
the way that I should go,
for I know I always can trust you.

2. Father, I place into your hands
my friends and family.
Father, I place into your hands
the things that trouble me.
Father I place into your hands
the person I would be,
for I know I always can trust you.

3. Father, we love to see your face,
we love to hear your voice,
Father, we love to sing your praise
and in your name rejoice.
Father, we love to walk with you
and in your presence rest,
for we know we always can trust you.

4. Father, I want to be with you
and do the things you do.
Father, I want to speak the words
that you are speaking too.
Father, I want to love the ones
that you will draw to you,
for I know that I am one with you.

68

Stewart Cross (1928-1989)

1. Father, Lord of all creation,
ground of Being, Life and Love;
height and depth beyond description
only life in you can prove:
you are mortal life's dependence:
thought, speech, sight are ours by grace;
yours is ev'ry hour's existence,
sov'reign Lord of time and space.

2. Jesus Christ, the Man for Others,
we, your people, make our prayer:
help us love – as sisters, brothers –
all whose burdens we can share.
Where your name binds us together
you, Lord Christ, will surely be;
where no selfishness can sever
there your love the world may see.

3. Holy Spirit, rushing, burning
wind and flame of Pentecost,
fire our hearts afresh with yearning
to regain what we have lost.
May your love unite our action,
nevermore to speak alone:
God, in us abolish faction,
God, through us your love make known.

69

Terrye Coelho (b. 1952)

1. Father, we adore you,
lay our lives before you.
How we love you!

2. Jesus, we adore you . . .

3. Spirit, we adore you . . .

70

Donna Adkins (b. 1940)

1. Father, we love you,
we worship and adore you,
glorify your name in all the earth.
Glorify your name, glorify your name,
glorify your name in all the earth.

2. Jesus, we love you . . .

3. Spirit, we love you . . .

71

John Raphael Peacey (1896-1971)

1. Filled with the Spirit's pow'r,
with one accord
the infant Church
confessed its risen Lord.
O Holy Spirit,
in the Church today
no less your pow'r
of fellowship display.

2. Now with the mind of Christ
set us on fire,
that unity
may be our great desire.
Give joy and peace;
give faith to hear your call,
and readiness
in each to work for all.

3. Widen our love, good Spirit,
to embrace
in your strong care
the people of each race.
Like wind and fire
with life among us move,
till we are known as Christ's,
and Christians prove.

72

Horatius Bonar (1808-1889) alt.

1. Fill thou my life, O Lord my God,
in ev'ry part with praise,
that my whole being may proclaim
thy being and thy ways.

2. Not for the lip of praise alone,
nor e'en the praising heart,
I ask, but for a life made up
of praise in ev'ry part.

3. Praise in the common things of life,
its goings out and in;
praise in each duty and each deed,
however small and mean.

4. Fill ev'ry part of me with praise:
let all my being speak
of thee and of thy love, O Lord,
poor though I be and weak.

5. So shalt thou, Lord, receive from me
the praise and glory due;
and so shall I begin on earth
the song for ever new.

Continued overleaf

6. So shall each fear, each fret, each care,
be turnèd into song;
and ev'ry winding of the way
the echo shall prolong.

7. So shall no part of day or night
unblest or common be;
but all my life, in ev'ry step,
be fellowship with thee.

73

Timothy Dudley-Smith (b. 1926)

1. Fill your hearts with joy and gladness,
sing and praise your God and mine!
Great the Lord in love and wisdom,
might and majesty divine!
He who framed the starry heavens
knows and names them as they shine.
Fill your hearts with joy and gladness,
sing and praise your God and mine!

2. Praise the Lord, his people, praise him!
Wounded souls his comfort know.
Those who fear him find his mercies,
peace for pain and joy for woe;
humble hearts are high exalted,
human pride and pow'r laid low.
Praise the Lord, his people, praise him!
Wounded souls his comfort know.

3. Praise the Lord for times and seasons,
cloud and sunshine, wind and rain;
spring to melt the snows of winter
till the waters flow again;
grass upon the mountain pastures,
golden valleys thick with grain.
Praise the Lord for times and seasons,
cloud and sunshine, wind and rain.

4. Fill your hearts with joy and gladness,
peace and plenty crown your days!
Love his laws, declare his judgements,
walk in all his words and ways;
he the Lord and we his children,
praise the Lord, all people, praise!
Fill your hearts with joy and gladness,
peace and plenty crown your days!

74

Unknown
trans. John Mason Neale (1818-1866) alt.

1. Finished the strife of battle now,
gloriously crowned the victor's brow;
sing with gladness, banish sadness:
Alleluia, alleluia!

2. After the death that him befell,
Jesus Christ has harrowed hell;
songs of praising we are raising:
Alleluia, alleluia!

3. On the third morning he arose,
shining with vict'ry o'er his foes;
earth is singing, heav'n is ringing:
Alleluia, alleluia!

4. Lord, by your wounds on you we call,
you, by your death, have freed us all;
may our living be thanksgiving:
Alleluia, alleluia!

75

Michael Cockett (b. 1938)

Follow me, follow me,
leave your home and family,
leave your fishing nets and boats
upon the shore.
Leave the seed that you have sown,
leave the crops that you've grown,
leave the people you have known
and follow me.

1. The foxes have their holes
and the swallows have their nests,
but the Son of Man
has no place to lie down.
I do not offer comfort,
I do not offer wealth,
but in me will all happiness be found.

2. If you would follow me,
you must leave old ways behind.
You must take my cross and
follow on my path.
You may be far from loved ones,
you may be far from home,
but my Father will welcome you at last.

3. Although I go away
you will never be alone,
for the Spirit will be
there to comfort you.
Though all of you may scatter,
each follow his own path,
still the Spirit of love will lead you home.

76

Dave Richards

For I'm building a people of power
and I'm making a people of praise,
that will move through this land by my Spirit,
and will glorify my precious name.
Build your church, Lord,
make us strong, Lord,
join our hearts, Lord,
through your Son.
Make us one, Lord, in your body,
in the Kingdom of your Son.

77

Fred Kaan (b. 1929)

1. For ourselves no longer living,
let us live for Christ alone;
of ourselves more strongly giving,
go as far as he has gone:
one with God who chose to be
one with us to set us free.

2. If we are to live for others,
share as equals human worth,
join the round of sisters, brothers,
that encircles all the earth:
all the fullness earth affords,
is the people's, is the Lord's.

3. Fighting fear and exploitation
is our daily common call;
finding selfhood, building nations,
sharing what we have with all.
As the birds that soar in flight,
let us rise towards the light.

4. Let us rise and join the forces
that combine to do God's will,
wisely using earth's resources,
human energy and skill.
Let us now, by love released,
celebrate the future's feast!

78

Fred Pratt Green (1903-2000)

1. For the fruits of his creation,
thanks be to God;
for his gifts to ev'ry nation,
thanks be to God;
for the ploughing, sowing, reaping,
silent growth while we are sleeping,
future needs in earth's safe keeping,
thanks be to God.

2. In the just reward of labour,
God's will is done;
in the help we give our neighbour,
God's will is done;
in our world-wide task of caring
for the hungry and despairing,
in the harvests we are sharing,
God's will is done.

3. For the harvests of his Spirit,
thanks be to God;
for the good we all inherit,
thanks be to God;
for the wonders that astound us,
for the truths that still confound us,
most of all, that love has found us,
thanks be to God.

79

Fred Kaan (b. 1929)

1. For the healing of the nations,
Lord, we pray with one accord;
for a just and equal sharing
of the things that earth affords.
To a life of love in action
help us rise and pledge our word.

Continued overleaf

2. Lead us, Father, into freedom,
from despair your world release;
that, redeemed from war and hatred,
all may come and go in peace.
Show us how through care and goodness
fear will die and hope increase.

3. All that kills abundant living,
let it from the earth be banned;
pride of status, race or schooling
dogmas that obscure your plan.
In our common quest for justice
may we hallow life's brief span.

4. You, creator-God, have written
your great name on humankind;
for our growing in your likeness
bring the life of Christ to mind;
that by our response and service
earth its destiny may find.

80

James Quinn (b. 1919)

1. Forth in the peace of Christ we go;
Christ to the world with joy we bring;
Christ in our minds, Christ on our lips,
Christ in our hearts, the world's
true King.

2. King of our hearts, Christ makes us kings;
kingship with him his servants gain;
with Christ, the Servant-Lord of all,
Christ's world we serve to share
Christ's reign.

3. Priests of the world, Christ sends us forth
this world of time to consecrate,
our world of sin by grace to heal,
Christ's world in Christ to re-create.

4. Prophets of Christ, we hear his Word:
he claims our minds to search his ways;
he claims our lips to speak his truth;
he claims our hearts to sing his praise.

5. We are his Church, he makes us one:
here is one hearth for all to find;
here is one flock, one Shepherd-King;
here is one faith, one heart, one mind.

81

Jean Holloway (b. 1939)

1. Forty days and forty nights
in Judah's desert Jesus stayed;
all alone he fought temptation,
all alone he fasted, prayed.
When the heat of passion rules me,
when I feel alone, betrayed,
Lord, you meet me in the desert,
strong in faith and unafraid.

2. In the garden, his disciples
slept the darkest hours away,
but our Lord did not condemn them
when they would not watch or pray.
Make me constant in your service,
keeping watch both night and day.
Give me grace that I may never
such a love as yours betray.

3. When the rooster crowed at daybreak,
Peter's fear and panic grew.
He denied three times the charge
that Jesus was a man he knew.
When my love for you is challenged,
when the faithful ones are few,
give me courage and conviction
to proclaim my Lord anew.

4. Soldiers came, the Galilean
was arrested, bound and tried,
and upon a wooden cross
the Son of God was crucified.
In the darkest hour of torture,
Jesus raised his head and cried,
'Why hast thou forsaken me?',
and faithful to the end, he died.

5. With a sword they pierced his side –
himself, they jeered, he could not save;
Joseph then prepared the body
with sweet spices for the grave.
This the precious, broken body
which for me my Saviour gave;
such a love as his I long for,
such a faith as his I crave.

82

Graham Kendrick (b. 1950)

1. From heav'n you came, helpless babe,
entered our world, your glory veiled;
not to be served but to serve,
and give your life that we might live.

This is our God, the Servant King,
he calls us now to follow him,
to bring our lives as a daily offering
of worship to the Servant King.

2. There in the garden of tears,
my heavy load he chose to bear;
his heart with sorrow was torn.
'Yet not my will but yours,' he said.

3. Come see his hands and his feet,
the scars that speak of sacrifice,
hands that flung stars into space,
to cruel nails surrendered.

4. So let us learn how to serve,
and in our lives enthrone him;
each other's needs to prefer,
for it is Christ we're serving.

83

Michael Forster (b. 1946), based on the Didaché

1. From many grains, once scattered far
and wide,
each one alone, to grow as best it may,
now safely gathered in and unified,
one single loaf we offer here today.
So may your Church, in ev'ry time
and place,
be in this meal united by your grace.

2. From many grapes, once living on the vine,
now crushed and broken under
human feet,
we offer here this single cup of wine:
the sign of love, unbroken and complete.
So may we stand among the crucified,
and live the risen life of him who died.

3. From many places gathered, we are here,
each with a gift that we alone can bring.
O Spirit of the living God, draw near,
make whole by grace our broken offering.
O crush the pride that bids us stand alone;
let flow the love that makes our spirits one.

84

Graham Kendrick (b. 1950)

1. From the sun's rising unto the sun's setting,
Jesus our Lord, shall be great in the earth;
and all earth's kingdoms shall be
his dominion,
all of creation shall sing of his worth.

Let ev'ry heart, ev'ry voice,
ev'ry tongue join with spirits ablaze;
one in his love, we will circle the world
with the song of his praise.
O let all his people rejoice,
and let all the earth hear his voice.

2. To ev'ry tongue, tribe and nation he
sends us,
to make disciples, to teach and baptise.
For all authority to him is given;
now, as his witnesses, we shall arise.

3. Come, let us join with the Church from
all nations,
cross ev'ry border, throw wide ev'ry door;
workers with him as he gathers his harvest,
till earth's far corners our Saviour adore.

85

Michael Forster (b. 1946)

1. From the very depths of darkness
springs a bright and living light;
out of falsehood and deceit
a greater truth is brought to sight;
in the halls of death, defiant,
life is dancing with delight!
The Lord is risen indeed!

Christ is risen! Hallelujah! (x3)
The Lord is risen indeed!

2. Jesus meets us at the dawning
of the resurrection day;
speaks our name with love, and gently
says that here we may not stay:
'Do not cling to me, but go to all
the fearful ones and say,
"The Lord is risen indeed!" '

3. So proclaim it in the high-rise,
in the hostel let it ring;
make it known in Cardboard City,
let the homeless rise and sing:
'He is Lord of life abundant,
and he changes everything;
the Lord is risen indeed!'

4. In the heartlands of oppression,
sound the cry of liberty;
where the poor are crucified,
behold the Lord of Calvary;
from the fear of death and dying,
Christ has set his people free;
the Lord is risen indeed!

5. To the tyrant, tell the gospel
of a love that can't be known
in a guarded palace-tomb,
condemned to live and die alone:
'Take the risk of love and freedom;
Christ has rolled away the stone!
The Lord is risen indeed!'

6. When our spirits are entombed
in mortal prejudice and pride;
when the gates of hell itself
are firmly bolted from inside;
at the bidding of his Spirit,
we may fling them open wide;
the Lord is risen indeed!.

86

Jean Holloway (b. 1939)

Gather around, for the table is spread,
welcome the food and rest!
Wide is our circle, with Christ at the head,
he is the honoured guest.
Learn of his love, grow in his grace,
pray for the peace he gives;
here at this meal, here in this place,
know that his Spirit lives!
Once he was known
in the breaking of bread,
shared with a chosen few;
multitudes gathered
and by him were fed,
so will he feed us too.

87

Traditional

1. Give me joy in my heart, keep me praising,
give me joy in my heart, I pray.
Give me joy in my heart, keep my praising,
keep me praising till the end of day.

Sing hosanna! Sing hosanna!
Sing hosanna to the King of kings!
Sing hosanna! Sing hosanna!
Sing hosanna to the King!

2. Give me peace in my heart,
keep me resting . . .

3. Give me love in my heart,
keep me serving . . .

4. Give me oil in my lamp,
keep me burning . . .

88

Henry Smith.

Give thanks with a grateful heart,
give thanks to the Holy One,
give thanks because he's given
Jesus Christ, his Son.
And now let the weak say, 'I am strong',
let the poor say, 'I am rich',
because of what the Lord has done for us.
And now let the weak say, 'I am strong',
let the poor say, 'I am rich',
because of what the Lord has done for us.

89

Isaac Watts (1674-1748), based on Psalm 136 alt.

1. Give to our God immortal praise;
mercy and truth are all his ways:
wonders of grace to God belong,
repeat his mercies in your song.

2. Give to the Lord of lords renown,
the King of kings with glory crown:
his mercies ever shall endure
when earthly pow'rs are known no more.

3. He sent his Son with pow'r to save
from guilt and darkness and the grave:
wonders of grace to God belong,
repeat his mercies in your song.

4. Through earthly life he guides our feet,
and leads us to his heav'nly seat:
his mercies ever shall endure
when earthly pow'rs are known no more.

90

Howard Charles Adie Gaunt (1902-1983)

1. Glory to thee, O God,
for all thy saints in light,
who nobly strove and conquered
in the well-fought fight.
Their praises sing,
who life outpoured
by fire and sword for Christ their King.

2. Thanks be to thee, O Lord,
for saints thy Spirit stirred
in humble paths to live thy life and
speak thy word.
Unnumbered they,
whose candles shine
to lead our footsteps after thine.

3. Lord God of truth and love,
'thy kingdom come', we pray;
give us thy grace to know thy truth and
walk thy way:
that here on earth
thy will be done,
till saints in earth and heav'n are one.

91

Carol Owens

1. God forgave my sin in Jesus' name.
I've been born again in Jesus' name.
And in Jesus' name I come to you
to share his love as he told me to.

He said: 'Freely, freely you have received;
freely, freely give.
Go in my name, and because you believe,
others will know that I live.'

2. All pow'r is giv'n in Jesus' name,
in earth and heav'n in Jesus' name.
And in Jesus' name I come to you
to share his pow'r as he told me to.

3. God gives us life in Jesus' name,
he lives in us in Jesus' name.
And in Jesus' name I come to you
to share his peace as he told me to.

92

John L. Bell (b. 1949) and Graham Maule (b. 1958)

1. God, in the planning and purpose of life,
hallowed the union of husband and wife:
this we embody where love is displayed,
rings are presented and promises made.

Continued overleaf

2. Jesus was found, at a similar feast,
taking the roles of both waiter and priest,
turning the worldly towards the divine,
tears into laughter and water to wine.

3. Therefore we pray that his Spirit preside
over the wedding of bridegroom
and bride,
fulfilling all that they've hoped will
come true,
lighting with love all they dream of and do.

4. Praise then the Maker, the Spirit, the Son,
source of the love through which two are
made one.
God's is the glory, the goodness and grace
seen in this marriage and known in
this place.

93

Graham Kendrick (b. 1950)

God is good, we sing and shout it,
God is good, we celebrate.
God is good, no more we doubt it,
God is good, we know it's true.
And when I think of his love for me,
my heart fills with praise
and I feel like dancing.
For in his heart there is room for me
and I run with arms opened wide.

94

Marie Lydia Pereira (b. 1920)

1. God is love, God is love,
God is love for us.
He lives by love, he works by love,
and his sun comes shining through.

2. God is life, God is life,
God is life for us.
His life keeps us from sin and strife,
and his sun comes shining through.

3. God is food, God is food,
God is food for us.
He is our food, our saving good,
and his sun comes shining through.

4. God is light, God is light,
God is light for us.
His light shines out through the
darkest night,
and his sun comes shining through.

5. God is peace, God is peace.
God is peace for us.
And through his peace all quarrels cease,
and his sun comes shining through.

6. God is joy, God is joy,
God is joy for us.
The purest joy, the deepest joy,
and his sun comes shining through.

7. God is strength, God is strength,
God is strength for us.
The greatest strength, unfailing strength,
and his sun comes shining through.

8. God is truth, God is truth,
God is truth for us.
The surest truth, unchanging truth,
and his sun comes shining through.

95

Percy Dearmer (1867-1936) alt.

1. God is love: his the care,
tending each, ev'rywhere.
God is love, all is there!
Jesus came to show him,
that we all might know him!

Sing aloud, loud, loud!
Sing aloud, loud, loud!
God is good! God is truth!
God is beauty! Praise him!

2. None can see God above;
we can share life and love;
thus may we Godward move,
seek him in creation,
holding ev'ry nation.

3. Jesus lived on the earth,
hope and life brought to birth
and affirmed human worth,
for he came to save us
by the truth he gave us.

4. To our Lord praise we sing,
light and life, friend and King,
coming down, love to bring,
pattern for our duty,
showing God in beauty.

96

Timothy Dudley-Smith (b.1926) based on Psalm 63

1. God is my great desire,
his face I seek the first;
to him my heart and soul aspire,
for him I thirst.
As one in desert lands,
whose very flesh is flame,
in burning love I lift my hands
and bless his name.

2. God is my true delight,
my richest feast his praise,
through silent watches of the night,
through all my days.
To him my spirit clings,
on him my soul is cast;
beneath the shadow of his wings
he holds me fast.

3. God is my strong defence
in ev'ry evil hour;
in him I face with confidence
the tempter's pow'r.
I trust his mercy sure,
with truth and triumph crowned:
my hope and joy for evermore
in him are found.

97

Richard Bewes (b. 1934) based on Psalm 46

1. God is our strength and refuge,
our present help in trouble;
and we therefore will not fear,
though the earth should change!
Though mountains shake and tremble,
though swirling floods are raging,
God the Lord of hosts is with us
evermore!

2. There is a flowing river,
within God's holy city;
God is in the midst of her –she shall not
be moved!
God's help is swiftly given,
thrones vanish at his presence
God the Lord of hosts is with us
evermore!

3. Come, see the works of our maker,
learn of his deeds all-powerful;
wars will cease across the world when he
shatters the spear!
Be still and know your creator,
uplift him in the nations –
God the Lord of hosts is with us
evermore!

98

Michael Forster (b. 1946)

1. God is our strength from days of old,
the hope of ev'ry nation;
whose pow'r conceived the universe
and set the earth's foundation.
Though hidden from our sight
in uncreated light,
his presence yet is known,
his wondrous purpose shown,
resplendent in creation!

Continued overleaf

2. That Word of Life, before all things
in primal darkness spoken,
became for us the Word made flesh
for our redemption broken.
His glory set aside,
for us he lived and died,
obedient to the death,
renewed in life and breath,
to endless glory woken!

3. That Breath of God, who brooded first
upon the new creation,
who lit with light the Virgin's womb
to bear the world's salvation;
that Dove whose shadow graced
th'anointed Saviour's face,
now challenges us all
to recognise the call
to hope and liberation.

4. O great Creator, Spirit, Word,
the well-spring of creation,
our Alpha and our Omega,
our hope and our salvation;
to Father, Spirit, Son,
the Three for ever One,
and One for ever Three,
mysterious Trinity,
be praise and adoration.

99

Arthur Campbell Ainger (1841-1919)
adapted by Michael Forster (b. 1946)

1. God is working his purpose out
as year succeeds to year.
God is working his purpose out,
and the day is drawing near.
Nearer and nearer draws the time,
the time that shall surely be,
when the earth shall be filled
with the glory of God
as the waters cover the sea.

2. From the east to the utmost west
wherever foot has trod,
through the mouths of his messengers
echoes forth the voice of God:
'Listen to me, ye continents,
ye islands, give ear to me,
that the earth shall be filled
with the glory of God
as the waters cover the sea.'

3. How can we do the work of God,
how prosper and increase
harmony in the human race,
and the reign of perfect peace?
What can we do to urge the time,
the time that shall surely be,
when the earth shall be filled
with the glory of God
as the waters cover the sea?

4. March we forth in the strength of God,
his banner is unfurled;
let the light of the gospel shine
in the darkness of the world:
strengthen the weary, heal the sick
and set ev'ry captive free,
that the earth shall be filled
with the glory of God
as the waters cover the sea.

5. All our efforts are nothing worth
unless God bless the deed;
vain our hopes for the harvest tide
till he brings to life the seed.
Yet ever nearer draws the time,
the time that shall surely be,
when the earth shall be filled
with the glory of God
as the waters cover the sea.

100

David Fellingham

God of glory, we exalt your name,
you who reign in majesty.
We lift our hearts to you
and we will worship, praise and magnify
your holy name.

In pow'r resplendent (in pow'r
resplendent)
you reign in glory (you reign in glory),
eternal King (eternal King),
you reign for ever.

Your word is mighty (your word is
mighty),
releasing captives (releasing captives),
your love is gracious (your love is
gracious),
you are my God.

101

Harry Emerson Fosdick (1878-1969) alt.

1. God of grace and God of glory,
on thy people pour thy pow'r;
now fulfil thy Church's story;
bring her bud to glorious flow'r.
Grant us wisdom, grant us courage,
for the facing of this hour.

2. Lo, the hosts of evil round us
scorn thy Christ, assail his ways;
from the fears that long have bound us
free our hearts to faith and praise.
Grant us wisdom, grant us courage,
for the living of these days.

3. Cure thy children's warring madness,
bend our pride to thy control;
shame our wanton selfish gladness,
rich in goods and poor in soul.
Grant us wisdom, grant us courage,
lest we miss thy kingdom's goal.

4. Set our feet on lofty places,
gird our lives that they may be
armoured with all Christlike graces
as we set your people free.
Grant us wisdom, grant us courage,
lest we fail the world or thee.

102

Michael Forster (b. 1946)

1. God of the Passover,
Author and Lord of salvation,
gladly we gather to bring
you our heart's adoration;
ransomed and free,
called and commissioned to be
signs of your love for creation.

2. Here we remember that evening
of wonder enthralling,
myst'ry of passion divine,
and betrayal appalling.
Breaking the bread,
'This is my body,' he said,
'do this, my passion recalling.'

3. God of the Eucharist,
humbly we gather before you
and, at your table,
for pardon and grace we implore you.
Under the cross,
counting as profit our loss,
safe in its shade, we adore you.

103

Traditional, alt.

1. God rest you merry, gentlemen,
let nothing you dismay,
for Jesus Christ our Saviour
was born on Christmas day,
to save us all from Satan's pow'r
when we were gone astray:

*O tidings of comfort and joy,
comfort and joy,
O tidings of comfort and joy.*

2. In Bethlehem, in Jewry,
this blessèd babe was born,
and laid within a manger,
upon this blessèd morn;
at which his mother Mary
did nothing take in scorn.

Continued overleaf

3. From God, our heav'nly Father,
a blessèd angel came,
and unto certain shepherds
brought tidings of the same,
how that in Bethlehem was born
the Son of God by name.

O tidings of comfort and joy,
comfort and joy,
O tidings of comfort and joy.

4. 'Fear not,' then said the angel,
'let nothing you affright,
this day is born a Saviour,
of virtue, pow'r and might;
by him the world is overcome
and Satan put to flight.'

5. The shepherds at those tidings
rejoicèd much in mind,
and left their flocks a-feeding,
in tempest, storm and wind,
and went to Bethlehem straightway
this blessèd babe to find.

6. But when to Bethlehem they came,
whereat this infant lay,
they found him in a manger,
where oxen feed on hay;
his mother Mary kneeling,
unto the Lord did pray.

7. Now to the Lord sing praises,
all you within this place,
and with true love and fellowship
each other now embrace;
this holy tide of Christmas
all others doth deface.

104

John Arlott (1914-1991) alt.

1. God, whose farm is all creation,
take the gratitude we give;
take the finest of our harvest,
crops we grow that all may live.

2. Take our ploughing, seeding, reaping,
hopes and fears of sun and rain,
all our thinking, planning, waiting,
ripened in this fruit and grain.

3. All our labour, all our watching,
all our calendar of care,
in these crops of your creation,
take, O God: they are our prayer.

105

Fred Kaan (b.1929)

1. God, whose love is all around us,
who in Jesus sought and found us,
who to freedom new unbound us,
keep our hearts with joy aflame.

2. For the sacramental breaking,
for the honour of partaking,
for your life our lives remaking,
young and old, we praise your name.

3. From the service of this table
lead us to a life more stable,
for our witness make us able;
blessings on our work we claim.

4. Through our calling closely knitted,
daily to your praise committed,
for a life of service fitted,
let us now your love proclaim.

Verse 1, lines 1 and 2 originally read:
Father, who in Jesus found us,
God, whose love is all around us,
(amended by the author.)

106

James Edward Seddon (1915-1983)

1. Go forth and tell!
O Church of God, awake!
God's saving news
to all the nations take:
proclaim Christ Jesus,
Saviour, Lord and King,
that all the world
his worthy praise may sing.

2. Go forth and tell!
God's love embraces all;
he will in grace
respond to all who call;
how shall they call
if they have never heard
the gracious invitation
of his word?

3. Go forth and tell!
where still the darkness lies;
in wealth or want,
the sinner surely dies:
give us, O Lord,
concern of heart and mind,
a love like yours
which cares for all mankind.

4. Go forth and tell!
the doors are open wide:
share God's good gifts –
let no-one be denied;
live out your life
as Christ your Lord shall choose,
your ransomed pow'rs
for his sole glory use.

5. Go forth and tell!
O Church of God, arise!
Go in the strength
which Christ your Lord supplies;
go till all nations
his great name adore
and serve him, Lord and King,
for evermore.

107

Michael Forster, (b. 1946)

1. Going home, moving on,
through God's open door;
hush, my soul, have no fear,
Christ has gone before.
Parting hurts, love protests,
pain is not denied;
yet, in Christ, life and hope
span the great divide.
Going home, moving on,
through God's open door;
hush, my soul, have no fear,
Christ has gone before,
Christ has gone before.

2. No more guilt, no more fear,
all the past is healed:
broken dreams now restored,
perfect grace revealed.
Christ has died, Christ is ris'n,
Christ will come again:
death destroyed, life restored,
love alone shall reign.
Going home, moving on,
through God's open door;
hush, my soul, have no fear,
Christ has gone before,
Christ has gone before.

108

John Mason Neale (1818-1866) alt.

1. Good Christians all, rejoice
with heart and soul and voice!
Give ye heed to what we say:
News! News! Jesus Christ is born today;
ox and ass before him bow,
and he is in the manger now:
Christ is born today, Christ is born today!

2. Good Christians all, rejoice
with heart and soul and voice!
Now ye hear of endless bliss:
Joy! Joy! Jesus Christ was born for this.
He hath opened heaven's door,
and we are blest for evermore:
Christ was born for this,
Christ was born for this.

3. Good Christians all, rejoice
with heart and soul and voice!
Now ye need not fear the grave:
Peace! Peace! Jesus Christ was born to save;
calls you one, and calls you all,
to gain his everlasting hall:
Christ was born to save,
Christ was born to save.

109 John Mason Neale (1818-1866) alt.

1. Good King Wenceslas looked out
on the feast of Stephen,
when the snow lay round about,
deep, and crisp, and even;
brightly shone the moon that night,
though the frost was cruel,
when a poor man came in sight,
gath'ring winter fuel.

2. 'Hither, page, and stand by me,
if thou know'st it, telling,
yonder peasant, who is he,
where and what his dwelling?'
'Sire, he lives a good league hence,
underneath the mountain,
right against the forest fence,
by Saint Agnes' fountain.'

3. 'Bring me flesh, and bring me wine,
bring me pine logs hither:
thou and I will see him dine,
when we bring him thither.'
Page and monarch, forth they went,
forth they went together;
through the rude wind's wild lament,
and the bitter weather.

4. 'Sire, the night is darker now,
and the wind blows stronger;
fails my heart, I know not how;
I can go no longer.'
'Mark my footsteps good, my page;
tread thou in them boldly:
thou shalt find the winter's rage
freeze thy blood less coldly.'

5. In his master's steps he trod,
where the snow lay dinted;
heat was in the very sod
which the Saint had printed.
Therefore, Christians all, be sure,
wealth or rank possessing,
ye who now will bless the poor,
shall yourselves find blessing.

110 Traditional

Go, tell it on the mountain,
over the hills and ev'rywhere.
Go, tell it on the mountain
that Jesus Christ is born.

1. While shepherds kept their watching
o'er wand'ring flocks by night,
behold, from out of heaven,
there shone a holy light.

2. And lo, when they had seen it,
they all bowed down and prayed;
they travelled on together
to where the babe was laid.

3. When I was a seeker,
I sought both night and day:
I asked my Lord to help me
and he showed me the way.

4. He made me a watchman
upon the city wall,
and, if I am a Christian,
I am the least of all.

111 Basil Bridge (b. 1927)

1. Gracious God, in adoration
saints with joy before you fall;
only when our hearts are leaden
can we fail to hear their call:
'Come with wonder, serve with gladness
God whose pow'r created all.'

2. Earth and sky in silent praises
speak to those with eyes to see;
all earth's living creatures echo
'God has made us!' So may we
come with wonder, serve with gladness
him through whom they came to be.

3. You have made us in your image,
breathed your Spirit, given us birth;
Jesus calls, whose cross has given
ev'ry life eternal worth,
'Come with wonder, serve with
gladness,
let God's will be done on earth!'

4. Earth by war and want is threatened;
deep the roots of fear and greed;
let your mercy be our measure
as we see our neighbour's need,
come with wonder, serve with
gladness,
share your gift of daily bread.

5. Holy Spirit, urging, striving,
give us love that casts out fear,
courage, seeking peace with justice,
faith to make this message clear –
'Come with wonder, serve with
gladness,
live in hope; the Lord is near!'

112

Steve McEwan

1. Great is the Lord and most worthy of
praise,
the city of God, the holy place,
the joy of the whole earth.
Great is the Lord in whom we have the
victory.
He aids us against the enemy,
we bow down on our knees.

2. And, Lord, we want to lift your name
on high,
and, Lord, we want to thank you
for the works you've done in our lives;
and, Lord, we trust in your unfailing
love,
for you alone are God eternal,
throughout earth and heaven above.

113

Thomas Obadiah Chisholm (1866-1960)

1. Great is thy faithfulness,
O God my Father,
there is no shadow
of turning with thee;
thou changest not,
thy compassions, they fail not;
as thou hast been
thou for ever wilt be.

Great is thy faithfulness!
Great is thy faithfulness!
Morning by morning
new mercies I see;
all I have needed
thy hand hath provided,
great is thy faithfulness,
Lord, unto me!

2. Summer and winter,
and springtime and harvest,
sun, moon and stars
in their courses above,
join with all nature
in manifold witness
to thy great faithfulness,
mercy and love.

3. Pardon for sin
and a peace that endureth,
thine own dear presence
to cheer and to guide;
strength for today
and bright hope for tomorrow,
blessings all mine,
with ten thousand beside!

114

Edwin Le Grice (1911-1992)

1. Great Son of God,
you once on Cal'vry's cross
fought the long fight
for truth and freedom's sake,
endured the scourge,
the crown of thorns,
the nails that fixed
your youthful body to a stake.
For six long hours
you suffered searing pain
to set your captive
people free again.

2. 'Give us a sign from heav'n,'
the people cried.
'If you are Christ,
leap down, alive and free.
Who could accept as Saviour
one who died
like some poor miscreant
skewered to a tree?'
Lord Christ, our Saviour,
you would not descend
until your glorious work
achieved its end.

3. 'My God, my God,
where have you gone?' you called,
alone and helpless,
willing still to share
through all the gath'ring
gloom of Calvary,
the depth of dying sinners'
deep despair.
But then triumphant,
ready now to die,
'The work is finished!'
was your glorious cry.

115

Greek (3rd century or earlier)
trans. John Keble (1792-1866)

1. Hail, gladdening Light,
of his pure glory poured
from th' immortal Father,
heav'nly, blest,
holiest of holies,
Jesus Christ our Lord.

2. Now we are come
to the sun's hour of rest,
the lights of evening
round us shine,
we hymn the Father,
Son and Holy Spirit divine.

3. Worthiest art thou at all times
to be sung with undefilèd tongue,
Son of our God,
giver of life, alone:
therefore in all the world thy glories,
Lord, they own.

116

John Bakewell (1721-1819) alt.

1. Hail, thou once despisèd Jesus,
hail, thou Galilean King!
Thou didst suffer to release us;
thou didst free salvation bring.
Hail, thou universal Saviour,
bearer of our sin and shame;
by thy merits we find favour;
life is given through thy name.

2. Paschal Lamb, by God appointed,
all our sins on thee were laid;
by almighty love anointed,
thou hast full atonement made.
All thy people are forgiven
through the virtue of thy blood;
opened is the gate of heaven,
we are reconciled to God.

3. Jesus, hail! enthroned in glory,
there for ever to abide;
all the heav'nly hosts adore thee,
seated at thy Father's side:
there for sinners thou art pleading,
there thou dost our place prepare;
ever for us interceding,
till in glory we appear.

4. Worship, honour, pow'r and blessing,
thou art worthy to receive;
loudest praises, without ceasing,
it is right for us to give:
help, ye bright angelic spirits!
bring your sweetest, noblest lays;
help to sing our Saviour's merits,
help to chant Immanuel's praise.

117 Halle, halle, halle (Traditional)

Hal- le, hal- le, hal - le - lu -
jah! Hal- le, hal- le, hal - le -
lu - jah! Hal- le, hal - le, hal-
- le - lu - jah! Hal- le -
lu-jah, hal - le - lu - jah!

118 Tim Cullen, alt.

Hallelujah, my Father,
for giving us your Son;
sending him into the world
to be given up for all,
knowing we would bruise him
and smite him from the earth!
Hallelujah, my Father,
in his death is my birth.
Hallelujah, my Father,
in his life is my life.

119 William Cowper (1731-1800) based on John 21:16

1. Hark, my soul, it is the Lord;
'tis thy Saviour, hear his word;
Jesus speaks, and speaks to thee,
'Say, poor sinner, lov'st thou me?

2. 'I delivered thee when bound,
and, when wounded, healed thy wound;
sought thee wand'ring, set thee right,
turned thy darkness into light.

3. 'Can a woman's tender care
cease towards the child she bare?
Yes, she may forgetful be,
yet will I remember thee.

4. 'Mine is an unchanging love,
higher than the heights above,
deeper than the depths beneath,
free and faithful, strong as death.

5. 'Thou shalt see my glory soon,
when the work of grace is done;
partner of my throne shalt be:
say, poor sinner, lov'st thou me?'

6. Lord, it is my chief complaint
that my love is weak and faint;
yet I love thee, and adore;
O for grace to love thee more!

120 Bryn Austin Rees (1911-1983)

1. Have faith in God, my heart,
trust and be unafraid;
God will fulfil in ev'ry part
each promise he has made.

Continued overleaf

2. Have faith in God, my mind,
though oft thy light burns low;
God's mercy holds a wiser plan
than thou canst fully know.

3. Have faith in God, my soul,
his Cross for ever stands;
and neither life nor death can pluck
his children from his hands.

4. Lord Jesus, make me whole;
grant me no resting-place,
until I rest, heart, mind and soul,
the captive of thy grace.

121

Christian Strover

1. Have you heard the raindrops
drumming on the rooftops?
Have you heard the raindrops
dripping on the ground?
Have you heard the raindrops
splashing in the streams
and running to the rivers all around?

There's water, water of life,
Jesus gives us the water of life;
there's water, water of life,
Jesus gives us the water of life.

2. There's a busy worker
digging in the desert,
digging with a spade that
flashes in the sun;
soon there will be water
rising in the well-shaft,
spilling from the bucket as it comes.

3. Nobody can live
who hasn't any water,
when the land is dry,
then nothing much grows;
Jesus gives us life if we drink
the living water,
sing it so that ev'rybody knows.

122

Michael Forster (b. 1946)

1. Heaven is open wide,
and Christ in glory stands,
with all authority endowed
and set at God's right hand.
Above the world of noise
extends his reign of peace,
and all the blood of martyrs calls
our angry ways to cease.

2. Heaven is open wide,
and perfect love we see
in God's eternal self revealed:
the blessèd Trinity.
Christ for the church has prayed,
that we may all be one,
and share the triune grace whereby
creation was begun.

3. Heaven is open wide,
and Christ in glory stands:
the Source and End, the First and Last,
with justice in his hands.
Let all the thirsty come
where life is flowing free,
and Christ, in splendour yet unknown,
our morning star will be.

123

John L. Bell (b. 1949) and Graham Maule (b. 1958)

1. Heav'n shall not wait
for the poor to lose their patience,
the scorned to smile,
the despised to find a friend:
Jesus is Lord,
he has championed the unwanted;
in him injustice
confronts its timely end.

2. Heav'n shall not wait
for the rich to share their fortunes,
the proud to fall,
the élite to tend the least:
Jesus is Lord;
he has shown the master's privilege –
to kneel and wash
servants' feet before they feast.

3. Heav'n shall not wait
for the dawn of great ideas,
thoughts of compassion
divorced from cries of pain:
Jesus is Lord;
he has married word and action;
his cross and company
make his purpose plain.

4. Heav'n shall not wait
for our legalised obedience,
defined by statute,
to strict conventions bound:
Jesus is Lord;
he has hallmarked true allegiance –
goodness appears
where his grace is sought and found.

5. Heav'n shall not wait
for triumphant hallelujahs,
when earth has passed
and we reach another shore:
Jesus is Lord
in our present imperfection;
his pow'r and love
are for now and then for evermore.

124

Twila Paris

He is exalted,
the King is exalted on high;
I will praise him.
He is exalted,
for ever exalted
and I will praise his name!

He is the Lord;
for ever his truth shall reign.
Heaven and earth rejoice
in his holy name.
He is exalted,
the King is exalted on high.

125

Unknown

1. He is Lord, he is Lord.
He is risen from the dead and he is Lord.
Ev'ry knee shall bow, ev'ry tongue confess
that Jesus Christ is Lord.

2. He is King, he is King,
He is risen from the dead and he is King.
Ev'ry knee shall bow, ev'ry tongue confess
that Jesus Christ is King.

3. He is love, he is love.
He is risen from the dead and he is love.
Ev'ry knee shall bow, ev'ry tongue confess
that Jesus Christ is love.

126

Charles Wesley (1707-1788) alt.

1. Help us to help each other, Lord,
each other's cross to bear;
let each a helping hand afford,
and feel each other's care.

2. Up into thee, our living head,
let us in all things grow,
and by thy sacrifice be led
the fruits of love to show.

3. Drawn by the magnet of thy love
let all our hearts agree;
and ever t'wards each other move,
and ever move t'wards thee.

4. This is the bond of perfectness,
thy spotless charity.
O let us still we pray, possess
the mind that was in thee.

127

Brian Wren (b. 1936)

1. Here hangs a man discarded,
a scarecrow hoisted high,
a nonsense pointing nowhere
to all who hurry by.

2. Can such a clown of sorrows
still bring a useful word
when faith and love seem phantoms
and ev'ry hope absurd?

3. Yet here is help and comfort
for lives by comfort bound,
when drums of dazzling progress
give strangely hollow sound:

4. Life, emptied of all meaning,
drained out in bleak distress,
can share in broken silence
our deepest emptiness;

5. And love that freely entered
the pit of life's despair,
can name our hidden darkness
and suffer with us there.

6. Christ, in our darkness risen,
help all who long for light
to hold the hand of promise,
till faith receives its sight.

128

Traditional

1. He's got the whole world in his hand. *(x4)*

2. He's got you and me, brother . . .

3. He's got you and me, sister . . .

4. He's got the little tiny baby . . .

5. He's got ev'rybody here . . .

129

Maggi Dawn

1. He was pierced for our transgressions,
and bruised for our iniquities;
and to bring us peace he was punished,
and by his stripes we are healed.

2. He was led like a lamb to the slaughter,
although he was innocent of crime;
and cut off from the land of the living,
he paid for the guilt that was mine.

We like sheep have gone astray,
turned each one to his own way,
and the Lord has laid on him
the iniquity of us all.

130

Jimmy Owens

1. Holy, holy, holy, holy.
Holy, holy, holy Lord God almighty;
and we lift our hearts before you
as a token of our love,
holy, holy, holy, holy.

2. Gracious Father, gracious Father,
we are glad to be your children,
gracious Father;
and we lift our heads before you
as a token of our love,
gracious Father, gracious Father.

3. Risen Jesus, risen Jesus,
we are glad you have redeemed us,
risen Jesus;
and we lift our hands before you
as a token of our love,
risen Jesus, risen Jesus.

4. Holy Spirit, Holy Spirit,
come and fill our hearts anew, Holy Spirit;
and we lift our voice before you
as a token of our love,
Holy Spirit, Holy Spirit.

5. Hallelujah, hallelujah,
hallelujah, hallelujah, hallelujah;
and we lift our hearts before you
as a token of our love,
hallelujah, hallelujah.

131 Unknown

1. Holy, holy, holy is the Lord,
   holy is the Lord God almighty.
   Holy, holy, holy is the Lord,
   holy is the Lord God almighty:
   who was, and is, and is to come;
   holy, holy, holy is the Lord.

2. Jesus, Jesus, Jesus is the Lord,
   Jesus is the Lord God almighty: *(Repeat)*
   who was, and is, and is to come;
   Jesus, Jesus, Jesus is the Lord.

3. Worthy, worthy, worthy is the Lord,
   worthy is the Lord God almighty: *(Repeat)*
   who was, and is and is to come;
   worthy, worth, worthy is the Lord God
   almighty.

4. Glory, glory, glory to the Lord,
   glory to the Lord God almighty: *(Repeat)*
   who was, and is, and is to come;
   glory, glory, glory to the Lord.

132 Carl Tuttle

1. Hosanna, hosanna,
   hosanna in the highest! *(Repeat)*

   Lord, we lift up your name,
   with hearts full of praise;
   be exalted, O Lord, my God!
   Hosanna in the highest!

2. Glory, glory, glory
   to the King of kings! *(Repeat)*

133 Stuart Townend

1. How deep the Father's love for us,
   how vast beyond all measure,
   that he should give his only Son
   to make a wretch his treasure.
   How great the pain of searing loss,
   the Father turns his face away,
   as wounds which mar the Chosen One
   bring many sons to glory.

2. Behold the man upon a cross,
   my sin upon his shoulders;
   ashamed, I hear my mocking voice
   call out among the scoffers.
   It was my sin that held him there
   until it was accomplished;
   his dying breath has brought me life –
   I know that it is finished.

3. I will not boast in anything,
   no gifts, no pow'r, no wisdom;
   but I will boast in Jesus Christ,
   his death and resurrection.
   Why should I gain from his reward?
   I cannot give an answer,
   but this I know with all my heart,
   his wounds have paid my ransom.

134 Richard Keen (c. 1787)

1. How firm a foundation,
   ye saints of the Lord,
   is laid for your faith
   in his excellent word;
   what more can he say
   than to you he hath said,
   you who unto Jesus
   for refuge have fled?

2. Fear not, he is with thee,
   O be not dismayed;
   for he is thy God,
   and will still give thee aid:
   he'll strengthen thee, help thee,
   and cause thee to stand,
   upheld by his righteous,
   omnipotent hand.

3. In ev'ry condition,
   in sickness, in health,
   in poverty's vale,
   or abounding in wealth;
   at home and abroad,
   on the land, on the sea,
   as thy days may demand
   shall thy strength ever be.

Continued overleaf

4. When through the deep waters
he calls thee to go,
the rivers of grief
shall not thee overflow;
for he will be with thee
in trouble to bless,
and sanctify to thee
thy deepest distress.

5. When through fiery trials
thy pathway shall lie,
his grace all-sufficient
shall be thy supply;
the flame shall not hurt thee,
his only design
thy dross to consume
and thy gold to refine.

6. The soul that on Jesus
has leaned for repose
he will not, he cannot,
desert to its foes;
that soul, though all hell
should endeavour to shake,
he never will leave,
he will never forsake.

135

Joseph Hart (1712-1768)

1. How good is the God we adore!
Our faithful, unchangeable friend:
his love is as great as his pow'r
and knows neither measure nor end.

2. For Christ is the first and the last;
his Spirit will guide us safe home;
we'll praise him for all that is past
and trust him for all that's to come.

136

v. 1 Leonard E. Smith Jnr. (b. 1942)
based on Isaiah 52; vs. 2-4 unknown.

1. How lovely on the mountains
are the feet of him
who brings good news, good news,
announcing peace,
proclaiming news of happiness:
our God reigns, our God reigns.

Our God reigns. (x4)

2. You watchmen, lift your voices
joyfully as one,
shout for your King, your King!
See eye to eye,
the Lord restoring Zion:
our God reigns, our God reigns.

3. Wasteplaces of Jerusalem,
break forth with joy!
We are redeemed, redeemed.
The Lord has saved
and comforted his people:
our God reigns, our God reigns.

4. Ends of the earth, see
the salvation of our God!
Jesus is Lord, is Lord!
Before the nations,
he has bared his holy arm:
our God reigns, our God reigns.

137

Dave Bilbrough

I am a new creation,
no more in condemnation,
here in the grace of God I stand.
My heart is overflowing,
my love just keeps on growing,
here in the grace of God I stand.
And I will praise you, Lord,
yes, I will praise you, Lord,
and I will sing of all that you have done.
A joy that knows no limit,
a lightness in my spirit,
here in the grace of God I stand.

138

Suzanne Toolan (b. 1927)

1. I am the bread of life.
   You who come to me shall not hunger;
   and who believe in me shall not thirst.
   No one can come to me
   unless the Father beckons.

   And I will raise you up,
   and I will raise you up,
   and I will raise you up on the last day.

2. The bread that I will give
   is my flesh for the life of the world,
   and if you eat of this bread,
   you shall live for ever,
   you shall live for ever.

3. Unless you eat
   of the flesh of the Son of Man,
   and drink of his blood,
   and drink of his blood,
   you shall not have life within you.

4. I am the resurrection,
   I am the life.
   If you believe in me,
   even though you die,
   you shall live for ever.

5. Yes, Lord, I believe
   that you are the Christ,
   the Son of God,
   who has come
   into the world.

139

Frances Ridley Havergal (1836-1879)

1. I am trusting thee, Lord Jesus,
   trusting only thee;
   trusting thee for full salvation,
   great and free.

2. I am trusting thee for pardon,
   at thy feet I bow;
   for thy grace and tender mercy,
   trusting now.

3. I am trusting thee for cleansing
   in the crimson flood;
   trusting thee to make me holy
   by thy blood.

4. I am trusting thee to guide me;
   thou alone shalt lead,
   ev'ry day and hour supplying
   all my need.

5. I am trusting thee for power,
   thine can never fail;
   words which thou thyself shalt give me
   must prevail.

6. I am trusting thee, Lord Jesus;
   never let me fall;
   I am trusting thee for ever,
   and for all.

140

Marc Nelson

1. I believe in Jesus;
   I believe he is the Son of God.
   I believe he died and rose again.
   I believe he paid for us all.
   And I believe he's here now
   standing in our midst;
   here with the power to heal now,
   and the grace to forgive.

2. I believe in you, Lord;
   I believe you are the Son of God.
   I believe you died and rose again.
   I believe you paid for us all.
   And I believe you're here now
   standing in our midst;
   here with the power to heal now,
   and the grace to forgive.

141

Ascribed to St Patrick (373-463),
trans. Cecil Frances Alexander (1818-1895) alt.

1. I bind unto myself today
the strong name of the Trinity,
by invocation of the same,
the Three in One and One in Three.

2. I bind this day to me for ever,
by pow'r of faith, Christ's incarnation,
his baptism in the Jordan river,
his death on cross for my salvation;
his bursting from the spicèd tomb,
his riding up the heav'nly way,
his coming at the day of doom,
I bind unto myself today.

3. I bind unto myself the pow'r
of the great love of cherubim;
the sweet 'Well done!' in judgement hour;
the service of the seraphim,
confessors' faith, apostles' word,
the patriarchs' prayers, the prophets' scrolls,
all good deeds done unto the Lord,
and purity of faithful souls.

PART TWO

4. Christ be with me, Christ within me,
Christ behind me, Christ before me.
Christ beside me, Christ to win me,
Christ to comfort and restore me.
Christ beneath me, Christ above me,
Christ in quiet, Christ in danger,
Christ in hearts of all that love me,
Christ in mouth of friend and stranger.

DOXOLOGY

5. I bind unto myself the name,
the strong name of the Trinity,
by invocation of the same,
the Three in One and One in Three,
of whom all nature hath creation,
eternal Father, Spirit, Word.
Praise to the Lord of my salvation:
salvation is of Christ the Lord.
Amen.

142

William Young Fullerton (1857-1932) alt.

1. I cannot tell
how he whom angels worship
should stoop to love
the peoples of the earth,
or why as shepherd
he should seek the wand'rer
with his mysterious promise
of new birth.
But this I know,
that he was born of Mary,
when Bethl'em's manger
was his only home,
and that he lived at
Nazareth and laboured,
and so the Saviour,
Saviour of the world, is come.

2. I cannot tell
how silently he suffered,
as with his peace
he graced this place of tears,
or how his heart
upon the cross was broken,
the crown of pain
to three and thirty years.
But this I know,
he heals the broken-hearted,
and stays our sin,
and calms our lurking fear,
and lifts the burden
from the heavy laden,
for yet the Saviour,
Saviour of the world, is here.

3. I cannot tell
how he will win the nations,
how he will claim
his earthly heritage,
how satisfy
the needs and aspirations
of east and west,
of sinner and of sage.

But this I know,
all flesh shall see his glory,
and he shall reap
the harvest he has sown,
and some glad day
his sun shall shine in splendour
when he the Saviour,
Saviour of the world, is known.

4. I cannot tell
how all the lands shall worship,
when, at his bidding,
ev'ry storm is stilled,
or who can say
how great the jubilation
when ev'ry heart
with perfect love is filled.
But this I know,
the skies will thrill with rapture,
and myriad, myriad
human voices sing,
and earth to heav'n,
and heav'n to earth, will answer:
'At last the Saviour,
Saviour of the world, is King!'

143

Brian A. Wren (b. 1936)

1. I come with joy, a child of God,
forgiven, loved and free,
the life of Jesus to recall,
in love laid down for me.

2. I come with Christians far and near
to find, as all are fed,
the new community of love
in Christ's communion bread.

3. As Christ breaks bread, and bids us share,
each proud division ends.
The love that made us, makes us one,
and strangers now are friends.

4. The Spirit of the risen Christ,
unseen, but ever near,
is in such friendship better known,
alive among us here.

5. Together met, together bound
by all that God has done,
we'll go with joy, to give the world
the love that makes us one.

144

Michael Forster (b. 1946)

1. 'I do not know the man,'
the fearful Peter said.
No sharper nail could pierce the hand
by which the world is fed,
by which the world is fed!

2. The great disciple failed;
his weakness we may own,
and stand with him where judgement
meets
with grace, at Calv'ry's throne,
with grace, at Calv'ry's throne.

3. Christ stands among us still,
in those the world denies,
and in the faces of the poor,
we see his grieving eyes,
we see his grieving eyes.

4. We cannot cleanse our hands
of that most shameful spot,
since of our brother we have said,
'His keeper, I am not!'
'His keeper, I am not!'

5. And yet, what love is this?
Forgiveness all divine!
Christ says of our poor faithless souls,
'I know them, they are mine.'
'I know them, they are mine.'

145

Brian Howard

1. If I were a butterfly,
   I'd thank you Lord, for giving me wings,
   and if I were a robin in a tree,
   I'd thank you, Lord, that I could sing,
   and if I were a fish in the sea,
   I'd wiggle my tail and I'd giggle with glee,
   but I just thank you, Father,
   for making me 'me'.

For you gave me a heart,
and you gave me a smile,
you gave me Jesus
and you made me your child,
and I just thank you, Father,
for making me 'me'.

2. If I were an elephant,
   I'd thank you, Lord, by raising my trunk,
   and if I were a kangaroo,
   you know I'd hop right up to you,
   and if I were an octopus,
   I'd thank you, Lord, for my fine looks,
   but I just thank you, Father,
   for making me 'me'.

3. If I were a wiggly worm,
   I'd thank you, Lord, that I could squirm,
   and if I were a billy goat,
   I'd thank you, Lord, for my strong throat,
   and if I were a fuzzy wuzzy bear,
   I'd thank you, Lord, for my fuzzy wuzzy hair,
   but I just thank you, Father,
   for making me 'me'.

146

Susan Sayers (b. 1946)

1. If we only seek peace
   when it's to our advantage,
   if we fail to release
   the down-trodden and poor,
   then let the gen'rous, caring, boundless
   sharing
   of the God
   who walked this earth
   nourish our roots until we fruit
   in the joy of the Lord.

The story of love he came to tell us,
bound in the making of the world.
We are the pages still unwritten:
let the story be told.

2. If we try to avoid
   inconvenient giving,
   or if love is destroyed
   by our failure to serve,
   then let the wide, unflinching, selfless
   giving
   of the God who walked this earth
   nourish our roots until we fruit
   in the joy of the Lord.

3. If we start to object
   to the path we are given
   and decide to select
   other ways of our own,
   then let the full acceptance, firm
   obedience
   of the God who walked this earth
   nourish our roots until we fruit
   in the joy of the Lord.

147

Carl Tuttle

1. I give you all the honour
   and praise that's due your name,
   for you are the King of Glory,
   the Creator of all things.

And I worship you,
I give my life to you,
I fall down on my knees.
Yes, I worship you,
I give my life to you,
I fall down on my knees.

2. As your Spirit moves upon me now,
   you meet my deepest need,
   and I lift my hands up to your throne,
   your mercy I've received.

3. You have broken chains that bound me,
   you've set this captive free,
   I will lift my voice to praise your name
   for all eternity.

148

Michael Forster (b. 1946)
based on the Good Friday 'Reproaches'.

1. I give you love, and how do you repay?
   When you were slaves I strove to set
   you free;
   I led you out from under Pharaoh's yoke,
   but you led out your Christ to Calvary.

   My people, tell me, what is my offence?
   What have I done to harm you? Answer me!

2. For forty years I was your constant guide,
   I fed you with my manna from on high.
   I led you out to live in hope and peace,
   but you led out my only Son to die.

3. With cloud and fire I marked the
   desert way,
   I heard your cries of rage and calmed
   your fear.
   I opened up the sea and led you through,
   but you have opened Christ with nail
   and spear.

4. When in distress you cried to me for food,
   I sent you quails in answer to your call,
   and saving water from the desert rock,
   but to my Son you offered bitter gall.

5. I gave you joy when you were in despair,
   with songs of hope, I set your hearts
   on fire;
   crowned you with grace, the people of
   my choice,
   but you have crowned my Christ with
   thorny briar.

6. When you were weak, exploited and
   oppressed,
   I heard you cry and listened to your plea.
   I raised you up to honour and renown,
   but you have raised me on a shameful tree.

149

Samuel Medley (1738-1799) alt.

1. I know that my Redeemer lives!
   What joy the blest assurance gives!
   He lives, he lives, who once was dead;
   he lives, my everlasting Head!

2. He lives, to bless me with his love;
   he lives, to plead for me above;
   he lives, my hungry soul to feed;
   he lives, to help in time of need.

3. He lives, and grants me daily breath;
   he lives – for me he conquered death;
   he lives, my mansion to prepare;
   he lives, to lead me safely there.

4. He lives, all glory to his name;
   he lives, my Saviour, still the same;
   what joy the blest assurance gives!
   I know that my Redeemer lives!

150

Laurie Klein

I love you, Lord,
and I lift my voice to worship you,
O my soul rejoice.
Take joy, my King, in what you hear.
May it be a sweet, sweet sound in your
ear.

151

Rob Hayward

I'm accepted, I'm forgiven,
I am fathered by the true and living God.
I'm accepted, no condemnation,
I am loved by the true and living God.
There's no guilt or fear as I draw near
to the Saviour and Creator of the world.
There is joy and peace as I release
my worship to you, O Lord.

152 Isaac Watts (1674-1748)

1. I'm not ashamed to own my Lord,
   or to defend his cause;
   maintain the honour of his word,
   the glory of his cross.

2. Jesus, my God, I know his name;
   his name is all my trust;
   nor will he put my soul to shame,
   nor let my hope be lost.

3. Firm as his throne his promise stands;
   and he can well secure
   what I've committed to his hands,
   till the decisive hour.

4. Then will he own my worthless name
   before his Father's face;
   and in the new Jerusalem
   appoint my soul a place.

153 Martin E. Leckebusch (b. 1962)

1. In an age of twisted values
   we have lost the truth we need;
   in sophisticated language
   we have justified our greed;
   by our struggle for possessions
   we have robbed the poor and weak –
   hear our cry and heal our nation:
   your forgiveness, Lord, we seek.

2. We have built discrimination
   on our prejudice and fear;
   hatred swiftly turns to cruelty
   if we hold resentments dear.
   For communities divided
   by the walls of class and race
   hear our cry and heal our nation:
   show us, Lord, your love and grace.

3. When our families are broken;
   when our homes are full of strife;
   when our children are bewildered,
   when they lose their way in life;
   when we fail to give the aged
   all the care we know we should –
   hear our cry and heal our nation
   with your tender fatherhood.

4. We who hear your word so often
   choose so rarely to obey;
   turn us from our wilful blindness,
   give us truth to light our way.
   In the power of your Spirit
   come to cleanse us, make us new:
   hear our cry and heal our nation
   till our nation honours you.

154 Annie Sherwood Hawks (1835-1918)

1. I need thee ev'ry hour,
   most gracious Lord;
   no tender voice like thine
   can peace afford.
   I need thee, O I need thee!
   ev'ry hour I need thee;
   O bless me now,
   my Saviour! I come to thee.

2. I need thee ev'ry hour;
   stay thou near by;
   temptations lose their pow'r
   when thou art nigh.

3. I need thee ev'ry hour,
   in joy or pain;
   come quickly and abide,
   or life is vain.

4. I need thee ev'ry hour;
   teach me thy will,
   and thy rich promises
   in me fulfil.

5. I need thee ev'ry hour,
most Holy One;
O make me thine indeed,
thou blessèd Son!

155

Trans. from the Polish by Edith Margaret Gellibrand Reed (1885-1933).

1. Infant holy, infant lowly,
for his bed a cattle stall;
oxen lowing, little knowing
Christ the babe is Lord of all.
Swift are winging angels singing,
nowells ringing, tidings bringing,
Christ the babe is Lord of all,
Christ the babe is Lord of all.

2. Flocks were sleeping, shepherds keeping
vigil till the morning new;
saw the glory, heard the story,
tidings of a gospel true.
Thus rejoicing, free from sorrow,
praises voicing, greet the morrow,
Christ the babe was born for you,
Christ the babe was born for you.

156

Frances Ridley Havergal (1836-1879)

1. In full and glad surrender,
I give myself to thee,
thine utterly and only
and evermore to be.

2. O Son of God, who lov'st me,
I will be thine alone;
and all I have and am, Lord,
shall henceforth be thine own!

3. Reign over me, Lord Jesus,
O make my heart thy throne;
it shall be thine, dear Saviour,
it shall be thine alone.

4. O come and reign, Lord Jesus,
rule over ev'rything!
And keep me always loyal
and true to thee, my King.

157

Anna Laetitia Waring (1820-1910) based on Psalm 23

1. In heav'nly love abiding,
no change my heart shall fear;
and safe is such confiding,
for nothing changes here.
The storm may roar without me,
my heart may low be laid,
but God is round about me,
and can I be dismayed?

2. Wherever he may guide me,
no want shall turn me back;
my Shepherd is beside me,
and nothing can I lack.
His wisdom ever waketh,
his sight is never dim,
he knows the way he taketh,
and I will walk with him.

3. Green pastures are before me,
which yet I have not seen;
bright skies will soon be o'er me,
where the dark clouds have been.
My hope I cannot measure,
my path to life is free,
my Saviour has my treasure,
and he will walk with me.

158

John L. Bell (b. 1949) and Graham Maule (b. 1958)

1. Inspired by love and anger,
disturbed by endless pain,
aware of God's own bias,
we ask him once again:
'How long must some folk suffer?
How long can few folk mind?
How long dare vain self-int'rest
turn prayer and pity blind?'

Continued overleaf

2. From those for ever victims
of heartless human greed,
their cruel plight composes
a litany of need:
'Where are the fruits of justice?
Where are the signs of peace?
When is the day when pris'ners
and dreams find their release?'

3. From those for ever shackled
to what their wealth can buy,
the fear of lost advantage
provokes the bitter cry:
'Don't query our position!
Don't criticise our wealth!
Don't mention those exploited
by politics and stealth!'

4. To God, who through the prophets
proclaimed a diff'rent age,
we offer earth's indiff'rence,
its agony and rage:
'When will the wronged be righted?
When will the kingdom come?
When will the world be gen'rous
to all instead of some?'

5. God asks: 'Who will go for me?
Who will extend my reach?
And who, when few will listen,
will prophesy and preach?
And who, when few bid welcome,
will offer all they know?
And who, when few dare follow,
will walk the road I show?'

6. Amused in someone's kitchen,
asleep in someone's boat,
attuned to what the ancients
exposed, proclaimed and wrote,
a Saviour without safety,
a tradesman without tools
has come to tip the balance
with fishermen and fools.

159

John Bowring (1792-1872) based on Galatians 6:14

1. In the Cross of Christ I glory,
tow'ring o'er the wrecks of time;
all the light of sacred story
gathers round its head sublime.

2. When the woes of life o'ertake me,
hopes deceive, and fears annoy,
never shall the Cross forsake me;
Lo! it glows with peace and joy.

3. When the sun of bliss is beaming
light and love upon my way,
from the Cross the radiance streaming
adds more lustre to the day.

4. Bane and blessing, pain and pleasure,
by the Cross are sanctified;
peace is there that knows no measure,
joys that through all time abide.

160

Francesca Leftley (b. 1955)

1. In you, my God,
may my soul find its peace;
you are my refuge,
my rock and my strength,
calming my fears
with the touch of your love.
Here in your presence
my troubles will cease.

2. In you, my God,
may my soul find its joy;
you are the radiance,
the song of my heart,
drying my tears
with the warmth of your love.
Here in your presence
my troubles will cease.

3. In you, my God,
may my soul find its rest;
you are the meaning,
the purpose of life,
drawing me near
to the fire of your love,
safe in your presence
my yearning will cease.

161

Charles H. Gabriel (1856-1932)

1. I stand amazed in the presence
of Jesus the Nazarene,
and wonder how he could love me,
a sinner, condemned, unclean.

O, how marvellous! O, how wonderful,
and my song shall ever be:
O, how marvellous! O, how wonderful!
is my Saviour's love for me.

2. For me it was in the garden
he prayed – 'Not my will, but thine';
he had no tears for his own griefs,
but sweat drops of blood for mine.

3. In pity angels beheld him,
and came from the world of light,
to comfort him in the sorrows
he bore for my soul that night.

4. He took my sins and my sorrows,
he made them his very own;
he bore the burden to Calvary,
and suffered, and died alone.

5. When with the ransomed in glory
his face I at last shall see,
'twill be my joy through the ages
to sing of his love for me.

162

Stopford Augustus Brooke (1832-1916) alt.

1. It fell upon a summer day,
when Jesus walked in Galilee,
the mothers from a village
brought their children to his knee.

2. He took them in his arms, and laid
his hands on each remembered head;
'Allow these little ones to come
to me,' he gently said.

3. 'Forbid them not: unless ye bear
the childlike heart your hearts within,
unto my kingdom ye may come,
but may not enter in.'

4. My Lord, I fain would enter there;
O let me follow thee, and share
thy meek and lowly heart, and be
freed from all worldly care.

5. O happy thus to live and move,
and sweet this world, where I shall find
God's beauty everywhere, his love,
his good in humankind.

6. Then, Father, grant this childlike heart,
that I may come to Christ, and feel
his hands on me in blessing laid,
love-giving, strong to heal.

163

Dan Schutte, based on Isaiah 6

1. I, the Lord of sea and sky,
I have heard my people cry.
All who dwell in dark and sin
my hand will save.
I who made the stars of night,
I will make their darkness bright.
Who will bear my light to them?
Whom shall I send?

Here I am, Lord. Is it I, Lord?
I have heard you calling in the night.
I will go, Lord, if you lead me.
I will hold your people in my heart.

Continued overleaf

2. I, the Lord of snow and rain,
I have borne my people's pain.
I have wept for love of them.
They turn away.
I will break their hearts of stone,
give them hearts for love alone.
I will speak my word to them.
Whom shall I send?

Here I am, Lord. Is it I, Lord?
I have heard you calling in the night.
I will go, Lord, if you lead me.
I will hold your people in my heart.

3. I, the Lord of wind and flame,
I will tend the poor and lame.
I will set a feast for them.
My hand will save.
Finest bread I will provide
till their hearts be satisfied.
I will give my life to them.
Whom shall I send?

164

Spiritual

It's me, it's me, it's me, O Lord,
standing in the need of prayer. (Repeat)

1. Not my brother or my sister,
but it's me, O Lord,
standing in the need of prayer. *(Repeat)*
2. Not my mother or my father . . .
3. Not the stranger or my neighbour . . .

165

John Glynn (b. 1948)

1. I watch the sunrise lighting the sky,
casting its shadows near.
And on this morning, bright though it be,
I feel those shadows near me.

But you are always close to me,
following all my ways.
May I be always close to you,
following all your ways, Lord.

2. I watch the sunlight shine through
the clouds,
warming the earth below.
And at the mid-day, life seems to say:
'I feel your brightness near me.'
For you are always . . .

3. I watch the sunset fading away,
lighting the clouds with sleep.
And as the evening closes its eyes,
I feel your presence near me.
For you are always . . .

4. I watch the moonlight guarding the night,
waiting till morning comes.
The air is silent, earth is at rest –
only your peace is near me.
Yes, you are always . . .

166

Leona von Brethorst

I will enter his gates
with thanksgiving in my heart,
I will enter his courts with praise,
I will say this is the day
that the Lord has made,
I will rejoice for he has made me glad.
He has made me glad, he has made me glad,
I will rejoice for he has made me glad.
He has made me glad, he had made me glad,
I will rejoice for he has made me glad.

167

Matt Redman

1. I will offer up my life
in spirit and truth,
pouring out the oil of love
as my worship to you.
In surrender I must give
my ev'ry part;
Lord, receive the sacrifice
of a broken heart.

Jesus, what can I give,
what can I bring
to so faithful a friend,
to so loving a King?
Saviour, what can be said,
what can be sung
as a praise of your name
for the things you have done?
O my words could not tell,
not even in part,
of the debt of love that is owed
by this thankful heart.

2. You deserve my ev'ry breath
for you've paid the great cost;
giving up your life to death,
even death on a cross.
You took all my shame away,
there defeated my sin,
opened up the gates of heav'n,
and have beckoned me in.

168

Francis Harold Rawley (1854-1952)

1. I will sing the wondrous story
of the Christ who died for me,
how he left the realms of glory
for the cross on Calvary.
Yes, I'll sing the wondrous story
of the Christ who died for me –
sing it with his saints in glory,
gathered by the crystal sea.

2. I was lost but Jesus found me,
found the sheep that went astray,
raised me up and gently led me
back into the narrow way.
Days of darkness still may meet me,
sorrow's path I oft may tread;
but his presence still is with me,
by his guiding hand I'm led.

3. He will keep me till the river
rolls its waters at my feet:
then he'll bear me safely over,
made by grace for glory meet.
Yes, I'll sing the wondrous story
of the Christ who died for me –
sing it with his saints in glory,
gathered by the crystal sea.

169

John L. Bell (b. 1949) and Graham Maule (b. 1958)

1. 'James and Andrew, Peter and John,
men of temper, talent and tide,
your nets are empty, empty and bare.
Cast them now on the opposite side.'

2. 'Jesus, you're only a carpenter's son:
joints and joists are part of your trade,
but ours the skill to harvest the deep.
Why presume to come to our aid?'

3. 'Friends of mine and brothers thro' love,
I mean more than fishing for food.
I call your skill to service my will,
call your lives to harvest the good.'

4. 'Cast your nets where you think is right;
spend your lives where you think is need;
but if you long for that which is best,
let it be on my word you feed.'

5. 'Stir then the waters, Lord, stir up the wind;
stir the hope that needs to be stretched;
stir up the love that needs to be ground;
stir the faith that needs to be fetched.'

6. James and Andrew, Peter and John,
and the women close by his side,
hear how the Lord calls each by their name,
asking all to turn like the tide.

170

Based on verses by F. B. P.,
an unknown author (c. 1600)

1. Jerusalem, my happy home,
   name ever dear to me,
   when shall my labours have an end?
   thy joys when shall I see?

2. Apostles, martyrs, prophets, there
   around my Saviour stand;
   and all I love in Christ below
   will join the glorious band.

3. Jerusalem, my happy home,
   when shall I come to thee?
   when shall my labours have an end?
   thy joys when shall I see?

4. O Christ, do thou my soul prepare
   for that bright home of love;
   that I may see thee and adore
   with all thy saints above.

171

Chris Bowater

Jesus, at your name we bow the knee.
Jesus, at your name we bow the knee.
Jesus, at your name we bow the knee,
and acknowledge you as Lord.
(Repeat)
You are the Christ, you are the Lord.
Through your Spirit in our lives
we know who you are.
(Repeat)

172

John L. Bell (b. 1949) and Graham Maule (b. 1958)

1. Jesus calls us here to meet him as,
   through word and song and prayer,
   we affirm God's promised presence
   where his people live and care.
   Praise the God who keeps his promise;
   praise the Son who calls us friends;
   praise the Spirit who, among us,
   to our hopes and fears attends.

2. Jesus calls us to confess him
   Word of life and Lord of All,
   sharer of our flesh and frailness
   saving all who fail or fall.
   Tell his holy human story;
   tell his tales that all may hear;
   tell the world that Christ in glory
   came to earth to meet us here.

3. Jesus calls us to each other:
   found in him are no divides.
   Race and class and sex and language –
   such are barriers he derides.
   Join the hand of friend and stranger;
   join the hands of age and youth;
   join the faithful and the doubter
   in their common search for truth.

4. Jesus calls us to his table,
   rooted firm in time and space,
   where the Church in earth and heaven
   finds a common meeting place.
   Share the bread and wine, his body;
   share the love of which we sing;
   share the feast for saints and sinners
   hosted by our Lord and King.

173

Matt Redman

1. Jesus Christ, I think upon your sacrifice,
   you became nothing, poured out to death.
   Many times I've wondered at your gift of
   life,
   and I'm in that place once again.
   I'm in that place once again.

*And once again I look upon the cross where
you died,*
*I'm humbled by your mercy and I'm broken
inside.*
Once again I thank you,
once again I pour out my life.
*Thank you for the cross, thank you for the
cross,*
thank you for the cross, my friend.

2. Now you are exalted to the highest place,
King of the heavens, where one day I'll bow.
But for now, I marvel at this saving grace,
and I'm full of praise once again.
I'm full of praise once again.

174

John L. Bell (b. 1949) and Graham Maule (b. 1958)

1. Jesus Christ is waiting,
waiting in the streets:
no one is his neighbour,
all alone he eats.
Listen, Lord Jesus,
I am lonely too;
make me, friend or stranger,
fit to wait on you.

2. Jesus Christ is raging,
raging in the streets
where injustice spirals
and all hope retreats.
Listen, Lord Jesus,
I am angry too;
in the kingdom's causes
let me rage with you.

3. Jesus Christ is healing,
healing in the streets
curing those who suffer,
touching those he greets.
Listen, Lord Jesus,
I have pity too;
let my care be active,
healing just like you.

4. Jesus Christ is dancing,
dancing in the streets,
where each sign of hatred
his strong love defeats.
Listen, Lord Jesus,
I feel triumph too;
on suspicion's graveyard,
let me dance with you.

5. Jesus Christ is calling,
calling in the streets,
'Come and walk faith's tightrope,
I will guide your feet.'
Listen, Lord Jesus,
let my fears be few;
walk one step before me,
I will follow you.

175

David J. Mansell

1. Jesus is Lord!
Creation's voice proclaims it,
for by his pow'r each tree and flow'r
was planned and made.
Jesus is Lord! The universe declares it;
sun, moon and stars in heaven cry:
Jesus is Lord!

Jesus is Lord! Jesus is Lord!
Praise him with alleluias
for Jesus is Lord!

2. Jesus is Lord!
Yet from his throne eternal
in flesh he came to die in pain
on Calv'ry's tree.
Jesus is Lord! From him all life proceeding,
yet gave his life as ransom
thus setting us free.

3. Jesus is Lord!
O'er sin the mighty conqu'ror,
from death he rose and all his foes
shall own his name.
Jesus is Lord! God sends his Holy Spirit
to show by works of power
that Jesus is Lord.

176

John Barnett

Jesus, Jesus,
holy and anointed One, Jesus.
Jesus, Jesus,
risen and exalted One, Jesus.

Your name is like honey on my lips,
your Spirit like water to my soul.
Your word is a lamp unto my feet.
Jesus, I love you, I love you.

177

Paul Oakley

Jesus, lover of my soul,
all consuming fire is in your gaze.
Jesus, I want you to know
I will follow you all my days.
For no one else in history is like you,
and history itself belongs to you.
Alpha and Omega, you have loved me,
and I will share eternity with you.

It's all about you, Jesus,
and all this is for you,
for your glory and your fame.
It's not about me,
as if you should do things my way;
you alone are God,
and I surrender to your ways.

178

Nadia Hearn (b. 1944)

Jesus, Name above all names,
beautiful Saviour, glorious Lord,
Emmanuel, God is with us,
blessed Redeemer, living Word.

179

Timothy Dudley-Smith (b. 1926)

1. Jesus, Prince and Saviour,
Lord of life who died;
Christ, the friend of sinners,
mocked and crucified;
for a world's salvation,
he his body gave,
lay at last death's victim,
lifeless in the grave.

Lord of life triumphant,
risen now to reign!
King of endless ages,
Jesus lives again!

2. In his pow'r and Godhead
ev'ry vict'ry won;
pain and passion ended,
all his purpose done.
Christ the Lord is risen!
sighs and sorrows past,
death's dark night is over,
morning comes at last!

3. Resurrection morning!
sinners' bondage freed;
Christ the Lord is risen –
he is ris'n indeed!
Jesus, Prince and Saviour,
Lord of Life who died,
Christ the King of Glory
now is glorified!

180

Graham Kendrick (b. 1950)

1. Jesus put this song into our hearts, *(x2)*
it's a song of joy no one can take away.
Jesus put this song into our hearts.

2. Jesus taught us how to live in
harmony, *(x2)*
diff'rent faces, diff'rent races, he made
us one.
Jesus taught us how to live in harmony.

3. Jesus turned our sorrow into dancing, *(x2)*
changed our tears of sadness into rivers
of joy.
Jesus turned our sorrow into a dance.

181

Chris Bowater

Jesus shall take the highest honour,
Jesus shall take the highest praise;
let all earth join heav'n in exalting
the Name which is above all other names.
Let's bow the knee in humble adoration,
for at his name ev'ry knee must bow.
Let ev'ry tongue confess
he is Christ, God's only Son,
Sov'reign Lord, we give you glory now.

For all honour and blessing and power
belongs to you, belongs to you.
All honour and blessing and power
belongs to you, belongs to you,
Lord Jesus Christ, Son of the living God.

182

Graham Kendrick (b. 1950)

1. Jesus, stand among us
at the meeting of our lives,
be our sweet agreement
at the meeting of our eyes.

O Jesus, we love you,
so we gather here,
join our hearts in unity
and take away our fear.

2. So to you we're gath'ring
out of each and ev'ry land,
Christ the love between us
at the joining of our hands.

Optional verse for Communion

3. Jesus stand among us
at the breaking of the bread;
join us as one body
as we worship you, our Head.

183

Nick Fawcett (b. 1957)

1. Jesus, the broken bread, we come to you;
empty, we would be fed – meet us anew.
Teach us to hunger after righteousness,
reach out in love, we pray, to guide
and bless.

2. Jesus, the poured out wine, we come
with awe;
thirsty, we take the cup – quench and
restore.
Teach us to seek your kingdom and
your will,
reach out in love, we pray, our lives
to fill.

3. Jesus, the crucified, we come with shame;
greedy, we've sought reward – made
that our aim.
Teach us to worship now through
word and deed,
reach out in love, we pray, to all in need.

4. Jesus, the risen Lord, we come with
praise;
gladly, we sing of you, our hearts ablaze.
Teach us to glimpse new life beyond
the grave,
reach out in love, we pray, to heal
and save.

5. Jesus, the living one, we come with joy,
truly, no evil can your love destroy.
Teach us to walk in faith, though hope
seems vain,
reach out in love, we pray, renew again.

6. Jesus, the King of kings, we come to
serve,
freely give all for you as you deserve.
Teach us to share the love you daily
show,
reach out in love, we pray, and bid us go.

184

Michael Forster (b. 1946)

Jesus took a piece of bread,
he shared a cup of wine.
'Eat and drink with me,' he said,
'because you're friends of mine!'

1. We eat and drink with Jesus
because we are his friends,
remembering his promise
of life that never ends.

2. We share with one another
the bread and wine he gives,
and celebrate together
the special life he lives.

3. We rise up from the table,
and go where Jesus sends,
to tell the world the gospel
of love that never ends.

185

Isaac Watts (1674-1748), based on Psalm 98, alt.

1. Joy to the world! The Lord is come;
let earth receive her King;
let ev'ry heart prepare him room,
and heav'n and nature sing,
and heav'n and nature sing,
and heav'n and heav'n and nature sing.

2. Joy to the earth! The Saviour reigns;
let us our songs employ;
while fields and floods, rocks,
hills and plains
repeat the sounding joy,
repeat the sounding joy,
repeat, repeat the sounding joy.

3. He rules the world with truth and grace,
and makes the nations prove
the glories of his righteousness,
and wonders of his love,
and wonders of his love,
and wonders, and wonders of his love.

186

Fred Dunn (1907-1979)

Jubilate, ev'rybody,
serve the Lord in all your ways and
come before his presence singing;
enter now his courts with praise.
For the Lord our God is gracious,
and his mercy everlasting.
Jubilate, jubilate, jubilate, Deo!

187

Henry Scott Holland (1847-1918) alt.

1. Judge eternal, throned in splendour,
Lord of lords and King of kings,
with thy living fire of judgement
purge this realm of bitter things:
solace all its wide dominion
with the healing of thy wings.

2. Still the weary folk are pining
for the hour that brings release:
and the city's crowded clangour
cries aloud for sin to cease;
and the homesteads and the woodlands
plead in silence for their peace.

3. Crown, O God, thine own endeavour;
cleave our darkness with thy sword;
feed thy people's hungry spirits
with the richness of thy word:
cleanse the body of this nation
through the glory of the Lord.

188

Traditional

1. Just a closer walk with thee,
grant it, Jesus, if you please;
daily walking close to thee,
let it be, dear Lord, let it be.

2. Through the day of toil that's near,
if I fall, dear Lord, who cares?
Who with me my burden shares?
None but thee, dear Lord, none but thee.

3. When my feeble life is o'er,
time for me will be no more.
Guide me gently, safely on
to the shore, dear Lord, to the shore.

189

Naomi Batya and Sophie Conty

King of kings and Lord of lords,
glory, hallelujah.
King of kings and Lord of lords,
glory, hallelujah.
Jesus, Prince of Peace,
glory, hallelujah.
Jesus, Prince of Peace,
glory, hallelujah.

190

Spiritual

1. Kum ba yah, my Lord, kum ba yah. *(x3)*
O Lord, kum ba yah.
2. Someone's crying, Lord,
kum ba yah, *(x3)*
O Lord, kum ba yah.
3. Someone's singing, Lord,
kum ba yah, *(x3)*
O Lord, kum ba yah.
4. Someone's praying, Lord,
kum ba yah, *(x3)*
O Lord, kum ba yah.

191

Chris Bowater

Lamb of God, Holy One,
Jesus Christ, Son of God,
lifted up willingly to die;
that I the guilty one may know
the blood once shed
still freely flowing,
still cleansing, still healing.

I exalt you, Jesus, my sacrifice,
I exalt you, my Redeemer and my Lord.
I exalt you, worthy Lamb of God,
and in honour I bow down before
your throne.

192

Graham Kendrick (b. 1950)

1. Led like a lamb to the slaughter,
in silence and shame,
there on your back you carried a world
of violence and pain.
Bleeding, dying, bleeding, dying.

You're alive, you're alive,
you have risen!
Alleluia! And the pow'r
and the glory is given,
alleluia! Jesus to you.

2. At break of dawn, poor Mary,
still weeping she came,
when through her grief she heard your
voice
now speaking her name.
Mary, Master, Mary, Master.
3. At the right hand of the Father
now seated on high
you have begun your eternal reign
of justice and joy.
Glory, glory, glory, glory.

193

Michael Forster (b.1946)

1. Let love be real, in giving and receiving,
without the need to manage and to own;
a haven free from posing and pretending,
where ev'ry weakness may be safely
known.
Give me your hand,
along the desert pathway,
give me your love
wherever we may go.

Continued overleaf

As God loves us,
so let us love each other:
with no demands,
just open hands and space to grow.

2. Let love be real, not grasping or confining,
that strange embrace that holds yet sets
us free;
and helps us face the risk of truly living,
and makes us brave to be what we might be.
Give me your strength
when all my words are weakness;
give me your love
in spite of all you know.

3. Let love be real, with no manipulation,
no secret wish to harness or control;
let us accept each other's incompleteness,
and share the joy of learning to be whole.
Give me your hope
through dreams and disappointments;
give me your trust
when all my failings show.

194

Dave Bilbrough

Let there be love shared among us,
let there be love in our eyes.
May now your love sweep this nation;
cause us, O Lord, to arise.
Give us a fresh understanding,
brotherly love that is real.
Let there be love shared among us,
let there be love.

195

Unknown

1. Let us break bread together
on our knees,
let us break bread together
on our knees.
When I fall on my knees
with my face to the rising sun,
O Lord, have mercy on me.

2. Let us share wine together
on our knees,
let us share wine together
on our knees.
When I fall on my knees
with my face to the rising sun,
O Lord, have mercy on me.

3. Let us praise God together
on our knees,
let us praise God together
on our knees.
When I fall on my knees
with my face to the rising sun,
O Lord, have mercy on me.

196

James Edward Seddon (1915-1983)

1. Let us praise God together, let us praise;
let us praise God together all our days.
He is faithful in all his ways,
he is worthy of all our praise,
his name be exalted on high.

2. Let us seek God together, let us pray;
let us seek his forgiveness as we pray.
He will cleanse us from all our sin,
he will help us the fight to win,
his name be exalted on high.

3. Let us serve God together, him obey;
let our lives show his goodness
through each day.
Christ the Lord is the world's true light,
let us serve him with all our might,
his name be exalted on high.

197

Fred Kaan (b. 1929)

1. Let us talents and tongues employ,
reaching out with a shout of joy:
bread is broken, the wine is poured,
Christ is spoken and seen and heard.

Jesus lives again,
earth can breathe again,
pass the word around:
loaves abound!

2. Christ is able to make us one,
at his table he sets the tone,
teaching people to live to bless,
love in word and in deed express.

3. Jesus calls us in, sends us out
bearing fruit in a world of doubt,
gives us love to tell, bread to share:
God-Immanuel everywhere!

198

George William Kitchin (1827-1912) and Michael Robert Newbolt (1874-1956) alt.

Lift high the Cross,
the love of Christ proclaim
till all the world adore his sacred name!

1. Come, Christians,
follow where our Saviour trod,
o'er death victorious,
Christ the Son of God.

2. Led on their way by this
triumphant sign,
the hosts of God in joyful
praise combine:

3. Each new disciple
of the Crucified
is called to bear the seal
of him who died:

4. Saved by the Cross
whereon their Lord was slain,
now Adam's children
their lost home regain:

5. From north and south,
from east and west they raise
in growing harmony
their song of praise:

6. O Lord, once lifted
on the glorious tree,
as thou hast promised,
draw us unto thee:

7. Let ev'ry race
and ev'ry language tell
of him who saves
from fear of death and hell:

8. From farthest regions,
let them homage bring,
and on his Cross
adore their Saviour King:

9. Set up thy throne,
that earth's despair may cease
beneath the shadow
of its healing peace:

10. For thy blest Cross
which doth for all atone,
creation's praises rise
before thy throne:

11. So let the world
proclaim with one accord
the praise of our
ever-living Lord.

199

Michael Perry (1942-96)

1. Like a mighty river flowing,
like a flow'r in beauty growing,
far beyond all human knowing
is the perfect peace of God.

2. Like the hills serene and even,
like the coursing clouds of heaven,
like the heart that's been forgiven
is the perfect peace of God.

3. Like the summer breezes playing,
like the tall trees softly swaying,
like the lips of silent praying
is the perfect peace of God.

Continued overleaf

4. Like the morning sun ascended,
like the scents of evening blended,
like a friendship never ended
is the perfect peace of God.

5. Like the azure ocean swelling,
like the jewel all-excelling,
far beyond our human telling
is the perfect peace of God.

200

Aniceto Nazareth

Listen, let your heart keep seeking;
listen to his constant speaking;
listen to the Spirit calling you.
Listen to his inspiration;
listen to his invitation;
listen to the Spirit calling you.

1. He's in the sound of the thunder,
in the whisper of the breeze.
He's in the might of the whirlwind,
in the roaring of the seas.

2. He's in the laughter of children,
in the patter of the rain.
Hear him in cries of the suff'ring,
in their moaning and their pain.

3. He's in the noise of the city,
in the singing of the birds.
And in the night-time the stillness
helps you listen to his word.

201

Christopher Massey (b. 1956)

1. Little Jesus, sleep away, in the hay,
while we worship, watch and pray.
We will gather at the manger,
worship this amazing stranger:
little Jesus born on earth,
sign of grace and human worth.

2. Little Jesus, sleep away, while you may;
pain is for another day.
While you sleep, we will not wake you,
when you cry we'll not forsake you.
Little Jesus, sleep away,
we will worship you today.

202

Traditional Czech carol
trans. Percy Dearmer (1867-1936)

1. Little Jesus, sweetly sleep, do not stir;
we will lend a coat of fur;
we will rock you, rock you, rock you,
we will rock you, rock you, rock you,
see the fur to keep you warm,
snugly round your tiny form.

2. Mary's little baby sleep, sweetly sleep,
sleep in comfort, slumber deep;
we will rock you, rock you, rock you,
we will rock you, rock you, rock you;
we will serve you all we can,
darling, darling little man.

203

Jan Berry (b. 1953)

1. Living God, your word has called us,
summoned us to live by grace,
make us one in hope and vision,
as we gather in this place.
Take our searching, take our praising,
take the silence of our prayer,
offered up in joyful worship,
springing from the love we share.

2. Living God, your love has called us
in the name of Christ your Son,
forming us to be his body,
by your Spirit making one.
Working, laughing, learning, growing,
old and young and black and white,
gifts and skills together sharing,
in your service all unite.

3. Living God, your hope has called us
to the world that you have made,
teaching us to live for others,
humble, joyful, unafraid.
Give us eyes to see your presence,
joy in laughter, hope in pain.
In our loving, in our living,
give us strength that Christ may reign.

5. Lord for ourselves;
in living power remake us –
self on the cross
and Christ upon the throne,
past put behind us,
for the future take us:
Lord of our lives,
to live for Christ alone.

204

Timothy Dudley-Smith (b. 1926)

1. Lord for the years
your love has kept and guided,
urged and inspired us,
cheered us on our way,
sought us and saved us,
pardoned and provided:
Lord of the years,
we bring our thanks today.

2. Lord, for that word,
the word of life which fires us,
speaks to our hearts
and sets our souls ablaze,
teaches and trains,
rebukes us and inspires us:
Lord of the word,
receive your people's praise.

3. Lord, for our land
in this our generation,
spirits oppressed by pleasure,
wealth and care:
for young and old,
for commonwealth and nation,
Lord of our land,
be pleased to hear our prayer.

4. Lord, for our world;
when we disown and doubt you,
loveless in strength,
and comfortless in pain,
hungry and helpless,
lost indeed without you:
Lord of the world,
we pray that Christ may reign.

205

Geoff Bullock

1. Lord, I come to you,
let my heart be changed, renewed,
flowing from the grace
that I found in you.
And, Lord, I've come to know
the weaknesses I see in me
will be stripped away
by the pow'r of your love.

Hold me close,
let your love surround me,
bring me near,
draw me to your side;
and as I wait,
I'll rise up like an eagle,
and I will soar with you;
your Spirit leads me on
in the pow'r of your love.

2. Lord, unveil my eyes,
let me see you face to face,
the knowledge of your love
as you live in me.
Lord, renew my mind
as your will unfolds in my life,
in living ev'ry day
in the pow'r of your love.

206

Rick Founds

Lord, I lift your name on high;
Lord, I love to sing your praises.
I'm so glad you're in my life;
I'm so glad you came to save us.
(Repeat)

You came from heaven to earth
to show the way,
from the earth to the cross,
my debt to pay,
from the cross to the grave,
from the grave to the sky,
Lord, I lift your name on high.

207

Patrick Appleford (b. 1925)

1. Lord Jesus Christ, you have come to us,
you are one with us, Mary's Son.
Cleansing our souls from all their sin,
pouring your love and goodness in,
Jesus, our love for you we sing,
living Lord.

2. Lord Jesus Christ, now and ev'ry day
teach us how to pray, Son of God.
You have commanded us to do
this in remembrance, Lord, of you.
Into our lives your pow'r breaks through,
living Lord.

3. Lord Jesus Christ, you have come to us,
born as one of us, Mary's Son.
Led out to die on Calvary,
risen from death to set us free,
living Lord Jesus, help us see
you are Lord.

4. Lord Jesus Christ, I would come to you,
live my life for you, Son of God.
All your commands I know are true,
your many gifts will make me new,
into my life your pow'r breaks through,
living Lord.

208

Timothy Dudley-Smith (b. 1926)

1. Lord of all life and power
at whose creative word
in nature's first primeval hour
our formless being stirred,
you made the light to shine,
O shine on us, we pray,
renew with light and life divine
your church in this our day.

2. Lord of the fertile earth
who caused the world to be,
whose life alone can bring to birth
the fruits of land and sea,
teach us to use aright
and share the gifts you give,
to tend the earth as in your sight
that all the world may live.

3. Lord of the cross and grave
who died and lives again,
who came in love to seek and save
and then to rise and reign,
we share, as once you shared,
in mortal birth and breath,
and ours the risen life that dared
to vanquish sin and death.

4. Lord of the wind and flame,
the promised Spirit's sign,
possess our hearts in Jesus' name,
come down, O Love divine!
Help us in Christ to grow,
from sin and self to cease,
and daily in our lives to show
your love and joy and peace.

5. Lord of the passing years
whose changeless purpose stands,
our lives and loves, our hopes and fears,
we place within your hands;
we bring you but your own,
forgiven, loved and free,
to follow Christ, and Christ alone,
through all the days to be.

209

Philip Pusey (1799-1855), based on the German of Matthäus Apelles von Löwenstern (1594-1648) alt.

1. Lord of our life,
   and God of our salvation,
   star of our night,
   and hope of ev'ry nation,
   hear and receive
   thy Church's supplication,
   Lord God almighty.

2. Lord, thou canst help
   when earthly armour faileth,
   Lord, thou canst save
   when deadly sin assaileth;
   Christ, o'er thy rock
   nor death nor hell prevaileth;
   grant us thy peace, Lord.

3. Peace in our hearts,
   our evil thoughts assuaging;
   peace in thy Church,
   where people are engaging;
   peace, when the world
   its busy war is waging:
   calm all our raging.

4. Grant us thy grace
   through trial and temptation,
   grant us thy truth,
   thy promise of salvation,
   grant us thy peace
   in ev'ry heart and nation,
   and in thy heaven.

210

Graham Kendrick (b. 1950)

1. Lord, the light of your love is shining,
   in the midst of the darkness, shining;
   Jesus, Light of the World, shine upon us,
   set us free by the truth you now bring us.
   Shine on me, shine on me.

Shine, Jesus, shine,
fill this land with the Father's glory;
blaze, Spirit, blaze,
set our hearts on fire.
Flow, river, flow,
flood the nations with grace and mercy;
send forth your word, Lord,
and let there be light.

2. Lord, I come to your awesome presence,
   from the shadows into your radiance;
   by the blood I may enter your brightness,
   search me, try me, consume all
   my darkness.
   Shine on me, shine on me.

3. As we gaze on your kingly brightness,
   so our faces display your likeness,
   ever changing from glory to glory;
   mirrored here may our lives tell your story.
   Shine on me, shine on me.

211

Jean Holloway (b. 1939)

1. Lord, we come to ask your healing,
   teach us of love;
   all unspoken shame revealing,
   teach us of love.
   Take our selfish thoughts and actions,
   petty feuds, divisive factions,
   hear us now to you appealing,
   teach us of love.

2. Soothe away our pain and sorrow,
   hold us in love;
   grace we cannot buy or borrow,
   hold us in love.
   Though we see but dark and danger,
   though we spurn both friend and stranger,
   though we often dread tomorrow,
   hold us in love.

Continued overleaf

3. When the bread is raised and broken,
fill us with love;
words of consecration spoken,
fill us with love.
As our grateful prayers continue,
make the faith that we have in you
more than just an empty token,
fill us with love.

4. Help us live for one another,
bind us in love;
stranger, neighbour, father, mother –
bind us in love.
All are equal at your table,
through your Spirit make us able
to embrace as sister, brother,
bind us in love.

212

Susan Sayers (b. 1946)

1. Lord, when I turn my back on you
the fears and darkness grow.
I need you, oh I need you, Lord,
to show me where to go.

2. With you beside me, Lord, I find
the evils that I face
become instead a joyfulness,
a fountain of your grace.

3. So shape me to your purpose, Lord,
and tell me what to do;
and if I start to turn away,
then turn me back to you.

4. And when the world is over Lord,
or over just for me,
there is nowhere but with you, Lord,
that I would rather be.

213

Christina Georgina Rossetti (1830-1894)

1. Love came down at Christmas,
Love all lovely, Love divine;
Love was born at Christmas,
star and angels gave the sign.

2. Worship we the Godhead,
Love incarnate, Love divine;
worship we our Jesus:
but wherewith for sacred sign?

3. Love shall be our token,
love be yours and love be mine,
love to God and all men,
love for plea and gift and sign.

214

Luke Connaughton (1917-1979)

1. Love is his word, love is his way,
feasting with all, fasting alone,
living and dying, rising again,
love only love, is his way.

Richer than gold is the love of my Lord:
better than splendour and wealth.

2. Love is his way, love is his mark,
sharing his last Passover feast,
Christ at the table, host to the twelve,
love, only love, is his mark.

3. Love is his mark, love is his sign,
bread for our strength, wine for our joy,
'This is my body, this is my blood.'
Love, only love, is his sign.

4. Love is his sign, love is his news,
'Do this,' he said, 'lest you forget
all my deep sorrow, all my dear blood.'
Love, only love, is his news.

5. Love is his news, love is his name,
we are his own, chosen and called,
family, brethren, cousins and kin.
Love, only love, is his name.

6. Love is his name, love is his law,
hear his command, all who are his,
'Love one another, I have loved you.'
Love, only love, is his law.

7. Love is his law, love is his word:
love of the Lord, Father and Word,
love of the Spirit, God ever one,
love, only love, is his word.

215

Pamela Hayes

1. Lovely in your littleness,
   longing for our lowliness,
   longing for our lowliness,
   searching for our meekness:
   Jesus is our joy, Jesus is our joy.

2. Peace within our powerlessness,
   hope within our helplessness,
   hope within our helplessness,
   love within our loneliness:
   Jesus is our joy, Jesus is our joy.

3. Held in Mary's tenderness,
   tiny hands are raised to bless,
   tiny hands are raised to bless,
   touching us with God's caress:
   Jesus is our joy, Jesus is our joy.

4. Joy, then, in God's graciousness,
   peace comes with gentleness,
   peace comes with gentleness,
   filling hearts with gladness:
   Jesus is our joy, Jesus is our joy.

216

Noel and Tricia Richards

1. Love songs from heaven are filling the
   earth,
   bringing great hope to all nations;
   evil has prospered, but truth is alive,
   in this dark world the light still shines.

2. Nothing has silenced this gospel of
   Christ;
   it echoes down through the ages.
   Blood of the martyrs has made your
   church strong,
   in this dark world the light still shines.

   For you we live, and for you we may die,
   through us may Jesus be seen;
   for you alone we will offer our lives,
   in this dark world our light will shine.

3. Let ev'ry nation be filled with your song;
   this is the cry of your people,
   'We will not settle for anything less,
   in this dark world our light must shine.'

217

Jane Elizabeth Leeson (1809-1881)

1. Loving Shepherd of thy sheep,
   keep me, Lord, in safety keep;
   nothing can thy pow'r withstand,
   none can pluck me from thy hand.

2. Loving Shepherd, thou didst give
   thine own life that I might live;
   may I love thee day by day,
   gladly thy sweet will obey.

3. Loving Shepherd, ever near,
   teach me still thy voice to hear;
   suffer not my steps to stray
   from the straight and narrow way.

4. Where thou leadest may I go,
   walking in thy steps below;
   then, before thy Father's throne,
   Jesu, claim me for thine own.

218

Robert Lowry (1826-1899)

1. Low in the grave he lay,
   Jesus, my Saviour;
   waiting the coming day,
   Jesus, my Lord.

   Up from the grave he arose,
   with a mighty triumph o'er his foes;
   he arose a victor
   from the dark domain,
   and he lives for ever
   with his saints to reign.
   He arose! He arose!
   Hallelujah! Christ arose!

Continued overleaf

2. Vainly they watch his bed,
Jesus, my Saviour;
vainly they seal the dead,
Jesus, my Lord.

Up from the grave he arose,
with a mighty triumph o'er his foes;
he arose a victor
from the dark domain,
and he lives for ever
with his saints to reign.
He arose! He arose!
Hallelujah! Christ arose!

3. Death cannot keep its prey,
Jesus, my Saviour;
he tore the bars away,
Jesus, my Lord.

219

Jack W. Hayford (b. 1934)

Majesty, worship his majesty;
unto Jesus be glory, honour and praise.
Majesty, kingdom authority
flow from his throne unto his own:
his anthem raise.
So exalt, lift up on high the name of Jesus;
magnify, come glorify Christ Jesus the King.
Majesty, worship his majesty,
Jesus who died, now glorified,
King of all kings.

220

Sebastian Temple (1928-1997)
based on the Prayer of St Francis

1. Make me a channel of your peace.
Where there is hatred, let me bring
your love.
Where there is injury, your pardon, Lord;
and where there's doubt, true faith in you.

O, Master, grant that I may never seek
so much to be consoled as to console,
to be understood as to understand,
to be loved as to love with all my soul.

2. Make me a channel of your peace.
Where there's despair in life, let me
bring hope.
Where there is darkness, only light,
and where there's sadness, ever joy.

3. Make me a channel of your peace.
It is in pardoning that we are pardoned,
in giving of ourselves that we receive,
and in dying that we're born to eternal life.

221

Graham Kendrick (b. 1950)

1. Make way, make way, for Christ the King
in splendour arrives;
fling wide the gates and welcome him
into your lives.

Make way (make way), make way (make way),
for the King of kings (for the King of kings);
make way (make way), make way (make way),
and let his kingdom in!

2. He comes the broken hearts to heal,
the pris'ners to free;
the deaf shall hear, the lame shall dance,
the blind shall see.

3. And those who mourn with heavy hearts,
who weep and sigh,
with laughter, joy and royal crown
he'll beautify.

4. We call you now to worship him
as Lord of all,
to have no gods before him,
their thrones must fall.

222

Philipp Bliss (1838-1876) alt.

1. Man of sorrows! What a name
for the Son of God who came
ruined sinners to reclaim!
Alleluia! What a Saviour!

2. Bearing shame and scoffing rude,
in my place condemned he stood;
sealed my pardon with his blood;
Alleluia! What a Saviour!

3. Guilty, vile and helpless we;
spotless Lamb of God was he:
full atonement – can it be?
Alleluia! What a Saviour!

4. Lifted up was he to die:
'It is finished!' was his cry;
now in heav'n exalted high;
Alleluia! What a Saviour!

5. When he comes, our glorious King,
all his ransomed home to bring,
then anew this song we'll sing:
Alleluia! what a Saviour!

223

Michael Forster (b. 1946)

1. Mary, blessèd grieving mother,
waiting by the cross of shame,
through your patient, prayerful vigil,
kindle hope's eternal flame;
crying in the pains of earth,
singing of redemption's birth.

2. Where the crosses of the nations
darken still the noon-day skies,
see the sad madonna weeping
through a million mothers' eyes.
Holy Mary, full of grace,
all our tears with yours embrace.

3. Standing with the suff'ring Saviour,
still oppressed by hate and fear,
where the gentle still are murdered
and protestors disappear:
mother of the crucified,
call his people to your side!

4. Holy mother, watching, waiting,
for the saving of the earth;
in the loneliness of dying,
speak of hope and human worth,
there for all the world to see,
lifted up at Calvary!

224

Michael Forster (b. 1946)

1. Mary, blessèd teenage mother,
with what holy joy you sing!
Humble, yet above all other,
from your womb shall healing spring.
Out of wedlock pregnant found,
full of grace with blessing crowned.

2. Mother of the homeless stranger
only outcasts recognise,
point us to the modern manger;
not a sight for gentle eyes!
Oh the joyful news we tell:
'Even here, Immanuel!'

3. Now, throughout the townships ringing,
hear the black madonna cry,
songs of hope and freedom singing,
poor and humble lifted high.
Here the Spirit finds a womb
for the breaker of the tomb!

4. Holy mother, for the nations
bring to birth the child divine:
Israel's strength and consolation,
and the hope of Palestine!
All creation reconciled
in the crying of a child!

225

Kate Barclay Wilkinson (1859-1928)

1. May the mind of Christ my Saviour
live in me from day to day,
by his love and pow'r controlling
all I do and say.

Continued overleaf

2. May the word of God dwell richly
in my heart from hour to hour,
so that I may triumph only
in his saving pow'r.

3. May the peace of God my Father
rule my life in ev'rything,
that I may be calm to comfort
sick and sorrowing.

4. May the love of Jesus fill me,
as the waters fill the sea;
him exalting, self abasing,
this is victory.

5. May I run the race before me,
strong and brave to face the foe,
looking only unto Jesus,
as I onward go.

226

Graham Kendrick (b. 1950)

1. Meekness and majesty,
manhood and deity,
in perfect harmony, the Man who is God.
Lord of eternity dwells in humanity,
kneels in humility and washes our feet.

O what a mystery, meekness and majesty.
Bow down and worship for this is your God,
this is your God.

2. Father's pure radiance,
perfect in innocence,
yet learns obedience to death on a cross.
Suff'ring to give us life,
conqu'ring through sacrifice,
and as they crucify prays: 'Father forgive.'

3. Wisdom unsearchable,
God the invisible,
love indestructible in frailty appears.
Lord of infinity, stooping so tenderly,
lifts our humanity to the heights of
his throne.

227

Eleanor Farjeon (1881-1965)

1. Morning has broken like the first morning,
blackbird has spoken like the first bird.
Praise for the singing!
Praise for the morning!
Praise for them, springing
fresh from the Word!

2. Sweet the rain's new fall, sunlit from heaven,
like the first dew-fall on the first grass.
Praise for the sweetness of the wet garden,
sprung in completeness where his feet pass.

3. Mine is the sunlight! Mine is the morning
born of the one light Eden saw play!
Praise with elation, praise ev'ry morning,
God's re-creation of the new day!

228

Estelle White (b. 1925)

1. 'Moses, I know you're the man,'
the Lord said.
'You're going to work out my plan,'
the Lord said.
'Lead all the Israelites out of slavery,
and I shall make them a wandering race
called the people of God.'

So ev'ry day we're on our way,
for we're a travelling, wandering race
called the people of God.

2. 'Don't get too set in your ways,'
the Lord said.
'Each step is only a phase,'
the Lord said.
'I'll go before you and I shall be a sign
to guide my travelling, wandering race.
You're the people of God.'

3. 'No matter what you may do,'
the Lord said,
'I shall be faithful and true,'
the Lord said.
'My love will strengthen you as you go along,
for you're my travelling, wandering race.
You're the people of God.'

4. 'Look at the birds in the air,'
the Lord said.
'They fly unhampered by care,'
the Lord said.
'You will move easier if you're trav'lling light,
for you're a wandering, vagabond race.'
You're the people of God.'

5. 'Foxes have places to go,'
the Lord said.
'but I've no home here below,'
the Lord said.
'So if you want to be with me all your days,
keep up the moving and travelling on.
You're the people of God.'

229

Ray Palmer (1808-1887)

1. My faith looks up to thee,
thou Lamb of Calvary,
Saviour divine!
Now hear me while I pray,
take all my guilt away,
O let me from this day
be wholly thine.

2. May thy rich grace impart
strength to my fainting heart,
my zeal inspire.
As thou hast died for me,
O may my love to thee
pure, warm and changeless be,
a living fire.

3. While life's dark maze I tread,
and griefs around me spread,
be thou my guide;
bid darkness turn to day,
wipe sorrow's tears away,
nor let me ever stray
from thee aside.

4. When ends life's transient dream,
when death's cold sullen stream
shall o'er me roll,
blest Saviour, then in love,
fear and distrust remove;
O bear me safe above,
a ransomed soul.

230

Henry Williams Baker (1821-1877)

1. My Father, for another night
of quiet sleep and rest,
for all the joy of morning light,
thy holy name be blest.

2. Now with the new-born day I give
myself anew to thee,
that as thou willest I may live,
and what thou willest be.

3. Whate'er I do, things great or small,
whate'er I speak or frame,
thy glory may I seek in all,
do all in Jesus' name.

4. My Father, for his sake, I pray,
thy child accept and bless;
and lead me by thy grace today
in paths of righteousness.

231

Robin Mark

1. My heart will sing to you
because of your great love,
a love so rich, so pure,
a love beyond compare;
the wilderness, the barren place,
become a blessing
in the warmth of your embrace.

Continued overleaf

May my heart sing your praise for ever,
may my voice lift your name, my God;
may my soul know no other treasure
than your love, than your love.

2. When earthly wisdom dims
the light of knowing you,
or if my search for understanding
clouds your way,
to you I fly, my hiding-place,
where revelation
is beholding face to face.

232

Darlene Zschech
© 1993 Darlene Zschech /Hillsong Music Australia/Kingsway's Thankyou Music

1. My Jesus, my Saviour,
Lord, there is none like you.
All of my days I want to praise
the wonders of your mighty love.

2. My comfort, my shelter,
tower of refuge and strength,
let ev'ry breath, all that I am,
never cease to worship you.

3. Shout to the Lord,
all the earth, let us sing
power and majesty,
praise to the King.
Mountains bow down
and the seas will roar
at the sound of your name.

4. I sing for joy
at the work of your hands.
Forever I'll love you,
forever I'll stand.
Nothing compares to the promise
I have in you.

233

Graham Kendrick (b. 1950)
© 1989 Make Way Music

1. My Lord, what love is this,
that pays so dearly,
that I, the guilty one,
may go free!

Amazing love, O what sacrifice,
the Son of God, giv'n for me.
My debt he pays, and my death he dies,
that I might live,
that I might live.

2. And so they watched him die,
despised, rejected;
but O, the blood he shed
flowed for me!

3. And now this love of Christ
shall flow like rivers;
come, wash your guilt away,
live again!

234

Timothy Dudley-Smith (b. 1926)
© Timothy Dudley-Smith

1. Name of all majesty,
fathomless mystery,
King of the ages
by angels adored;
power and authority,
splendour and dignity,
bow to his mastery –
Jesus is Lord!

2. Child of our destiny,
God from eternity,
love of the Father
on sinners outpoured;
see now what God has done
sending his only Son,
Christ the belovèd One,
Jesus is Lord!

3. Saviour of Calvary,
costliest victory,
darkness defeated
and Eden restored;
born as a man to die,
nailed to a cross on high,
cold in the grave to lie,
Jesus is Lord!

4. Source of all sovereignty,
light, immortality,
life everlasting
and heaven assured;
so with the ransomed, we
praise him eternally,
Christ in his majesty,
Jesus is Lord!

235 Sarah Flower Adams (1805-1848)

1. Nearer, my God, to thee,
nearer to thee!
E'en though it be a cross
that raiseth me:
still all my song would be,
'Nearer, my God, to thee,
nearer to thee.'

2. Though, like the wanderer,
the sun gone down,
darkness be over me,
my rest a stone;
yet in my dreams I'd be
nearer, my God, to thee,
nearer to thee!

3. There let the way appear,
steps unto heav'n;
all that thou sendest me
in mercy giv'n:
angels to beckon me
nearer, my God, to thee,
nearer to thee!

4. Then, with my waking thoughts
bright with thy praise,
out of my stony griefs
Bethel I'll raise;
so by my woes to be
nearer, my God, to thee,
nearer to thee!

5. Or if on joyful wing
cleaving the sky,
sun, moon and stars forgot,
upwards I fly,
still all my song shall be,
'Nearer, my God, to thee,
nearer to thee.'

236 Erik Routley (1917-1982)

1. New songs of celebration render
to him who has great wonders done.
Love sits enthroned in ageless splendour:
come and adore the mighty one.
He has made known his great salvation
which all his friends with joy confess:
he has revealed to ev'ry nation
his everlasting righteousness.

2. Joyfully, heartily resounding,
let ev'ry instrument and voice
peal out the praise of grace abounding,
calling the whole world to rejoice.
Trumpets and organs, set in motion
such sounds as make the heavens ring;
all things that live in earth and ocean,
make music for your mighty King.

3. Rivers and seas and torrents roaring,
honour the Lord with wild acclaim;
mountains and stones look up adoring
and find a voice to praise his name.
Righteous, commanding, ever glorious,
praises be his that never cease:
just is our God, whose truth victorious
establishes the world in peace.

237 Elizabeth Ann Porter Head (1850-1936)

1. O Breath of Life,
come sweeping through us,
revive your Church with life and pow'r;
O Breath of Life, come cleanse,
renew us,
and fit your Church to meet this hour.

Continued overleaf

2. O Breath of Love,
   come breathe within us,
renewing thought and will and heart;
come, love of Christ, afresh to win us,
revive your Church in ev'ry part!

3. O Wind of God,
   come bend us, break us,
till humbly we confess our need;
then, in your tenderness remake us,
revive, restore – for this we plead.

4. Revive us, Lord; is zeal abating
while harvest fields are vast and white?
Revive us, Lord, the world is waiting –
equip thy Church to spread the light.

238

Charles Wesley (1707-1788)

1. O for a thousand tongues to sing
my dear Redeemer's praise,
my dear Redeemer's praise,
the glories of my God and King,
the triumphs of his grace,
the triumphs of his grace,
the triumphs of his grace!

2. Jesus! the name that charms our fears,
that bids our sorrows cease,
that bids our sorrows cease;
'tis music in the sinner's ears,
'tis life and health and peace. *(x3)*

3. He breaks the pow'r of cancelled sin,
he sets the pris'ner free,
he sets the pris'ner free;
his blood can make the foulest clean;
his blood availed for me. *(x3)*

4. He speaks; and, list'ning to his voice,
new life the dead receive,
new life the dead receive,
the mournful broken hearts rejoice,
the humble poor believe. *(x3)*

5. Hear him, ye deaf; his praise, ye dumb,
your loosened tongues employ,
your loosened tongues employ;
ye blind, behold your Saviour come;
and leap, ye lame, for joy! *(x3)*

6. My gracious Master and my God,
assist me to proclaim,
assist me to proclaim
and spread through all the earth abroad
the honours of thy name. *(x3)*

239

Graham Kendrick (b. 1950)

O give thanks to the Lord,
for his love will never end.
O give thanks to the Lord,
for his love it never will end.
(Repeat)

1. Sing to him, sing your praise to him,
tell the world of all he has done.
Fill the nations with celebrations
to welcome him as he comes.

2. Give him thanks for the fruitful earth,
for the sun, the seasons, the rain.
For the joys of his good creation,
the life and breath he sustains.

3. Let the heavens rejoice before him,
the earth and all it contains.
All creation in jubilation,
join in the shout, 'The Lord reigns!'

4. Let the hearts of those who seek him
be happy now in his love.
Let their faces look up and gaze
at his gracious smile from above.

240

Michael Perry (1942-1996)
© Mrs B. Perry/Jubilate Hymns

1. O God beyond all praising,
 we worship you today,
 and sing the love amazing
 that songs cannot repay;
 for we can only wonder
 at ev'ry gift you send,
 at blessings without number
 and mercies without end:
 we lift our hearts before you
 and wait upon your word,
 we honour and adore you,
 our great and mighty Lord.

2. Then hear, O gracious Saviour,
 accept the love we bring,
 that we who know your favour
 may serve you as our King;
 and whether our tomorrows
 be filled with good or ill,
 we'll triumph through our sorrows
 and rise to bless you still:
 to marvel at your beauty
 and glory in your ways,
 and make a joyful duty
 our sacrifice of praise.

241

Gilbert Keith Chesterton (1874-1936)
© Copyright control

1. O God of earth and altar,
 bow down and hear our cry,
 our earthly rulers falter,
 our people drift and die;
 the walls of gold entomb us,
 the swords of scorn divide,
 take not thy thunder from us,
 but take away our pride.

2. From all that terror teaches,
 from lies of tongue and pen,
 from all the easy speeches
 that comfort cruel men,
 from sale and profanation
 of honour and the sword,
 from sleep and from damnation,
 deliver us, good Lord!

3. Tie in a living tether
 the prince and priest and thrall,
 bind all our lives together,
 smite us and save us all;
 in ire and exultation
 aflame with faith and free,
 lift up a living nation,
 a single sword to thee.

242

Philip Doddridge (1702-1751) alt.

1. O happy day! that fixed my choice
 on thee, my Saviour and my God!
 Well may this glowing heart rejoice,
 and tell its raptures all abroad.

2. 'Tis done, the work of grace is done!
 I am my Lord's, and he is mine!
 He drew me, and I followed on,
 glad to confess the voice divine.

3. Now rest, my long-divided heart,
 fixed on this blissful centre, rest;
 nor ever from thy Lord depart,
 with him of ev'ry good possessed.

4. High heav'n, that heard the solemn vow,
 that vow renewed shall daily hear;
 till in life's latest hour I bow,
 and bless in death a bond so dear.

When a tune with a Refrain is used this is sung after each verse:

O happy day! O happy day!
When Jesus washed my sins away,
he taught me how to watch and pray,
and live rejoicing ev'ry day;
O happy day! O happy day!
When Jesus washed my sins away.

243 Traditional

O, how good is the Lord! (x3)
I never will forget what he has done for me.

1. He gives us salvation,
   how good is the Lord. *(x3)*
   I never will forget
   what he has done for me.

2. He gives us his Spirit . . .

3. He gives us healing . . .

4. He gives us his body . . .

5. He gives us his freedom . . .

6. He gives us each other . . .

7. He gives us his glory . . .

244 Michael Forster (b. 1946) based on the German

1. O Lamb of God, most holy,
   salvation's perfect sign,
   by your redeeming passion,
   we share the life divine.
   The cost of our deliv'rance
   in flowing blood is shown,
   and life in all its fullness
   is found in you alone.

2. Upon the cross you carried
   a universe of shame,
   your dying breath atoning
   for centuries of blame.
   So now accept your servant,
   who on your love relied,
   to rest in peace eternal
   redeemed and purified.

3. O draw us to your presence,
   beyond the sundered veil,
   to stand in silent wonder,
   where words and senses fail.
   In fellowship unbroken
   with all who went before,
   we join with saints and angels
   to worship and adore.

245 John Wimber (1934-1997)

1. O let the Son of God enfold you
   with his Spirit and his love,
   let him fill your heart and satisfy your
   soul.
   O let him have the things that hold you,
   and his Spirit like a dove
   will descend upon your life and make
   you whole.

Jesus, O Jesus,
come and fill your lambs.
Jesus, O Jesus,
come and fill your lambs.

2. O come and sing this song with gladness
   as your hearts are filled with joy,
   lift your hands in sweet surrender to his
   name.
   O give him all your tears and sadness,
   give him all your years of pain,
   and you'll enter into life in Jesus' name.

246 Samuel Scheidt (1650)

trans. Percy Dearmer (1867-1936) alt.

1. O little one sweet, O little one mild,
   thy Father's purpose thou hast fulfilled;
   thou cam'st from heav'n to dwell below,
   to share the joys and tears we know.
   O little one sweet, O little one mild.

2. O little one sweet, O little one mild,
with joy thou hast the whole world filled;
thou camest here from heav'n's domain,
to bring us comfort in our pain,
O little one sweet, O little one mild.

3. O little one sweet, O little one mild,
in thee Love's beauties are all distilled;
then light in us thy love's bright flame,
that we may give thee back the same,
O little one sweet, O little one mild.

247

Patrick Appleford

1. O Lord, all the world belongs to you,
and you are always making all things new.
What is wrong you forgive,
and the new life you give
is what's turning the world upside down.

2. The world's only loving to its friends,
but you have brought us love that
never ends;
loving enemies too,
and this loving with you
is what's turning the world upside down.

3. This world lives divided and apart.
You draw us all together and we start,
in your body, to see
that in a fellowship we
can be turning the world upside down.

4. The world wants the wealth to live
in state,
but you show us a new way to be great:
like a servant you came,
and if we do the same,
we'll be turning the world upside down.

5. O Lord, all the world belongs to you,
and you are always making all things new.
Send your Spirit on all
in your Church, whom you call
to be turning the world upside down.

248

Karl Boberg (1859-1940)
trans. Stuart K. Hine (1899-1989)

1. O Lord, my God,
when I in awesome wonder
consider all the works
thy hand has made,
I see the stars,
I hear the rolling thunder,
thy pow'r throughout
the universe displayed.

Then sings my soul,
my Saviour God, to thee:
how great thou art, how great thou art.
Then sings my soul,
my Saviour God, to thee;
how great thou art, how great thou art.

2. When through the woods
and forest glades I wander
and hear the birds sing
sweetly in the trees;
when I look down
from lofty mountain grandeur,
and hear the brook,
and feel the gentle breeze.

3. And when I think that God,
his Son not sparing,
sent him to die,
I scarce can take it in
that on the cross,
my burden gladly bearing,
he bled and died
to take away my sin.

4. When Christ shall come
with shout of acclamation
and take me home,
what joy shall fill my heart;
when I shall bow
in humble adoration,
and there proclaim:
my God, how great thou art.

249

Michael Forster (b. 1946)

1. O Lord of our salvation,
 the pains of all creation
 are borne upon your cross:
 the failure of compassion,
 revealed in starkest fashion,
 exposes all our gold as dross.

2. We hear your voice protesting,
 to love and hope attesting,
 where justice is denied.
 Where innocents are dying,
 where hate is crucifying,
 you call us to your bleeding side.

3. O give us faith to stay here,
 to wait, to watch and pray here,
 and witness to your cry;
 in scarred and tearful faces,
 in countless painful places,
 you give us hope that will not die.

250

Graham Kendrick (b. 1950)

O Lord, your tenderness,
melting all my bitterness,
O Lord, I receive your love.
O Lord, your loveliness,
changing all my ugliness,
O Lord, I receive your love.
O Lord, I receive your love.
O Lord, I receive your love.

251

George Matheson (1842-1906)

1. O Love that wilt not let me go,
 I rest my weary soul in thee;
 I give thee back the life I owe,
 that in thine ocean depths its flow
 may richer, fuller be.

2. O Light that follow'st all my way,
 I yield my flick'ring torch to thee;
 my heart restores its borrowed ray,
 that in thy sunshine's blaze its day
 may brighter, fairer be.

3. O Joy that seekest me through pain,
 I cannot close my heart to thee;
 I trace the rainbow through the rain,
 and feel the promise is not vain
 that morn shall tearless be.

4. O Cross that liftest up my head,
 I dare not ask to fly from thee:
 I lay in dust life's glory dead,
 and from the ground there blossoms red
 life that shall endless be.

252

William Walsham How (1823-1897)

1. O my Saviour, lifted
 from the earth for me,
 draw me, in thy mercy,
 nearer unto thee.

2. Lift my earth-bound longings,
 fix them, Lord, above;
 draw me with the magnet
 of thy mighty love.

3. Lord, thine arms are stretching
 ever far and wide,
 to enfold thy children
 to thy loving side.

4. And I come, O Jesus:
 dare I turn away?
 No, thy love hath conquered,
 and I come today.

5. Bringing all my burdens,
 sorrow, sin and care;
 at thy feet I lay them,
 and I leave them there.

253

George Bennard (1873-1958)

1. On a hill far away
stood an old rugged cross,
the emblem of suff'ring and shame;
and I loved that old cross
where the dearest and best
for a world of lost sinners was slain.

So I'll cherish the old rugged cross,
till my trophies at last I lay down;
I will cling to the old rugged cross
and exchange it some day for a crown.

2. O that old rugged cross,
so despised by the world,
has a wondrous attraction for me:
for the dear Lamb of God
left his glory above
to bear it to dark Calvary.

3. In the old rugged cross,
stained with blood so divine,
a wondrous beauty I see.
For t'was on that old cross
Jesus suffered and died
to pardon and sanctify me.

4. To the old rugged cross
I will ever be true,
its shame and reproach gladly bear.
Then he'll call me some day
to my home far away;
there his glory for ever I'll share.

254

Traditional English carol, alt.

1. On Christmas night all Christians sing,
to hear the news the angels bring,
on Christmas night all Christians sing,
to hear the news the angels bring,
news of great joy, news of great mirth,
news of our merciful King's birth.

2. Then why should we on earth be so sad,
since our Redeemer made us glad,
then why should we on earth be so sad,
since our Redeemer made us glad,
when from our sin he set us free,
all for to gain our liberty?

3. When sin departs before his grace,
then life and health come in its place,
when sin departs before his grace,
then life and health come in its place,
angels and earth with joy may sing,
all for to see the new-born King.

4. All out of darkness we have light,
which made the angels sing this night:
all out of darkness we have light,
which made the angels sing this night:
'Glory to God and peace to men,
now and for evermore. Amen.'

255

Sydney Carter (b. 1915)

1. One more step along the world I go,
one more step along the world I go.
From the old things to the new
keep me travelling along with you.

And it's from the old
I travel to the new,
keep me travelling
along with you.

2. Round the corners of the world I turn,
more and more about the world
I learn.
All the new things that I see
you'll be looking at along with me.

3. As I travel through the bad and good,
keep me travelling the way I should.
Where I see no way to go,
you'll be telling me the way, I know.

Continued overleaf

4. Give me courage when the world
   is rough,
keep me loving though the world
   is tough.
Leap and sing in all I do,
keep me travelling along with you.

And it's from the old
I travel to the new,
keep me travelling
along with you.

5. You are older than the world can be,
you are younger than the life in me.
Ever old and ever new,
keep me travelling along with you.

256

Graham Kendrick (b. 1950)
© 1981 Kingsway's Thankyou Music

1. One shall tell another,
and he shall tell his friend,
husbands, wives and children
shall come following on.
From house to house in families
shall more be gathered in,
and lights will shine in every street,
so warm and welcoming.

Come on in and taste the new wine,
the wine of the kingdom,
the wine of the kingdom of God.
Here is healing and forgiveness,
the wine of the kingdom,
the wine of the kingdom of God.

2. Compassion of the Father
is ready now to flow,
through acts of love and mercy
we must let it show.
He turns now from his anger
to show a smiling face,
and longs that all should stand beneath
the fountain of his grace.

3. He longs to do much more than
our faith has yet allowed,
to thrill us and surprise us
with his sovereign power.
Where darkness has been darkest
the brightest light will shine;
his invitation comes to us,
it's yours and it is mine.

257

Gerrit Gustafson
© 1990 Integrity's Hosanna! Music/Kingsway's Thankyou Music

Only by grace can we enter,
only by grace can we stand;
not by our human endeavour,
but by the blood of the Lamb.

Into your presence you call us,
you call us to come.
Into your presence you draw us,
and now by your grace we come,
now by your grace we come.

Lord, if you mark our transgressions,
who would stand?
Thanks to your grace we are cleansed
by the blood of the Lamb.
(Repeat)

258

Graham Kendrick (b. 1950)
© 1998 Ascent Music

1. On the blood-stained ground, where the
   shadow falls,
of a cross and a crown of thorns,
I kneel down, I kneel down,
I lift my eyes to a tear-stained face;
who is this dying in my place?
I kneel down, I kneel down.

I come just as I am,
this is my only plea,
one hope in which I trust,
this blood was shed for me.

2. As you wash the stains of my guilty heart,
'til I'm clean in ev'ry part,
I kneel down, I kneel down.
Wash away my shame, my pain, my pride,
ev'ry sin that I once denied,
I kneel down, I kneel down.

This is where I'll always come,
this is where I'll always run,
to worship you, Jesus.
This is where I'll always come,
this is where I'll always run,
to worship you, Jesus.

259

18th century trans. Henry Williams Baker (1821-1877) adapted by the editors of 'English Praise'

1. On this day, the first of days,
God the Father's name we praise,
who, creation's Lord and spring,
did the world from darkness bring.

2. On this day his only Son
over death the triumph won;
on this day the Spirit came
with his gifts of living flame.

3. On this day his people raise
one pure sacrifice of praise,
and, with all the saints above,
tell of Christ's redeeming love.

4. Praise, O God, to thee be giv'n,
praise on earth and praise in heav'n,
praise to thy eternal Son,
who this day our vict'ry won

260

Michael Forster (b. 1946)

1. Onward, Christian pilgrims,
Christ will be our light;
see, the heav'nly vision
breaks upon our sight!
Out of death's enslavement
Christ has set us free,
on then to salvation,
hope and liberty.

Onward, Christian pilgrims,
Christ will be our light;
see, the heav'nly vision
breaks upon our sight!

2. Onward, Christian pilgrims,
up the rocky way,
where the dying Saviour
bids us watch and pray.
Through the darkened valley
walk with those who mourn,
share the pain and anger,
share the promised dawn!

3. Onward, Christian pilgrims,
in the early dawn;
death's great seal is broken,
life and hope reborn!
Faith in resurrection
strengthens pilgrims' hearts,
ev'ry load is lightened,
ev'ry fear departs.

4. Onward, Christian pilgrims,
hearts and voices raise,
till the whole creation
echoes perfect praise;
swords are turned to ploughshares,
pride and envy cease,
truth embraces justice,
hope resolves in peace.

261

Robert Cull (b. 1949)

Open our eyes, Lord, we want to see Jesus,
to reach out and touch him
and say that we love him;
open our ears, Lord, and help us to listen;
O, open our eyes, Lord,
we want to see Jesus!

262

Matt Redman

O sacred King, O holy King,
how can I honour you rightly,
honour that's fit for your name?
O sacred friend, O holy friend,
I don't take what you give lightly;
friendship instead of disgrace.

For it's the myst'ry of the universe;
you're the God of holiness,
and yet you welcome souls like me.
And with the blessing of your Father's heart,
you discipline the ones you love;
there's kindness in your majesty.
Jesus, those who recognise your pow'r
know just how wonderful you are
that you draw near.

263

Traditional Caribbean,
based on Matthew 6:9-13 and Luke 11:2-4

1. Our Father, who art in heaven,
hallowed be thy name.
Thy kingdom come, thy will be done,
hallowed be thy name. (x2)

2. On earth as it is in heaven.
hallowed be thy name.
Give us this day our daily bread,
hallowed be thy name. (x2)

3. Forgive us our trespasses,
hallowed be thy name.
as we forgive those who trespass against us.
hallowed be thy name. (x2)

4. Lead us not into temptation,
hallowed be thy name.
but deliver us from all that is evil.
hallowed be thy name. (x2)

5. For thine is the kingdom,
the power, and the glory,
hallowed be thy name.
for ever, and for ever and ever.
hallowed be thy name. (x2)

6. Amen, amen, it shall be so.
hallowed be thy name.
Amen, amen, it shall be so.
hallowed be thy name. (x2)

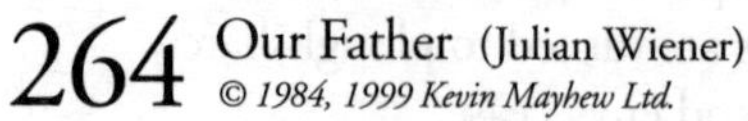

264 Our Father (Julian Wiener)

Our Fa - ther, who art in hea - ven, hal - lowed be thy name;
thy king - dom come; thy will be done on earth as it is in hea -
ven. Give us this day our dai - ly bread; and for - give us our tres - pas - ses
as we for - give those who tres - pass a - gainst us; and lead us not in - to temp -
ta - tion, but de - li - ver us from all that is e - vil.
Doxology
For the king - dom,
the pow'r and the glo - ry are yours, now and for e - ver. A - men.

265

v. 1-4 unknown, v. 5 © 1999 Kevin Mayhew Ltd.

1. Peace is flowing like a river,
flowing out through you and me,
spreading out into the desert,
setting all the captives free.

(This refrain is not always sung.)

Let it flow through me,
let it flow through me,
let the mighty peace of God
flow out through me. (Repeat)

2. Love is flowing like a river,
flowing out through you and me,
spreading out into the desert,
setting all the captives free.

3. Joy is flowing like a river,
flowing out through you and me,
spreading out into the desert,
setting all the captives free.

4. Hope is flowing like a river,
flowing out through you and me,
spreading out into the desert,
setting all the captives free.

5. Christ brings peace to all creation,
flowing out through you and me,
love, joy, hope and true salvation,
setting all the captives free.

266

Edward Henry Bickersteth (1825-1906)

1. Peace, perfect peace,
in this dark world of sin?
The blood of Jesus
whispers peace within.

2. Peace, perfect peace,
by thronging duties pressed?
To do the will of Jesus,
this is rest.

3. Peace, perfect peace,
with sorrows surging round?
In Jesus' presence
naught but calm is found.

4. Peace, perfect peace,
with loved ones far away?
In Jesus' keeping
we are safe, and they.

5. Peace, perfect peace,
our future all unknown?
Jesus we know,
and he is on the throne.

6. Peace, perfect peace,
death shad'wing us and ours?
Jesus has vanquished death
and all its pow'rs.

7. It is enough: earth's struggles
soon shall cease,
and Jesus call us
to heav'n's perfect peace.

267

Kevin Mayhew (b. 1942)
© 1976 Kevin Mayhew Ltd.

1. Peace, perfect peace
is the gift of Christ our Lord.
Peace, perfect peace,
is the gift of Christ our Lord.
Thus says the Lord,
will the world know my friends.
Peace, perfect peace,
is the gift of Christ our Lord.

2. Love, perfect love . . .

3. Faith, perfect faith . . .

4. Hope, perfect hope . . .

5. Joy, perfect joy . . .

268

Graham Kendrick (b. 1950)

Peace to you.
We bless you now
in the name of the Lord.
Peace to you.
We bless you now
in the name of the Prince of Peace.
Peace to you.

269

Unknown, based on Acts 3

Peter and John went to pray,
they met a lame man on the way.
He asked for alms
and held out his palms
and this is what Peter did say:
'Silver and gold have I none,
but such as I have I give thee,
in the name of Jesus Christ of Nazareth,
rise up and walk!'
He went walking and leaping
and praising God,
walking and leaping and praising God.
'In the name of Jesus Christ of Nazareth,
rise up and walk.'

270

Brian Wren (b. 1936)

1. Praise God for the harvest of orchard and field,
praise God for the people who gather their yield,
the long hours of labour, the skills of a team,
the patience of science, the pow'r of machine.

2. Praise God for the harvest that comes from afar,
from market and harbour, the sea and the shore:
foods packed and transported, and gathered and grown
by God-given neighbours, unseen and unknown.

3. Praise God for the harvest that's quarried and mined,
then sifted, and smelted, or shaped and refined:
for oil and for iron, for copper and coal,
praise God, who in love has provided them all.

4. Praise God for the harvest of science and skill,
the urge to discover, create and fulfil:
for dreams and inventions that promise to gain
a future more hopeful, a world more humane.

5. Praise God for the harvest of mercy and love
from leaders and peoples who struggle and serve
with patience and kindness, that all may be led
to freedom and justice, and all may be fed.

271

Andy Piercy and Dave Clifton

Praise God, from whom all blessings flow,
praise him, all creatures here below.
Praise him above, you heav'nly host,
praise Father, Son and Holy Ghost.
(Repeat)

Give glory to the Father,
give glory to the Son,
give glory to the Spirit
while endless ages run.
'Worthy the Lamb,' all heaven cries,
'to be exalted thus.'
'Worthy the Lamb,' our hearts reply,
'for he was slain for us.'

272 Thomas Ken (1637-1710)

Praise God, from whom all blessings flow,
praise him, all creatures here below,
praise him above ye heav'nly host,
praise Father, Son and Holy Ghost.

273 John Kennett, based on Psalm 150

Praise him on the trumpet,
the psalt'ry and harp;
praise him on the timbrel and the dance;
praise him with stringed instruments
too;
praise him on the loud cymbals,
praise him on the loud cymbals;
let ev'rything that has breath praise
the Lord!

Hallelujah, praise the Lord;
hallelujah, praise the Lord:
let ev'rything that has breath
praise the Lord!
Hallelujah, praise the Lord;
hallelujah, praise the Lord:
let ev'rything that has breath
praise the Lord!

274 Frances Jane van Alstyne (Fanny J. Crosby) (1820-1915)

1. Praise him, praise him!
Jesus, our blessèd Redeemer!
Sing, O earth,
his wonderful love proclaim!
Hail him, hail him!
highest archangels in glory;
strength and honour
give to his holy name!
Like a shepherd,
Jesus will guard his children,
in his arms he carries
them all day long.
Praise him, praise him!
tell of his excellent greatness;
praise him, praise him
ever in joyful song!

2. Praise him, praise him!
Jesus, our blessèd Redeemer!
For our sins
he suffered, and bled, and died!
He – our rock,
our hope of eternal salvation,
hail him, hail him!
Jesus the crucified!
Sound his praises –
Jesus who bore our sorrows,
love unbounded, wonderful,
deep and strong.

3. Praise him, praise him!
Jesus, our blessèd Redeemer!
Heav'nly portals,
loud with hosannas ring!
Jesus, Saviour,
reigneth for ever and ever:
crown him, crown him!
Prophet, and Priest, and King!
Christ is coming,
over the world victorious,
pow'r and glory
unto the Lord belong.

275 Unknown

1. Praise him, praise him,
   praise him in the morning,
   praise him in the noontime.
   Praise him, praise him,
   praise him when the sun goes down.
2. Love him, love him, . . .
3. Trust him, trust him, . . .
4. Serve him, serve him, . . .
5. Jesus, Jesus, . . .

276 Henry Williams Baker (1821-1877)

1. Praise, O praise our God and King;
   hymns of adoration sing:

   for his mercies still endure
   ever faithful, ever sure.
2. Praise him that he made the sun
   day by day his course to run:
3. And the silver moon by night,
   shining with her gentle light:
4. Praise him that he gave the rain
   to mature the swelling grain:
5. And hath bid the fruitful field
   crops of precious increase yield:
6. Praise him for our harvest-store;
   he hath filled the garner-floor:
7. And for richer food than this,
   pledge of everlasting bliss:
8. Glory to our bounteous King;
   glory let creation sing:
   glory to the Father, Son
   and blest Spirit, Three in One.

277 Timothy Dudley-Smith (b. 1926), based on Psalm 148

1. Praise the Lord of heaven,
   praise him in the height;
   praise him, all his angels,
   praise him, hosts of light.
   Sun and moon together,
   shining stars aflame,
   planets in their courses,
   magnify his name!
2. Earth and ocean praise him;
   mountains, hills and trees;
   fire and hail and tempest,
   wind and storm and seas.
   Praise him, fields and forests,
   birds on flashing wings,
   praise him, beasts and cattle,
   all created things.
3. Now by prince and people
   let his praise be told;
   praise him, men and maidens,
   praise him, young and old.
   He, the Lord of glory!
   We, his praise proclaim!
   High above all heavens
   magnify his name!

278 Howard Charles Adie Gaunt (1902-1983)

1. Praise the Lord, rise up rejoicing,
   worship, thanks, devotion voicing:
   glory be to God on high!
   Christ, your cross and passion sharing,
   by this Eucharist declaring
   yours th'eternal victory.
2. Scattered flock, one Shepherd sharing,
   lost and lonely, one voice hearing,
   ears are open to your word;
   by your blood new life receiving,
   in your body firm, believing,
   we are yours, and you the Lord.

3. Send us forth alert and living,
sins forgiven, wrongs forgiving,
in your Spirit strong and free.
Finding love in all creation,
bringing peace in ev'ry nation,
may we faithful foll'wers be.

279

Michael Forster (b. 1946)

1. Praise to God for saints and martyrs
inspiration to us all;
in the presence of our Saviour,
their example we recall:
lives of holy contemplation,
sacrifice or simple love,
witnesses to truth and justice,
honoured here and crowned above.

2. How we long to share their story,
faithful in response to grace,
signs of God's eternal presence
in the realm of time and space.
Now, their pilgrimage completed,
cross of Christ their only boast,
they unite their own rejoicing
with the great angelic host.

3. Saints and martyrs, now in glory,
robed before your Saviour's face,
let us join your intercession
for God's holy human race.
Let us join with you in singing
Mary's liberation song,
till a just and free creation sings,
with the angelic throng:

4. Praise and honour to the Father,
adoration to the Son,
with the all-embracing Spirit
wholly Three and holy One.
All the universe, united
in complete diversity,
sings as one your endless praises,
ever-blessèd Trinity!

280

Brian Doerksen

1. Purify my heart,
let me be as gold and precious silver.
Purify my heart,
let me be as gold, pure gold.

Refiner's fire,
my heart's one desire
is to be holy,
set apart for you, Lord.
I choose to be holy,
set apart for you, my master,
ready to do your will.

2. Purify my heart,
cleanse me from within and make me holy.
Purify my heart,
cleanse me from my sin, deep within.

281

Fred Kaan (b. 1929)

1. Put peace into each other's hands
and like a treasure hold it,
protect it like a candle-flame,
with tenderness enfold it.

2. Put peace into each other's hands
with loving expectation;
be gentle in your words and ways,
in touch with God's creation.

3. Put peace into each other's hands
like bread we break for sharing;
look people warmly in the eye:
our life is meant for caring.

4. As at communion, shape your hands
into a waiting cradle;
the gift of Christ receive, revere,
united round the table.

5. Put Christ into each other's hands,
he is love's deepest measure;
in love make peace, give peace a chance,
and share it like a treasure.

282
Paul Gerhardt (1607-1676)
trans. John Wesley (1703-1791) and others

1. Put thou thy trust in God,
in duty's path go on;
walk in his strength with faith and hope,
so shall thy work be done.

2. Commit thy ways to him,
thy works into his hands,
and rest on his unchanging word,
who heav'n and earth commands.

3. Though years on years roll on,
his cov'nant shall endure;
though clouds and darkness hide his path,
the promised grace is sure.

4. Give to the winds thy fears;
hope, and be undismayed:
God hears thy sighs and counts thy tears;
God shall lift up thy head.

5. Through waves and clouds and storms
his pow'r will clear thy way:
wait thou his time; the darkest night
shall end in brightest day.

6. Leave to his sov'reign sway
to choose and to command;
so shalt thou, wond'ring, own his way,
how wise, how strong his hand.

283
Unknown
Based on Philippians 4:4

Rejoice in the Lord always and again
I say rejoice. *(Repeat)*
Rejoice, rejoice and again I say rejoice.
(Repeat)

284
Based on the Latin (c. 4th century)
trans. the Editors of 'The New English Hymnal'

1. Rejoice, the year upon its way
has brought again that blessèd day
when on the Church by Christ our Lord
the Holy Spirit was outpoured.

2. From out the heav'ns a rushing noise
came like the tempest's sudden voice,
and mingled with th'Apostles' prayer,
proclaiming loud that God was there.

3. Like quiv'ring tongues of light and flame,
upon each one the Spirit came:
tongues, that the earth might hear
their call,
and fire, that love might burn in all.

4. And so to all were spread abroad
the wonders of the works of God;
they knew the prophet's word fulfilled,
and owned the gift which God had
willed.

5. Look down, most gracious God, this day
upon thy people as we pray;
and Christ the Lord upon us pour
the Spirit's gift for evermore.
Amen.

285
Graham Kendrick (b. 1950) and Chris Rolinson
(b. 1958)

1. Restore, O Lord,
the honour of your name,
in works of sov'reign power
come shake the earth again,
that all may see,
and come with rev'rent fear
to the living God,
whose kingdom shall outlast the years.

2. Restore, O Lord,
in all the earth your fame,
and in our time revive
the church that bears your name.
And in your anger,
Lord, remember mercy,
O living God,
whose mercy shall outlast the years.

3. Bend us, O Lord,
where we are hard and cold,
in your refiner's fire:
come purify the gold.
Though suff'ring comes
and evil crouches near,
still our living God
is reigning, he is reigning here.

4. *As verse 1*

286 Unknown, based on Genesis 6:4

Rise and shine,
and give God his glory, glory, (x3)
children of the Lord.

1. The Lord said to Noah,
'There's gonna be a floody, floody.'
Lord said to Noah,
'There's gonna be a floody, floody,'
Get those children out of the muddy,
muddy,
children of the Lord.'

2. So Noah, he built him,
he built him an arky, arky,
Noah, he built him,
he built him an arky, arky,
built it out of hickory barky, barky,
children of the Lord.

3. The animals, they came on,
they came on, by twosies, twosies,
animals, they came on, they came on,
by twosies, twosies,
elephants and kangaroosies, roosies,
children of the Lord.

4. It rained and poured
for forty daysies, daysies,
rained and poured
for forty daysies, daysies,
nearly drove those animals
crazies, crazies,
children of the Lord.

5. The sun came out
and dried up the landy, landy,
sun came out
and dried up the landy, landy,
ev'rything was fine and dandy, dandy,
children of the Lord.

6. If you get to heaven
before I do-sies, do-sies,
you get to heaven
before I do-sies, do-sies,
tell those angels I'm comin'
too-sies, too-sies,
children of the Lord.

287 Edward Caswall (1814-1878)

1. See, amid the winter's snow,
born for us on earth below,
see, the tender Lamb appears,
promised from eternal years.

Hail, thou ever-blessèd morn,
hail, redemption's happy dawn!
Sing through all Jerusalem,
Christ is born in Bethlehem.

2. Lo, within a manger lies
he who built the starry skies;
he, who, throned in heights sublime,
sits amid the cherubim.

3. Say, you holy shepherds, say,
what your joyful news today?
Wherefore have you left your sheep
on the lonely mountain steep?

4. 'As we watched at dead of night,
there appeared a wondrous light;
angels, singing peace on earth,
told us of the Saviour's birth.'

5. Sacred infant, all divine,
what a tender love was thine,
thus to come from highest bliss,
down to such a world as this!

Continued overleaf

6. Virgin mother, Mary, blest,
by the joys that fill thy breast,
pray for us, that we may prove
worthy of the Saviour's love.

288

Michael Perry (1942-1996)

1. See him lying on a bed of straw:
a draughty stable with an open door.
Mary cradling the babe she bore:
the Prince of Glory is his name.

*O now carry me to Bethlehem
to see the Lord of Love again:
just as poor as was the stable then,
the Prince of Glory when he came!*

2. Star of silver, sweep across the skies,
show where Jesus in the manger lies;
shepherds, swiftly from your stupor rise
to see the Saviour of the world!

3. Angels, sing again the song you sang,
sing the glory of God's gracious plan;
sing that Bethlehem's little baby can
be the Saviour of us all.

4. Mine are riches, from your poverty;
from your innocence, eternity;
mine, forgiveness by your death for me,
child of sorrow for my joy.

289

v. 1 Karen Lafferty (b. 1948), vs. 2 and 3 unknown, based on Matthew 6:33; 7:7

1. Seek ye first the kingdom of God,
and his righteousness,
and all these things shall be added
unto you;
allelu, alleluia.

*Alleluia, alleluia,
alleluia, allelu, alleluia.*

2. You shall not live by bread alone,
but by ev'ry word
that proceeds from the mouth of God;
allelu, alleluia.

3. Ask and it shall be given unto you,
seek and ye shall find;
knock, and it shall be opened unto you;
allelua, alleluia.

290

Michael Forster (b. 1946), based on Psalm 104

*Send forth your Spirit, Lord,
renew the face of the earth. (Repeat)*

1. Bless the Lord, O my soul,
O Lord God, how great you are;
you are clothed in honour and glory,
you set the world on its foundations.

2. Lord, how great are your works,
in wisdom you made them all;
all the earth is full of your creatures,
your hand always open to feed them.

3. May your wisdom endure,
rejoice in your works, O Lord.
I will sing for ever and ever,
in praise of my God and my King.

291

Robert Lowry (1826-1899)

1. Shall we gather at the river,
where bright angel feet have trod,
with its crystal tide for ever
flowing from the throne of God?

*Yes, we'll gather at the river,
the beautiful, the beautiful river,
gather with the saints at the river,
that flows from the throne of God.*

2. On the margin of the river,
washing up its silver spray,
we will walk and worship ever,
all the happy golden day.

3. Ere we reach the shining river,
lay we ev'ry burden down;
grace our spirits will deliver,
and provide a robe and crown.

4. At the smiling of the river,
mirror of the Saviour's face,
saints, whom death will never sever,
lift their songs of saving grace.

5. Soon we'll reach the shining river,
soon our pilgrimage will cease;
soon our happy hearts will quiver
with the melody of peace.

292

Henry Williams Baker (1821-1877)

1. Shall we not love thee, Mother dear,
whom Jesus loves so well,
and to his glory year by year
thy praise and honour tell?

2. Thee did he choose from whom to take
true flesh, his flesh to be;
in it to suffer for our sake,
and by it make us free.

3. O wondrous depth of love divine,
that he should bend so low;
and, Mary, O what joy was thine
the Saviour's love to know.

4. Joy to be mother of the Lord,
yet thine the truer bliss,
in ev'ry thought and deed and word
to be for ever his.

5. Now in the realm of life above
close to thy Son thou art,
while on thy soul glad streams of love
flow from his sacred heart.

6. Jesu, the Virgin's holy Son,
praise we thy mother blest;
grant when our earthly course is run,
life with the saints at rest.

293

David Fellingham

Shout for joy and sing your praises to the King,
lift your voice and let your hallelujahs ring;
come before his throne to worship and adore,
enter joyfully now the presence of the Lord.

You are my Creator, you are my Deliverer,
you are my Redeemer, you are Lord,
and you are my Healer.
You are my Provider,
you are now my Shepherd, and my Guide,
Jesus, Lord and King, I worship you.

294

Joseph Mohr, (1792-1848)
trans. John Freeman Young (1820-1885)

1. Silent night, holy night.
All is calm, all is bright,
round yon virgin mother and child;
holy infant, so tender and mild,
sleep in heavenly peace,
sleep in heavenly peace.

2. Silent night, holy night.
Shepherds quake at the sight,
glories stream from heaven afar,
heav'nly hosts sing alleluia:
Christ, the Saviour is born,
Christ, the Saviour is born.

3. Silent night, holy night.
Son of God, love's pure light,
radiant beams from thy holy face,
with the dawn of redeeming grace:
Jesus, Lord, at thy birth,
Jesus, Lord, at thy birth.

295

Michael Saward (b. 1932)

1. Sing glory to God the Father,
   the King of the universe, changelessly
   the same.
   Sing praise to the world's creator
   and magnify his holy name.

He made all that is round us and all that is beyond,
his hands uphold the planets, to him they all respond.

2. Sing glory to God the Saviour,
   the Lord of the galaxies, bearer of our
   shame.
   Sing praise to the world's redeemer
   and magnify his holy name.

He suffered grief and torment, for sin he paid the price,
he rose in glorious triumph, both priest and sacrifice.

3. Sing glory to God the Spirit,
   the power of the elements, setting
   hearts aflame.
   Sing praise to the world's life-giver
   and magnify his holy name.

His gifts to all are given, his fruit transforms our hearts,
his fellowship enriches, a grace which he imparts.

4. Sing glory, the whole creation!
   Give thanks to the Trinity, heaven's
   love proclaim.
   Sing praise to our God almighty,
   and magnify his holy name.

296

Mike Anderson (b. 1956)

Sing it in the valleys,
shout it from the mountain tops,
Jesus came to save us,
and his saving never stops.
He is King of kings,
and new life he brings,
sing it in the valleys,
shout it from the mountain tops,
Oh, shout it from the mountain tops.

1. Jesus, you are by my side,
   you take all my fears.
   If I only come to you,
   you will heal the pain of years.

2. You have not deserted me,
   though I go astray.
   Jesus, take me in your arms,
   help me walk with you today.

3. Jesus, you are living now,
   Jesus, I believe.
   Jesus, take me, heart and soul,
   yours alone I want to be.

297

Sabine Baring-Gould (1834-1924)

1. Sing lullaby!
   Lullaby baby, now reclining,
   sing lullaby!
   Hush, do not wake the infant king.
   Angels are watching,
   stars are shining
   over the place where he is lying:
   sing lullaby!

2. Sing lullaby!
   Lullaby baby, now a-sleeping,
   sing lullaby!
   Hush, do not wake the infant king.
   Soon will come sorrow
   with the morning,
   soon will come bitter grief and weeping:
   sing lullaby!

3. Sing lullaby!
Lullaby baby, now a-dozing,
sing lullaby!
Hush, do not wake the infant king.
Soon comes the cross,
the nails, the piercing,
then in the grave at last reposing:
sing lullaby!

4. Sing lullaby!
Lullaby! is the babe awaking?
Sing lullaby.
Hush, do not stir the infant king.
Dreaming of Easter,
gladsome morning,
conquering death, its bondage breaking:
sing lullaby!

298

Michael Baughen (b. 1930) from Psalm 98

1. Sing to God new songs of worship,
all his deeds are marvellous;
he has brought salvation to us
with his hand and holy arm:
he has shown to all the nations
righteousness and saving pow'r;
he recalled his truth and mercy
to his people Israel.

2. Sing to God new songs of worship,
earth has seen his victory;
let the lands of earth be joyful
praising him with thankfulness:
sound upon the harp his praises,
play to him with melody;
let the trumpets sound his triumph,
show your joy to God the king!

3. Sing to God new songs of worship,
let the sea now make a noise;
all on earth and in the waters
sound your praises to the Lord:
let the hills rejoice together,
let the rivers clap their hands,
for with righteousness and justice
he will come to judge the earth.

299

George Bourne Timms (b. 1910)

1. Sing we of the blessèd Mother
who received the angel's word,
and obedient to his summons
bore in love the infant Lord;
sing we of the joys of Mary
at whose breast that child was fed,
who is Son of God eternal
and the everlasting Bread.

2. Sing we, too, of Mary's sorrows,
of the sword that pierced her through,
when beneath the cross of Jesus
she his weight of suff'ring knew,
looked upon her Son and Saviour
reigning high on Calv'ry's tree,
saw the price of our redemption
paid to set the sinner free.

3. Sing again the joys of Mary
when she saw the risen Lord,
and, in prayer with Christ's apostles,
waited on his promised word:
from on high the blazing glory
of the Spirit's presence came,
heav'nly breath of God's own being,
manifest through wind and flame.

4. Sing the greatest joy of Mary
when on earth her work was done,
and the Lord of all creation
brought her to his heav'nly home:
virgin mother, Mary blessèd,
raised on high and crowned with grace,
may your Son, the world's redeemer,
grant us all to see his face.

300

'Anima Christi'. Ascribed to John XXII (1249-1334)
trans. unknown

1. Soul of my Saviour,
sanctify my breast;
Body of Christ,
be thou my saving guest;
Blood of my Saviour,
bathe me in thy tide,
wash me with water
flowing from thy side.

2. Strength and protection
may thy passion be;
O blessèd Jesus,
hear and answer me;
deep in thy wounds, Lord,
hide and shelter me;
so shall I never,
never part from thee.

3. Guard and defend me
from the foe malign;
in death's dread moments
make me only thine;
call me, and bid me
come to thee on high,
when I may praise thee
with thy saints for aye.

301

Helen Kennedy

1. Spirit of God, come dwell within me.
Open my heart, O come set me free,
fill me with love for Jesus, my Lord,
O fill me with living water.

Jesus is living, Jesus is here.
Jesus, my Lord, come closer to me.
Jesus, our Saviour dying for me,
and rising to save his people.

2. Lord, how I thirst, O Lord, I am weak.
Lord, come to me, you alone do I seek.
Lord, you are life, and love and hope,
O fill me with living water.

3. Lord, I am blind, O Lord, I can't see.
Stretch out your hand, O Lord,
comfort me.
Lead me your way in light and in truth,
O fill me with living water.

302

Paul Armstrong

Spirit of the living God,
fall afresh on me;
Spirit of the living God,
fall afresh on me;
fill me anew, fill me anew;
Spirit of the Lord,
fall afresh on me.

303

Daniel Iverson (1890-1972)

1. Spirit of the living God, fall afresh on me.
Spirit of the living God, fall afresh on me.
Melt me, mould me, fill me, use me.
Spirit of the living God, fall afresh on me.

2. Spirit of the living God, fall afresh on us.
Spirit of the living God, fall afresh on us.
Melt us, mould us, fill us, use us.
Spirit of the living God, fall afresh on us.

When appropriate a third verse may be added, singing 'on them', for example, before Confirmation, or at a service for the sick.

304

Jean Holloway (b. 1939)

1. Stand up, stand up for Jesus,
stand up before his cross,
an instrument of torture
inflicting pain and loss;
transformed by his obedience
to God's redeeming plan,
the cross was overpowered
by Christ, both God and man.

2. Stand up, stand up for Jesus,
be counted as his own;
his gospel of forgiveness
he cannot spread alone.
The love which draws us to him,
he calls us out to share;
he calls us to the margins
to be his presence there.

3. Stand up, stand up for Jesus,
in faith and hope be strong,
stand firm for right and justice,
opposed to sin and wrong.
Give comfort to the wounded,
and care for those in pain,
for Christ, in those who suffer,
is crucified again.

4. Stand up, stand up for Jesus,
who reigns as King of kings,
be ready for the challenge
of faith his kingship brings.
He will not force obedience,
he gives to each the choice
to turn from all that's holy,
or in his love rejoice.

5. Stand up, stand up for Jesus,
give courage to the weak,
be unashamed to praise him,
be bold his name to speak.
Confront the cross unflinching,
Christ's love has set us free;
he conquered death for ever
and lives eternally.

305 Spiritual

Steal away, steal away,
steal away to Jesus.
Steal away, steal away home.
I ain't got long to stay here.

1. My Lord, he calls me,
he calls me by the thunder.
The trumpet sounds within my soul;
I ain't got long to stay here.

2. Green trees are bending,
the sinner stands a-trembling.
The trumpet sounds within my soul;
I ain't got long to stay here.

3. My Lord, he calls me,
he calls me by the lightning.
The trumpet sounds within my soul;
I ain't got long to stay here.

306 Graham Kendrick (b. 1950)

1. Such love, pure as the whitest snow;
such love weeps for the shame I know;
such love, paying the debt I owe;
O Jesus, such love.

2. Such love, stilling my restlessness;
such love, filling my emptiness;
such love, showing me holiness;
O Jesus, such love.

3. Such love springs from eternity;
such love, streaming through history;
such love, fountain of life to me;
O Jesus, such love.

307 Francis Stanfield (1835-1914), alt.

1. Sweet sacrament divine,
hid in thy earthly home,
lo, round thy lowly shrine,
with suppliant hearts we come;
Jesus, to thee our voice we raise,
in songs of love and heartfelt praise,
sweet sacrament divine,
sweet sacrament divine.

Continued overleaf

2. Sweet sacrament of peace,
dear home of ev'ry heart,
where restless yearnings cease,
and sorrows all depart,
there in thine ear all trustfully
we tell our tale of misery,
sweet sacrament of peace,
sweet sacrament of peace.

3. Sweet sacrament of rest,
Ark from the ocean's roar,
within thy shelter blest
soon may we reach the shore;
save us, for still the tempest raves;
save, lest we sink beneath the waves,
sweet sacrament of rest,
sweet sacrament of rest.

4. Sweet sacrament divine,
earth's light and jubilee,
in thy far depths doth shine
thy Godhead's majesty;
sweet light, so shine on us, we pray,
that earthly joys may fade away,
sweet sacrament divine,
sweet sacrament divine.

308

Francesca Leftley (b. 1955)

1. Take me, Lord, use my life
in the way you wish to do.
Fill me, Lord, touch my heart
till it always thinks of you.
Take me now, as I am,
this is all I can offer.

Here today I, the clay,
will be moulded by my Lord.

2. Lord, I pray that each day
I will listen to your will.
Many times I have failed
but I know you love me still.
Teach me now, guide me,
Lord, keep me close to you always.

3. I am weak, fill me now
with your strength and set me free.
Make me whole, fashion me
so that you will live in me.
Hold me now in your hands,
form me now with your Spirit.

309

Frances Ridley Havergal (1836-1879)

1. Take my life, and let it be
consecrated, Lord, to thee;
take my moments and my days,
let them flow in ceaseless praise.

2. Take my hands, and let them move
at the impulse of thy love;
take my feet, and let them be
swift and beautiful for thee.

3. Take my voice, and let me sing
always, only, for my King;
take my lips, and let them be
filled with messages from thee.

4. Take my silver and my gold;
not a mite would I withhold;
take my intellect, and use
ev'ry pow'r as thou shalt choose.

5. Take my will, and make it thine:
it shall be no longer mine;
take my heart: it is thine own;
it shall be thy royal throne.

6. Take my love; my Lord, I pour
at thy feet its treasure-store;
take myself, and I will be
ever, only, all for thee.

310

Susan Sayers (b. 1946), based on Mark 8 and John 14

'Take up your cross,' he says, 'and follow me,
and in my love and comfort you shall hide.
I am the Way,' he says, 'so follow me;
do not fear, I am here at your side!'

1. What if the wind is howling round
my house
'til the walls are trembling like a leaf?
What if the windows rattle in the storm
as doubts come battering belief?

2. What if the rocks are blistering my feet,
and the sun's heat beats upon my head?
Near me a grass path beckons with its
flowers,
I'm tempted to go that way instead.

3. What if the tiredness aches behind my eyes
and my boat is impossible to steer?
Out on an ocean, drifting and alone,
am I still, even then, to persevere?

4. Strangest of wonders, wonderfully strange,
that the cross can set me free.
Nothing is stronger than the love of God:
I know very well that he loves me.

311

Jean Holloway (b. 1939)

Thanks for the fellowship found at this meal,
thanks for a day refreshed;
thanks to the Lord for his presence we feel,
thanks for the food he blessed.
Joyfully sing praise to the Lord,
praise to the risen Son,
alleluia, ever adored,
pray that his will be done.
As he was known in the breaking of bread,
now is he known again,
and by his hand have the hungry been fed,
thanks be to Christ. Amen!

312

Diane Davis Andrew
adapted by Geoffrey Marshall-Taylor

1. Thank you, Lord, for this new day, *(x3)*
right where we are.

Alleluia, praise the Lord, (x3)
right where we are.

2. Thank you, Lord, for food to eat, *(x3)*
right where we are.

3. Thank you, Lord, for clothes to wear, *(x3)*
right where we are.

4. Thank you, Lord, for all your gifts, *(x3)*
right where we are.

313

Sabine Baring-Gould (1834-1924),
based on 'Birjina gaztettobat zegoen

1. The angel Gabriel from heaven came,
his wings as drifted snow, his eyes
as flame.
'All hail,' said he,
'thou lowly maiden, Mary,
most highly favoured lady.' Gloria!

2. 'For known a blessèd Mother thou shalt be.
All generations laud and honour thee.
Thy Son shall be Emmanuel,
by seers foretold,
most highly favoured lady.' Gloria!

3. Then gentle Mary meekly bowed her head.
'To me be as it pleaseth God,' she said.
'My soul shall laud and magnify
his holy name.'
Most highly favoured lady! Gloria!

4. Of her, Emmanuel, the Christ, was born
in Bethlehem, all on a Christmas morn;
and Christian folk throughout
the world will ever say:
'Most highly favoured lady.' Gloria!

314

From William Sandys' 'Christmas Carols,
Ancient and Modern', alt.

1. The first Nowell the angel did say
was to certain poor shepherds in fields as
they lay:
in fields where they lay keeping their sheep,
on a cold winter's night that was so deep.

Nowell, Nowell, Nowell, Nowell,
born is the King of Israel!

Continued overleaf

2. They lookèd up and saw a star,
shining in the east, beyond them far,
and to the earth it gave great light,
and so it continued both day and night.

Nowell, Nowell, Nowell, Nowell,
born is the King of Israel!

3. And by the light of that same star,
three wise men came from country far;
to seek for a king was their intent,
and to follow the star wherever it went.

4. This star drew nigh to the north-west,
o'er Bethlehem it took its rest,
and there it did both stop and stay
right over the place where Jesus lay.

5. Then entered in those wise men three,
full rev'rently upon their knee,
and offered there in his presence,
their gold and myrrh and frankincense.

6. Then let us all with one accord
sing praises to our heav'nly Lord,
who with the Father we adore
and Spirit blest for evermore.

315

Traditional

1. The holly and the ivy,
when they are both full grown,
of all the trees that are in the wood
the holly bears the crown.

The rising of the sun
and the running of the deer,
the playing of the merry organ,
sweet singing in the choir.

2. The holly bears a blossom,
white as the lily flower,
and Mary bore sweet Jesus Christ
to be our sweet Saviour.

3. The holly bears a berry,
as red as any blood,
and Mary bore sweet Jesus Christ
to do poor sinners good.

4. The holly bears a prickle,
as sharp as any thorn,
and Mary bore sweet Jesus Christ
on Christmas day in the morn.

5. The holly bears a bark,
as bitter as any gall,
and Mary bore sweet Jesus Christ
to redeem us all.

6. The holly and the ivy,
when they are both full grown,
of all the trees that are in the wood
the holly bears the crown.

316

David Arkin

1. The ink is black, the page is white,
together we learn to read and write,
to read and write;
and now a child can understand
this is the law of all the land,
all the land;
the ink is black, the page is white,
together we learn to read and write,
to read and write.

2. The slate is black, the chalk is white,
the words stand out so clear and bright,
so clear and bright;
and now at last we plainly see
the alphabet of liberty,
liberty;
the slate is black, the chalk is white,
together we learn to read and write,
to read and write.

3. A child is black, a child is white,
the whole world looks upon the sight,
upon the sight;
for very well the whole world knows,
this is the way that freedom grows,
freedom grows;
a child is black, a child is white,
together we learn to read and write,
to read and write.

4. The world is black, the world is white,
it turns by day and then by night,
and then by night;
it turns so each and ev'ry one
can take his station in the sun,
in the sun;
the world is black, the world is white,
together we learn to read and write,
to read and write.

317

Bryn A. Rees (1911-1983)

1. The kingdom of God
is justice and joy,
for Jesus restores
what sin would destroy;
God's power and glory
in Jesus we know,
and here and hereafter
the kingdom shall grow.

2. The kingdom of God
is mercy and grace,
the captives are freed,
the sinners find place,
the outcast are welcomed
God's banquet to share,
and hope is awakened
in place of despair.

3. The kingdom of God
is challenge and choice,
believe the good news,
repent and rejoice!
His love for us sinners
brought Christ to his cross,
our crisis of judgement
for gain or for loss.

4. God's kingdom is come,
the gift and the goal,
in Jesus begun,
in heaven made whole;
the heirs of the kingdom
shall answer his call,
and all things cry 'Glory!'
to God all in all.

318

Mike Anderson (b. 1956), based on Matthew 5:3-10

The kingdom of heaven,
the kingdom of heaven is yours.
A new world in Jesus
a new world in Jesus is yours.

1. Blessèd are you in sorrow and grief,
for you shall all be consoled;
blessèd are you, the gentle of heart,
you shall inherit the earth.

2. Blessèd are you who hunger for right,
for you shall be satisfied;
blessèd are you the merciful ones,
for you shall be pardoned too.

3. Blessèd are you whose hearts are pure,
your eyes shall gaze on the Lord;
blessèd are you who strive after peace,
the Lord will call you his own.

4. Blessèd are you who suffer for right,
the heav'nly kingdom is yours;
blessèd are you who suffer for me,
for you shall reap your reward.

319

Graham Kendrick (b. 1950)

1. The King is among us,
his Spirit is here,
let's draw near and worship,
let songs fill the air.

2. He looks down upon us,
delight in his face,
enjoying his children's love,
enthralled by our praise.

3. For each child is special,
accepted and loved,
a love gift from Jesus
to his Father above.

Continued overleaf

4. And now he is giving
his gifts to us all,
for no one is worthless
and each one is called.

5. The Spirit's anointing
on all flesh comes down,
and we shall be channels
for works like his own.

6. We come now believing
your promise of pow'r,
for we are your people
and this is your hour.

7. The King is among us,
his Spirit is here,
let's draw near and worship,
let songs fill the air.

320

Josiah Conder (1789-1855) alt.

1. The Lord is King! lift up thy voice,
O earth, and all ye heav'ns, rejoice;
from world to world the joy shall ring:
'The Lord omnipotent is King!'

2. He reigns! ye saints, exalt your strains;
your God is King, your Saviour reigns;
and he is at the Father's side,
the Man of Love, the Crucified.

3. Alike pervaded by his eye
all parts of his dominion lie:
this world of ours and worlds unseen,
and thin the boundary between.

4. One Lord one empire all secures;
he reigns, and endless life is yours;
through earth and heav'n one song
shall ring:
'The Lord omnipotent is King!'

321

Taizé Community

The Lord is my song, the Lord is my praise:
all my hope comes from God.
The Lord is my song, the Lord is my praise:
God the well-spring of life

322

John Gowans (b. 1934)

1. There are hundreds of sparrows,
thousands, millions,
they're two a penny, far too many there
must be;
there are hundreds and thousands,
millions of sparrows,
but God knows ev'ry one, and God
knows me.

2. There are hundreds of flowers,
thousands, millions,
and flowers fair the meadows wear for all
to see;
there are hundreds and thousands,
millions of flowers,
but God knows ev'ry one, and God
knows me.

3. There are hundreds of planets,
thousands, millions,
way out in space each has a place by
God's decree;
there are hundreds and thousands,
millions of planets,
but God knows ev'ry one, and God
knows me.

4. There are hundreds of children,
thousands, millions,
and yet their names are written on God's
memory;
there are hundreds and thousands,
millions of children,
but God knows ev'ry one, and God
knows me.

323

Melody Green, based on Scripture

1. There is a Redeemer,
   Jesus, God's own Son,
   precious Lamb of God, Messiah,
   Holy One.

   Thank you, O my Father,
   for giving us your Son,
   and leaving your Spirit
   till the work on earth is done.

2. Jesus, my Redeemer,
   name above all names,
   precious Lamb of God, Messiah,
   O for sinners slain.

3. When I stand in glory,
   I will see his face,
   and there I'll serve my King for ever,
   in that holy place.

324

Frederick William Faber (1814-1863) alt.

1. There's a wideness in God's mercy,
   like the wideness of the sea;
   there's a kindness in his justice,
   which is more than liberty.
   There is no place where earth's sorrows
   are more felt than up in heav'n;
   there is no place where earth's failings
   have such kindly judgement giv'n.

2. But we make his love too narrow
   by false limits of our own;
   and we magnify his strictness
   with a zeal he will not own.
   There is plentiful redemption
   in the blood that has been shed,
   there is joy for all the members
   in the sorrows of the Head.

3. For the love of God is broader
   than the scope of human mind,
   and the heart of the Eternal
   is most wonderfully kind.
   If our love were but more simple,
   we should take him at his word;
   and our hearts would find assurance
   in the promise of the Lord.

325

Michael Forster (b. 1946), based on Isaiah 35

1. The Saviour will come,
   resplendent in joy;
   the lame and the sick
   new strength will enjoy.
   The desert, rejoicing,
   shall burst into flower,
   the deaf and the speechless
   will sing in that hour!

2. The Saviour will come,
   like rain on the earth,
   to harvest at last
   his crop of great worth.
   In patience await him,
   with firmness of mind;
   both mercy and judgement
   his people will find.

3. The Saviour will come,
   his truth we shall see:
   where lepers are cleansed
   and captives set free.
   No finely clad princeling
   in palace of gold,
   but Christ with his people,
   O wonder untold!

326

Damian Lundy (1944-1997)

1. The Spirit lives to set us free,
   walk, walk in the light.
   He binds us all in unity,
   walk, walk in the light.

Continued overleaf

Walk in the light (x3)
walk in the light of the Lord.

2. Jesus promised life to all,
walk, walk in the light.
The dead were wakened by his call,
walk, walk in the light.

3. He died in pain on Calvary,
walk, walk in the light,
to save the lost like you and me,
walk, walk in the light.

4. We know his death was not the end,
walk, walk in the light.
He gave his Spirit to be our friend,
walk, walk in the light.

5. By Jesus' love our wounds are healed,
walk, walk in the light.
The Father's kindness is revealed,
walk, walk in the light.

6. The Spirit lives in you and me,
walk, walk in the light.
His light will shine for all to see,
walk, walk in the light.

327

Michael Forster (b. 1946)

1. The universe was waiting
in dark, chaotic night,
until the word was spoken:
'Let there be glorious light!'
From darkness and from chaos
were light and order born;
the God of new beginnings
rejoiced to see their dawn.

2. And as in that beginning,
in every age the same,
creation's Re-creator
is keeping hope aflame.
From Eden to the desert,
the manger to the tomb,
each fall becomes a rising,
and every grave a womb.

3. Wherever people languish
in darkness or despair,
the God of new beginnings
is pierced, and rises there.
We join with him, to listen,
to care, and to protest,
to see the mighty humbled
and all the humble blessed.

4. We join with our Creator
to keep the vision bright:
in places of oppression
we call for freedom's light:
a glorious new beginning,
a universe at peace,
where justice flows like fountains
and praises never cease.

328

Traditional West Indian

1. The Virgin Mary had a baby boy,
the Virgin Mary had a baby boy,
the Virgin Mary had a baby boy,
and they said that his name was Jesus.

He came from the glory,
he came from the glorious kingdom.
He came from the glory,
he came from the glorious kingdom.
O yes, believer. O yes, believer.
He came from the glory,
he came from the glorious kingdom.

2. The angels sang when the baby
was born, *(x3)*
and proclaimed him the Saviour Jesus.

3. The wise men saw where the baby
was born, *(x3)*
and they saw that his name was Jesus.

329

Doreen Newport

1. Think of a world without any flowers,
   think of a world without any trees,
   think of a sky without any sunshine,
   think of the air without any breeze.
   We thank you, Lord, for flow'rs and trees
   and sunshine,
   we thank you, Lord, and praise your
   holy name.

2. Think of a world without any animals,
   think of a field without any herd,
   think of a stream without any fishes,
   think of a dawn without any bird.
   We thank you, Lord, for all your living
   creatures,
   we thank you, Lord, and praise your
   holy name.

3. Think of a world without any people,
   think of a street with no one living there,
   think of a town without any houses,
   no one to love and nobody to care.
   We thank you, Lord, for families and
   friendships,
   we thank you, Lord, and praise your
   holy name.

330

vs. 1 & 2: Jimmy Owens
vs. 3-5: Damian Lundy (1944-1997)

1. This is my body, broken for you,
   bringing you wholeness, making you free.
   Take it and eat it, and when you do,
   do it in love for me.

2. This is my blood, poured out for you,
   bringing forgiveness, making you free.
   Take it and drink it, and when you do,
   do it in love for me.

3. Back to my Father soon I shall go.
   Do not forget me; then you will see
   I am still with you, and you will know
   you're very close to me.

4. Filled with my Spirit, how you will grow!
   You are my branches; I am the tree.
   If you are faithful, others will know
   you are alive in me.

5. Love one another; I have loved you,
   and I have shown you how to be free;
   serve one another, and when you do,
   do it in love for me.

331

James Quinn (b. 1919)

1. This is my will, my one command,
   that love should dwell among you all.
   This is my will that you should love
   as I have shown that I love you.

2. No greater love can be than this:
   to choose to die to save one's friends.
   You are my friends if you obey
   all I command that you should do.

3. I call you now no longer slaves;
   no slave knows all his master does.
   I call you friends, for all I hear
   my Father say, you hear from me.

4. You chose not me, but I chose you,
   that you should go and bear much fruit.
   I called you out that you in me
   should bear much fruit that will abide.

5. All that you ask my Father dear
   for my name's sake you shall receive.
   This is my will, my one command,
   that love should dwell in each, in all.

332

Les Garrett (b. 1944)

1. This is the day, this is the day
   that the Lord has made,
   that the Lord has made;
   we will rejoice, we will rejoice
   and be glad in it, and be glad in it.
   This is the day that the Lord has made;
   we will rejoice and be glad in it.
   This is the day, this is the day
   that the Lord has made.

2. This is the day, this is the day
   when he rose again,
   when he rose again;
   we will rejoice, we will rejoice
   and be glad in it, and be glad in it.
   This is the day when he rose again;
   we will rejoice and be glad in it.
   This is the day, this is the day
   when he rose again.

3. This is the day, this is the day
   when the Spirit came,
   when the Spirit came;
   we will rejoice, we will rejoice
   and be glad in it, and be glad in it.
   This is the day when the Spirit came;
   we will rejoice and be glad in it.
   This is the day, this is the day
   when the Spirit came.

333

George Ratcliffe Woodward (1848-1934)

1. This joyful Eastertide,
   away with sin and sorrow.
   My love, the Crucified,
   hath sprung to life this morrow.

   Had Christ, that once was slain,
   ne'er burst his three-day prison,
   our faith had been in vain:
   but now hath Christ arisen,
   arisen, arisen, arisen.

2. My flesh in hope shall rest,
   and for a season slumber;
   till trump from east to west
   shall wake the dead in number.

3. Death's flood hath lost its chill,
   since Jesus crossed the river:
   lover of souls, from ill
   my passing soul deliver.

334

Traditional

This little light of mine,
I'm gonna let it shine, (x3)
let it shine, let it shine, let it shine.

1. The light that shines is the light of love,
   lights the darkness from above,
   it shines on me and it shines on you,
   and shows what the power of love can do.
   I'm gonna shine my light both far
   and near,
   I'm gonna shine my light both bright
   and clear.
   Where there's a dark corner in this land,
   I'm gonna let my little light shine.

2. On Monday he gave me the gift of love,
   Tuesday peace came from above.
   On Wednesday he told me to have
   more faith,
   on Thursday he gave me a little more grace.
   On Friday he told me to watch and pray,
   on Saturday he told me just what to say,
   on Sunday he gave me the pow'r divine
   to let my little light shine.

335

Susan Sayers (b. 1946)

This world you have made
is a beautiful place;
it tells the pow'r of your love.
We rejoice in the beauty
of your world,
from the seas
to the heavens above.

1. The morning whispers of purity;
the evening of your peace;
the thunder booms your exuberance
in the awesome pow'r you release.

2. The tenderness of a new-born child;
the gentleness of the rain;
simplicity in a single cell;
and complexity in a brain.

3. Your stillness rests in a silent pool;
infinity drifts in space;
your grandeur straddles the mountain tops;
and we see your face in each face.

336

Horatius Bonar (1808-1889)

1. Thy way, not mine, O Lord,
however dark it be;
lead me by thine own hand,
choose out the path for me.

2. Smooth let it be or rough,
it will be still the best;
winding or straight, it leads
right onward to thy rest.

3. I dare not choose my lot;
I would not if I might:
choose thou for me, my God,
so shall I walk aright.

4. The kingdom that I seek
is thine, so let the way
that leads to it be thine,
else I must surely stray.

5. Take thou my cup, and it
with joy or sorrow fill,
as best to thee may seem;
choose thou my good and ill.

6. Choose thou for me my friends,
my sickness or my health;
choose thou my cares for me,
my poverty or wealth.

7. Not mine, not mine, the choice
in things or great or small;
be thou my guide, my strength,
my wisdom, and my all.

337

Noel Richards

1. To be in your presence,
to sit at your feet,
where your love surrounds me
and makes me complete.

This is my desire, O Lord, this is my desire,
this is my desire, O Lord, this is my desire.

2. To rest in your presence,
not rushing away,
to cherish each moment,
here I would stay.

338

Frances Jane van Alstyne
(Fanny J. Crosby) (1820-1915)

1. To God be the glory!
great things he hath done;
so loved he the world
that he gave us his Son;
who yielded his life
an atonement for sin,
and opened the life-gate
that all may go in.

Praise the Lord, praise the Lord!
let the earth hear his voice;
praise the Lord, praise the Lord!
let the people rejoice:
O come to the Father,
through Jesus the Son,
and give him the glory;
great things he hath done.

Continued overleaf

2. O perfect redemption,
the purchase of blood!
to ev'ry believer
the promise of God;
the vilest offender
who truly believes,
that moment from Jesus
a pardon receives.

Praise the Lord, praise the Lord!
let the earth hear his voice;
praise the Lord, praise the Lord!
let the people rejoice:
O come to the Father,
through Jesus the Son,
and give him the glory;
great things he hath done.

3. Great things he hath taught us,
great things he hath done,
and great our rejoicing
through Jesus the Son;
but purer, and higher,
and greater will be
our wonder, our rapture,
when Jesus we see.

339

'Puer nobis nascitur'
15th century trans. Percy Dearmer (1867-1936) alt.

1. Unto us a boy is born!
King of all creation;
came he to a world forlorn,
the Lord of ev'ry nation,
the Lord of ev'ry nation.

2. Cradled in a stall was he,
watched by cows and asses;
but the very beasts could see
that he the world surpasses,
that he the world surpasses.

3. Then the fearful Herod cried,
'Pow'r is mine in Jewry!'
So the blameless children died
the victims of his fury,
the victims of his fury.

4. Now may Mary's Son, who came
long ago to love us,
lead us all with hearts aflame
unto the joys above us,
unto the joys above us.

5. Omega and Alpha he!
Let the organ thunder,
while the choir with peals of glee
shall rend the air asunder,
shall rend the air asunder.

340

Michael Forster (b. 1946)

1. Waken, O sleeper, wake and rise,
salvation's day is near,
and let the dawn of light and truth
dispel the night of fear.

2. Let us prepare to face the day
of judgement and of grace,
to live as people of the light,
and perfect truth embrace.

3. Watch then and pray, we cannot know
the moment or the hour,
when Christ, unheralded, will come
with life-renewing power.

4. Then shall the nations gather round
to learn his ways of peace,
when spears are turned to pruning-hooks
and all our conflicts cease.

341

Philipp Nicolai (1556-1608)
trans. Francis Crawford Burkitt (1864-1935) alt.

1. Wake, O wake! with tidings thrilling
the watchmen all
the air are filling:
arise, Jerusalem, arise!
Midnight strikes! no more delaying,
'The hour has come!'
we hear them saying.
Where are ye all, ye maidens wise?
The Bridegroom comes in sight,
raise high your torches bright!
Alleluia!
The wedding song
swells loud and strong:
go forth and join the festal throng.

2. Sion hears the watchmen shouting,
her heart leaps up
with joy undoubting,
she stands and waits with eager eyes;
see her Friend from heav'n descending,
adorned with truth
and grace unending!
Her light burns clear, her star doth rise.
Now come, thou precious Crown,
Lord Jesu, God's own son!
Hosanna!
Let us prepare
to follow there,
where in thy supper we may share.

3. Ev'ry soul in thee rejoices;
from earthly and
angelic voices
be glory giv'n to thee alone!
Now the gates of pearl receive us,
thy presence never more
shall leave us,
we stand with angels round thy throne.
Earth cannot give below
the bliss thou dost bestow.
Alleluia!
Grant us to raise,
to length of days,
the triumph-chorus of thy praise.

342

Marie Lydia Pereira (b. 1920)

Wake up, O people, the Lord is very near!
Wake up, and stand for the Lord. (Repeat)

1. Your saving Lord is near. Wake up!
His glory will appear. Wake up!
Your hour of grace is nearer than it
ever was.

2. The night of sin has passed. Wake up!
The light is near at last. Wake up!
The day star, Christ, the Son of God, will
soon appear.

3. To live in love and peace. Wake up!
To let all quarrels cease. Wake up!
To live that all you do may stand the
light of day.

4. That Christ may be your shield.
Wake up!
That death to life may yield. Wake up!
That heaven's gate be opened wide again
for you.

343

Graham Kendrick (b. 1950)

1. We are his children, the fruit of
his suff'ring,
saved and redeemed by his blood;
called to be holy, a light to the nations:
clothed with his pow'r, filled with his love.

Go forth in his name,
proclaiming, 'Jesus reigns!'
Now is the time for the church to arise
and proclaim him
'Jesus, Saviour, Redeemer and Lord.'

2. Countless the souls that are stumbling
in darkness,
why do we sleep in the light?
Jesus commands us to go make disciples,
this is our case, this is our fight.

Continued overleaf

3. Listen, the wind of the Spirit is blowing,
   the end of the age is so near;
   pow'rs in the earth and the heavens
      are shaking,
   Jesus our Lord soon shall appear!

344

Traditional South African
v.1 trans. Anders Nyberg vs. 2 & 3 trans. Andrew Maries

1. We are marching in the light of God. *(x4)*

   We are marching,
   Oo-oooh! We are marching in the light
      of God. *(Repeat)*

2. We are living in the love of God . . .

3. We are moving in the pow'r of God . . .

345

Graham Kendrick (b. 1950)

1. We believe in God the Father,
   maker of the universe,
   and in Christ, his Son our Saviour,
   come to us by virgin birth.
   We believe he died to save us,
   bore our sins, was crucified;
   then from death he rose victorious,
   ascended to the Father's side.

   Jesus, Lord of all, Lord of all; (x4)
   name above all names,
   name above all names!

2. We believe he sends his Spirit
   on his Church with gifts of pow'r;
   God, his word of truth affirming,
   sends us to the nations now.
   He will come again in glory,
   judge the living and the dead:
   ev'ry knee shall bow before him,
   then must ev'ry tongue confess.

346

Viola Grafstrom

1. We bow down and confess
   you are Lord in this place.
   We bow down and confess
   you are Lord in this place.

2. You are all I need;
   it's your face I seek.
   In the presence of your light
   we bow down, we bow down.

347

The Iona Community

1. We cannot measure how you heal
   or answer ev'ry suff'rer's prayer,
   yet we believe your grace responds
   where faith and doubt unite to care.
   Your hands, though bloodied on the cross,
   survive to hold and heal and warn,
   to carry all through death to life
   and cradle children yet unborn.

2. The pain that will not go away,
   the guilt that clings from things long past,
   the fear of what the future holds,
   are present as if meant to last.
   But present too is love which tends
   the hurt we never hoped to find,
   the private agonies inside,
   the memories that haunt the mind.

3. So some have come who need your help
   and some have come to make amends,
   as hands which shaped and saved
      the world
   are present in the touch of friends.
   Lord, let your Spirit meet us here
   to mend the body, mind and soul,
   to disentangle peace from pain
   and make your broken people whole.

348

Michael Forster (b. 1946)
based on the speech by Martin Luther King Jr.

1. We have a dream:
this nation will arise,
and truly live
according to its creed,
that all are equal
in their maker's eyes,
and none shall suffer
through another's greed.

2. We have a dream
that one day we shall see
a world of justice,
truth and equity,
where sons of slaves
and daughters of the free
will share the banquet
of community.

3. We have a dream
of deserts brought to flow'r,
once made infertile
by oppression's heat,
when love and truth
shall end oppressive pow'r,
and streams of righteousness
and justice meet.

4. We have a dream:
our children shall be free
from judgements based on
colour or on race;
free to become
whatever they may be,
of their own choosing
in the light of grace.

5. We have a dream
that truth will overcome
the fear and anger
of our present day;
that black and white
will share a common home,
and hand in hand
will walk the pilgrim way.

6. We have a dream:
each valley will be raised,
and ev'ry mountain,
ev'ry hill brought down;
then shall creation
echo perfect praise,
and share God's glory
under freedom's crown!

349

Graham Kendrick (b. 1950)

1. We'll walk the land with hearts on fire;
and ev'ry step will be a prayer.
Hope is rising, new day dawning;
sound of singing fills the air.

2. Two thousand years, and still the flame
is burning bright across the land.
Hearts are waiting, longing, aching,
for awak'ning once again.

Let the flame burn brighter
in the heart of the darkness,
turning night to glorious day.
Let the song grow louder,
as our love grows stronger;
let it shine! Let it shine!

3. We'll walk for truth, speak out for love;
in Jesus' name we shall be strong,
to lift the fallen, to save the children,
to fill the nation with your song.

350

Pierre-Marie Hoog and Robert B. Kelly (b. 1948)

Advent 1

We shall stay awake
and pray at all times,
ready to welcome Christ,
the Prince of Justice.
We shall set aside
all fears and worries,
ready to welcome Christ,
the Prince of Peace.

Continued overleaf

Advent 2

We shall set our sights
on what is righteous,
ready to welcome Christ,
the Prince of Justice.
We shall smooth the path,
prepare the Lord's way,
ready to welcome Christ,
the Prince of Peace.

Advent 3

We shall plunge into
the saving water,
ready to welcome Christ,
the Prince of Justice.
We shall be reborn
and rise to new life,
ready to welcome Christ,
the Prince of Peace.

Advent 4

We shall hold with faith
to what God promised,
ready to welcome Christ,
the Prince of Justice.
We shall be
attentive to his Spirit,
ready to welcome Christ,
the Prince of Peace.

351

John Henry Hopkins (1820-1891) alt.

1. We three kings of Orient are;
bearing gifts we traverse afar;
field and fountain, moor and mountain,
following yonder star.

O star of wonder, star of night,
star with royal beauty bright,
westward leading still proceeding,
guide us to thy perfect light.

2. Born a King on Bethlehem plain,
gold I bring, to crown him again,
King for ever, ceasing never,
over us all to reign.

3. Frankincense to offer have I,
incense owns a Deity nigh,
prayer and praising, gladly raising,
worship him, God most high.

4. Myrrh is mine, its bitter perfume
breathes a life of gathering gloom;
sorrowing, sighing, bleeding, dying,
sealed in the stone-cold tomb.

5. Glorious now behold him arise,
King and God and sacrifice;
alleluia, alleluia,
earth to heav'n replies.

352

Doug Horley

We want to see Jesus lifted high,
a banner that flies across this land,
that all men might see the truth
and know he is the way to heaven.
(Repeat)

We want to see, we want to see,
we want to see Jesus lifted high.
We want to see, we want to see,
we want to see Jesus lifted high.

Step by step we're moving forward,
little by little taking ground,
ev'ry prayer a powerful weapon,
strongholds come tumbling down,
and down, and down, and down.

353

John L. Bell (b. 1949) and Graham Maule (b. 1958)

1. We will lay our burden down,
we will lay our burden down,
we will lay our burden down
in the hands of the risen Lord.

2. We will light the flame of love,
we will light the flame of love,
we will light the flame of love,
as the hands of the risen Lord.

3. We will show both hurt and hope,
we will show both hurt and hope,
we will show both hurt and hope,
like the hands of the risen Lord.

4. We will walk the path of peace,
we will walk the path of peace,
we will walk the path of peace,
hand in hand with the risen Lord.

354

Joseph Medlicott Scriven (1819-1886)

1. What a friend we have in Jesus,
all our sins and griefs to bear!
What a privilege to carry
ev'rything to him in prayer!
O what peace we often forfeit,
O what needless pain we bear,
all because we do not carry
ev'rything to God in prayer!

2. Have we trials and temptations?
Is there trouble anywhere?
We should never be discouraged:
take it to the Lord in prayer!
Can we find a friend so faithful,
who will all our sorrows share?
Jesus knows our ev'ry weakness –
take it to the Lord in prayer!

3. Are we weak and heavy-laden,
cumbered with a load of care?
Jesus only is our refuge,
take it to the Lord in prayer!
Do thy friends despise, forsake thee?
Take it to the Lord in prayer!
In his arms he'll take and shield thee,
thou wilt find a solace there.

355

William Chatterton Dix (1837-1898) alt.

1. What child is this who, laid to rest,
on Mary's lap is sleeping?
Whom angels greet with anthems sweet,
while shepherds watch are keeping?
This, this is Christ the King,
whom shepherds guard and angels sing:
come, greet the infant Lord,
the babe, the Son of Mary!

2. Why lies he in such mean estate,
where ox and ass are feeding?
Good Christians, fear: for sinners here
the silent Word is pleading.
Nails, spear, shall pierce him through,
the cross be borne for me, for you;
hail, hail the Word made flesh,
the babe, the Son of Mary!

3. So bring him incense, gold and myrrh,
come rich and poor, to own him.
The King of kings salvation brings,
let loving hearts enthrone him.
Raise, raise the song on high,
the Virgin sings her lullaby:
joy, joy for Christ is born,
the babe the Son of Mary!

356

John L. Bell (b. 1949) and Graham Maule (b. 1958)

1. When God Almighty came to earth,
he took the pain of Jesus' birth,
he took the flight of refugee,
and whispered: 'Humbly follow me.'

2. When God Almighty went to work,
carpenter's sweat he didn't shirk,
profit and loss he didn't flee,
and whispered: 'Humbly follow me.'

3. When God Almighty walked the street,
the critic's curse he had to meet,
the cynic's smile he had to see,
and whispered: 'Humbly follow me.'

Continued overleaf

4. When God Almighty met his folk,
of peace and truth he boldly spoke
to set the slave and tyrant free,
and whispered: 'Humbly follow me.'

5. When God Almighty took his place
to save the sometimes human race,
he took it boldly on a tree,
and whispered: 'Humbly follow me.'

6. When God Almighty comes again,
he'll meet us incognito as then;
and though no words may voice
his plea,
he'll whisper: 'Are you following me?'

357

Keri Jones and David Matthew

When I feel the touch
of your hand upon my life,
it causes me to sing a song
that I love you, Lord.
So from deep within
my spirit singeth unto thee,
you are my King,
you are my God,
and I love you, Lord.

358

Wayne and Cathy Perrin

When I look into your holiness,
when I gaze into your loveliness,
when all things that surround
become shadows in the light of you;
when I've found the joy
of reaching your heart,
when my will becomes
enthrall'd in your love,
when all things that surround
become shadows in the light of you:
I worship you, I worship you,
the reason I live is to worship you.
I worship you, I worship you,
the reason I live is to worship you.

359

Sydney Carter (b. 1915)

1. When I needed a neighbour,
were you there, were you there?
When I needed a neighbour,
were you there?

And the creed and the colour
and the name won't matter,
were you there?

2. I was hungry and thirsty,
were you there, were you there?
I was hungry and thirsty,
were you there?

3. I was cold, I was naked,
were you there, were you there?
I was cold, I was naked,
were you there?

4. When I needed a shelter,
were you there, were you there?
When I needed a shelter,
were you there?

5. When I needed a healer,
were you there, were you there?
When I needed a healer,
were you there?

6. Wherever you travel,
I'll be there, I'll be there,
wherever you travel,
I'll be there.

360

Fred Pratt Green (1903-2000)

1. When, in our music,
God is glorified,
and adoration leaves
no room for pride,
it is as though
the whole creation cried:
Alleluia.

2. How often, making music,
we have found
a new dimension
in the world of sound,
as worship moved us
to a more profound
Alleluia!

3. So has the Church,
in liturgy and song,
in faith and love,
through centuries of wrong,
borne witness to the truth
in ev'ry tongue:
Alleluia!

4. And did not Jesus sing
a psalm that night
when utmost evil strove
against the Light?
Then let us sing,
for whom he won the fight:
Alleluia!

5. Let ev'ry instrument
be tuned for praise!
Let all rejoice
who have a voice to raise!
And may God give us
faith to sing always:
Alleluia!

361

Michael Forster (b. 1946)

1. When our God came to earth,
not for him noble birth:
he affirmed human worth
from a humble manger,
just another stranger.

Let the poor rejoice!
Let the mute give voice!
Love is shown,
God is known,
Christ is born of Mary.

2. Not for kings was the word
which the poor shepherds heard:
hope renewed, grace conferred,
and the hillside ringing
with the angels' singing.

3. Bethlehem, humble town
where the babe wears the crown,
turns the world upside down:
God so unexpected,
homeless and rejected.

4. Let us sing Mary's song,
bringing hope, righting wrong,
heard with fear by the strong,
poor and humble raising,
God of justice praising.

362

John Henry Sammis (1846-1919)

1. When we walk with the Lord
in the light of his word,
what a glory he sheds on our way!
While we do his good will,
he abides with us still,
and with all who will trust and obey.

Trust and obey,
for there's no other way
to be happy in Jesus,
but to trust and obey.

2. Not a burden we bear,
not a sorrow we share,
but our toil he doth richly repay;
not a grief nor a loss,
not a frown nor a cross,
but is blest if we trust and obey.

3. But we never can prove
the delights of his love
until all on the altar we lay;
for the favour he shows,
and the joy he bestows,
are for them who will trust and obey.

Continued overleaf

4. Then in fellowship sweet
we will sit at his feet,
or we'll walk by his side in the way.
What he says he will do,
where he sends we will go,
never fear, only trust and obey.

363

Graham Kendrick (b. 1950)

1. Who can sound the depths of sorrow
in the Father heart of God,
for the children we've rejected,
for the lives so deeply scarred?
And each light that we've extinguished
has brought darkness to our land:
upon our nation, upon our nation
have mercy, Lord.

2. We have scorned the truth you gave us,
we have bowed to other lords.
We have sacrificed the children
on the altar of our gods.
O let truth again shine on us,
let your holy fear descend:
upon our nation, upon our nation
have mercy, Lord.

(Men)

3. Who can stand before your anger?
Who can face your piercing eyes?
For you love the weak and helpless,
and you hear the victims' cries.

(All)

Yes, you are a God of justice,
and your judgement surely comes:
upon our nation, upon our nation
have mercy, Lord.

(Women)

4. Who will stand against the violence?
Who will comfort those who mourn?
In an age of cruel rejection,
who will build for love a home?

(All)

Come and shake us into action,
come and melt our hearts of stone:
upon your people, upon your people
have mercy, Lord.

5. Who can sound the depths of mercy
in the Father heart of God?
For there is a Man of sorrows
who for sinners shed his blood.
He can heal the wounds of nations,
he can wash the guilty clean:
because of Jesus, because of Jesus
have mercy, Lord.

364

William Walsham How (1823-1897) alt.

1. Who is this so weak and helpless,
child of lowly Hebrew maid,
rudely in a stable sheltered,
coldly in a manger laid?
'Tis the Lord of all creation,
who this wondrous path hath trod;
he is God from everlasting,
and to everlasting God.

2. Who is this – a Man of Sorrows,
walking sadly life's hard way;
homeless, weary, sighing, weeping
over sin and Satan's sway?
'Tis our God, our glorious Saviour,
who beyond our mortal sight
now for us a place prepareth
free from grief and full of light.

3. Who is this – behold him raining
drops of blood upon the ground?
Who is this – despised, rejected,
mocked, insulted, beaten, bound?
'Tis our God, who gifts and graces
on his Church now poureth down;
all his faithful ones empow'ring
to partake in cross and crown.

4. Who is this that hangeth dying,
with the thieves on either side?
Nails his hands and feet are tearing,
and the spear hath pierced his side.
'Tis the God who ever liveth
'mid the shining ones on high,
in the glorious golden city
reigning everlastingly.

365

Paul Booth (1931-1995)

1. Who put the colours in the rainbow?
Who put the salt into the sea?
Who put the cold into the snowflake?
Who made you and me?
Who put the hump upon the camel?
Who put the neck on the giraffe?
Who put the tail upon the monkey?
Who made hyenas laugh?
Who made whales and snails and quails?
Who made hogs and dogs and frogs?
Who made bats and cats and rats?
Who made ev'rything?

2. Who put the gold into the sunshine?
Who put the sparkle in the stars?
Who put the silver in the moonlight?
Who made Earth and Mars?
Who put the scent into the roses?
Who taught the honey-bee to dance?
Who put the tree inside the acorn?
It surely can't be chance!
Who made seas and leaves and trees?
Who made snow and winds that blow?
Who made streams and rivers flow?
God made all of these!

366

Graham Kendrick (b. 1950)

1. Who sees it all, before whose gaze
is darkest night bright as the day;
watching as in the secret place
his likeness forms upon a face?

God sees, God knows,
God loves the broken heart;
and holds, and binds,
and heals the broken heart.

2. Who sees it all, the debt that's owed
of lives unlived, of love unknown?
Who weighs the loss of innocence,
or feels the pain of our offence?

3. Who knows the fears that drive a choice,
unburies pain and gives it voice?
And who can wash a memory,
or take the sting of death away?

4. Whose anger burns at what we've done,
then bears our sin as if his own?
Who will receive us as we are,
whose arms are wide and waiting now?

5. Whose broken heart upon a cross
won freedom, joy and peace for us?
Whose blood redeems, who ever lives
and all because of love forgives?

367

C. Austin Miles (1868-1946)

Wide, wide as the ocean,
high as the heavens above;
deep, deep as the deepest sea
is my Saviour's love.
I, though so unworthy,
still am a child of his care,
for his word teaches me that
his love reaches me ev'rywhere.

368

John L. Bell (b. 1949) and Graham Maule (b. 1958)

1. Will you come and follow me
if I but call your name?
Will you go where you don't know,
and never be the same?
Will you let my love be shown,
will you let my name be known,
will you let my life be grown
in you, and you in me?

Continued overleaf

2. Will you leave yourself behind
if I but call your name?
Will you care for cruel and kind,
and never be the same?
Will you risk the hostile stare
should your life attract or scare,
will you let me answer prayer
in you, and you in me?

3. Will you let the blinded see
if I but call your name?
Will you set the pris'ners free,
and never be the same?
Will you kiss the leper clean
and do such as this unseen,
and admit to what I mean
in you, and you in me?

4. Will you love the 'you' you hide
if I but call your name?
Will you quell the fear inside,
and never be the same?
Will you use the faith you've found
to reshape the world around
through my sight and touch and sound
in you, and you in me?

5. Lord, your summons echoes true
when you but call my name.
Let me turn and follow you,
and never be the same.
In your company I'll go
where your love and footsteps show.
Thus I'll move and live and grow
in you, and you in me.

369

Priscilla Jane Owens (1829-1899)

1. Will your anchor hold
in the storms of life,
when the clouds unfold
their wings of strife?
When the strong tides lift,
and the cables strain,
will your anchor drift,
or firm remain?

We have an anchor
that keeps the soul
steadfast and sure
while the billows roll;
fastened to the rock
which cannot move,
grounded firm and deep
in the Saviour's love!

2. Will your anchor hold
in the straits of fear,
when the breakers roar
and the reef is near?
While the surges rage,
and the wild winds blow,
shall the angry waves
then your bark o'erflow?

3. Will your anchor hold
in the floods of death,
when the waters cold
chill your latest breath?
On the rising tide
you can never fail,
while your anchor holds
within the veil.

4. Will your eyes behold
through the morning light,
the city of gold
and the harbour bright?
Will you anchor safe
by the heav'nly shore,
when life's storms are past
for evermore?

370

John Pantry

1. Wonderful grace, that gives what I don't
deserve,
pays me what Christ has earned,
then lets me go free.
Wonderful grace, that gives me the time
to change,
washes away the stains that once covered
me.

And all that I have
I lay at the feet
of the wonderful Saviour
who loves me.

2. Wonderful grace, that held in the face of death,
breathed in its latest breath
forgiveness for me.
Wonderful love, whose pow'r can break ev'ry chain,
giving us life again, setting us free.

371

Mark Altrogge

You are beautiful beyond description,
too marvellous for words,
too wonderful for comprehension,
like nothing ever seen or heard.
Who can grasp your infinite wisdom?
Who can fathom the depth of your love?
You are beautiful beyond description,
majesty, enthroned above.

And I stand, I stand in awe of you.
I stand, I stand in awe of you.
Holy God, to whom all praise is due,
I stand in awe of you.

372

Graham Jeffrey

1. You are beneath me,
Lord, you uphold me,
you are above me,
Lord, you sustain.
You are beside me
through ev'ry weather,
summer and winter,
sunshine and rain.

2. You go before me
you come behind me,
you are my spirit,
you are my guide.
You are my star, Lord
leading me onwards,
you my companion,
here by my side.

3. You are my father,
always sustaining,
you are my saviour,
you are my friend.
You my beginning,
you my true ending,
yours be the glory,
world without end.

373

Mavis Ford

You are the King of Glory,
you are the Prince of Peace,
you are the Lord of heav'n and earth,
you're the Son of righteousness.
Angels bow down before you,
worship and adore, for
you have the words of eternal life,
you are Jesus Christ the Lord.
Hosanna to the Son of David!
Hosanna to the King of kings!
Glory in the highest heaven,
for Jesus the Messiah reigns.

374

Margaret Rizza (b. 1929)

1. You are the light that is ever bright,
you fill my heart, giving life;
you give the work
I endeavour to do,
meaning and purpose
are blessings from you.

Continued overleaf

O hold me, enfold me in your love.

2. You are the beauty that fills my soul,
you, by your wounds, make me whole.
You paid the price
to redeem me from death;
yours is the love that
sustains my ev'ry breath.

3. You still the storms and the fear of night,
you turn despair to delight.
You feel the anguish,
and share in my tears,
you give the hope from
the depth of my fears.

4. You are the word full of life and truth,
you guide my feet since my youth;
you are my refuge,
my firm cornerstone,
you I will worship
and honour alone.

5. You have restored me and pardoned sin,
you give me strength from within.
You called me forth,
and my life you made new.
Love is the binding
that holds me to you.

6. You are the Way, you are Truth and Life,
you keep me safe in the strife.
You give me love
I cannot comprehend,
you guide the way
to a life without end.

375

Noel Richards

You laid aside your majesty,
gave up ev'rything for me,
suffered at the hands of those you had
created.
You took all my guilt and shame,
when you died and rose again;
now today you reign,
in heav'n and earth exalted.

I really want to worship you, my Lord,
you have won my heart and I am yours
for ever and ever;
I will love you.
You are the only one who died for me,
gave your life to set me free,
so I lift my voice to you in adoration.

376

Mike Anderson (b. 1956)

Your love's greater (greater),
greater than the greatest mountain,
your love's deeper (deeper),
deeper than the deepest sea;
a love that never dies,
a love that reaches deep inside,
more wondrous than all the universe.

1. You made the heavens,
the earth and sea;
your power is awesome,
and you still love me.

2. Your ways are righteous,
your laws are just,
love is your promise,
and in you I trust.

3. Your love is healing,
your love endures;
my life is changed, Lord,
now I know I'm yours.

377

Wes Sutton

1. Your mercy flows upon us like a river.
Your mercy stands unshakeable and true.
Most holy God, of all good things the giver,
we turn and lift our fervent prayer to you.

Hear our cry (hear our cry),
O Lord (O Lord),
be merciful (be merciful)
once more (once more).
Let your love (let your love)
your anger stem (your anger stem),
remember mercy, O Lord, again.

2. Your Church once great, though standing clothed in sorrow,
is even still the bride that you adore;
revive your Church, that we again may honour
our God and King, our Master and our Lord.

3. As we have slept, this nation has been taken
by ev'ry sin we have every known,
so at its gates, thought burnt by fire and broken,
in Jesus' name we come to take our stand.

378

Steffi Geiser Rubin and Stuart Dauermann

You shall go out with joy
and be led forth with peace,
and the mountains and the hills
shall break forth before you.
There'll be shouts of joy
and the trees of the field shall clap,
shall clap their hands.
And the trees of the field
shall clap their hands,
and the trees of the field
shall clap their hands,
and the trees of the field
shall clap their hands,
and you'll go out with joy.

CHANTS

379

Taizé Community

Adoramus te, Domine

1. With the angels and archangels:
2. With the patriarchs and prophets:
3. With the Virgin Mary, mother of God:
4. With the apostles and evangelists:
5. With all the martyrs of Christ:
6. With all who witness to the Gospel of
   the Lord:
7. With all your people of the Church
   throughout the world.

380

Traditional

Adoramus te, Domine Deus.

Translation: We adore you, O Lord God.

381

Taizé Community, from Psalm 103

Bless the Lord, my soul,
and bless God's holy name.
Bless the Lord, my soul,
who leads me into life.

1. It is God who forgives all your guilt,
   who heals ev'ry one of your ills,
   who redeems your life from the grave,
   who crowns you with love and
   compassion.

2. The Lord is compassion and love,
   the Lord is patient and rich in mercy.
   God does not treat us according to our sins
   nor repay us according to our faults.

3. As a father has compassion on
   his children,
   the Lord has mercy on those who
   revere him;
   for God knows of what we are made,
   and remembers that we are dust.

382

David Adam.

Calm me, Lord, as you calmed the storm;
still me, Lord, keep me from harm.
Let all the tumult within me cease;
enfold me, Lord, in your peace.

Last time:
Lord enfold me in your peace.

383

Psalm 118

Confitemini Domino quoniam bonus.
Confitemini Domino. Alleluia!

Translation: Give thanks to the Lord for he is good

384

Taizé Community, based on Scripture

Eat this bread, drink this cup,
come to him and never be hungry.
Eat this bread, drink this cup,
trust in him and you will not thirst.

1. Christ is the Bread of Life,
   the true bread sent from the Father.

2. Your ancestors ate manna in the desert,
   but this is the bread come down
   from heaven.

3. Eat his flesh, and drink his blood,
   and Christ will raise you up on the last day.

4. Anyone who eats this bread
   will live for ever.

5. If we believe and eat this bread
   we will have eternal life.

385
Traditional

Exaudi nos, Domine,
donna nobis pacem tuam.

Translation: Hear us, O Lord, give us your peace.

386
Kevin Mayhew (b. 1942)
based on the Aaronic Blessing, Numbers 6: 24-26

Holy God,
we place ourselves into your hands.
Bless us and care for us,
be gracious and loving to us;
look kindly upon us, and give us peace.

387
Taizé Community

In the Lord I'll be ever thankful,
in the Lord, I will rejoice!
Look to God, do not be afraid;
lift up your voices: the Lord is near,
lift up your voices: the Lord is near.

388
Margaret Rizza (b. 1929)

In the Lord is my joy and salvation,
he gives light to all his creation.
In the Lord is my joy and salvation,
he gives peace and true consolation.
In the Lord is my salvation.
In the Lord is my salvation.

389
Taizé Community, based on Scripture

Jesus, remember me
when you come into your kingdom.

390
John L. Bell (b. 1949) and Graham Maule (b. 1958)

Kindle a flame to lighten the dark
and take all fear away.

391
Taizé Community, based on Scripture

Laudate Dominum,
laudate Dominum,
omnes gentes, alleluia. (Repeat)

or

Sing praise and bless the Lord,
sing praise and bless the Lord,
peoples, nations, alleluia. (Repeat)

1. Praise the Lord, all you nations,
praise God all you peoples.
Alleluia.
Strong is God's love and mercy,
always faithful for ever. Alleluia

2. Alleluia, alleluia.
Let ev'rything living give praise to the Lord.
Alleluia, alleluia.
Let ev'rything living give praise to the Lord.

392
Colin Mawby (b. 1936)

Lord of creation,
may your will be done.
Lord of creation,
may your will be done.

393
Based on Luke 1:46

Magnificat, magnificat
anima mea Dominum. *(Repeat)*

Translation: My soul praises and magnifies the Lord

394

Gaelic Blessing, adapted by Margaret Rizza (b. 1929)

May the Lord bless you,
may the Lord protect you and guide you,
may his strength uphold you,
his light shine upon you,
his peace surround you,
his love enfold you.

Last time:
May the Lord bless you,
the Lord bless you,
the Lord bless you.

395

St Teresa of Avila

Nada te turbe,
nada te espante.
Quien a Dios tiene nada le falta.
Nada te turbe,
nada te espante.
Solo Dios basta.

or
Nothing can trouble,
nothing can frighten.
Those who seek God shall never go wanting.
Nothing can trouble,
nothing can frighten.
God alone fills us.

396

Taizé Community

O Lord, hear my prayer.
O Lord, hear my prayer:
when I call answer me.
O Lord, hear my prayer.
O Lord, hear my prayer.
Come and listen to me.

397

From Psalm 131

O Lord, my heart is not proud,
nor haughty my eyes.
I have not gone after things too great,
nor marvels beyond me.
Truly I have set my soul in silence and peace;
at rest, as a child in its mother's arms,
so is my soul.

398

Traditional

Sanctum nomen Domini
magnificat anima mea. *(Repeat)*

Last time:
Sanctum, sanctum nomen Domini.

Translation: My soul magnifies the holy name of the Lord

399

v. 1 Pamela Hayes; v. 2 Margaret Rizza (b. 1929)

Silent, surrendered, calm and still,
open to the word of God.
Heart humbled to his will,
offered is the servant of God.

*Come, Holy Spirit, bring us light,
teach us, heal us, give us life.
Come, Lord, O let our hearts
flow with love and all that is true.

* *for use at Pentecost*

400

Based on Matthew 26:36-42

*Stay with me, remain here with me,
watch and pray, watch and pray.*

1. Stay here and keep watch with me.
Watch and pray, watch and pray!

2. Watch and pray not to give way to
temptation.

3. The Spirit is eager, but the flesh is weak.
4. My heart is nearly broken with sorrow. Remain here with me, stay awake and pray.
5. Father, if it is possible let this cup pass me by.
6. Father, if this cannot pass me by without my drinking it, your will be done.

401

From Daniel 3

Surrexit Christus, alleluia!
Cantate Domino, alleluia!

Translation: Christ is risen. Sing to the Lord.

1. All you heavens, bless the Lord. Stars of the heavens, bless the Lord.
2. Sun and moon, bless the Lord. And you, night and day, bless the Lord.
3. Frost and cold, bless the Lord. Ice and snow, bless the Lord.
4. Fire and heat, bless the Lord. And you, light and darkness, bless the Lord.
5. Spirits and souls of the just, bless the Lord. Saints and the humble-hearted, bless the Lord.

402

Based on Psalm 27

The Lord is my light,
my light and salvation:
in God I trust,
in God I trust.

403

From Psalm 27

The Lord is my light, in him I trust. *(x2)*
The Lord is my light, in him I trust,
in him I trust.

404

Taizé Community

Ubi caritas et amor.
Ubi caritas Deus ibi est.

Translation: Where there is charity and love, there is God.

1. Your love, O Jesus Christ, has gathered us together.
2. May your love, O Jesus Christ, be foremost in our lives.
3. Let us love one another as God has loved us.
4. Let us be one in love together in the one bread of Christ.
5. The love of God in Jesus Christ bears eternal joy.
6. The love of God in Jesus Christ will never have an end.

405

Stephen Langton (1160-1228)

Veni, lumen cordium.
Veni, Sancte Spiritus.

Translation: Come, light of our hearts. Come, Holy Spirit, come

406

From the sequence for Pentecost Sunday ascribed to Stephen Langton (1160-1228)

Veni, veni,
veni, Sancte Spiritus.

Translation: Come, Holy Spirit

407

Taizé Community, based on Scripture

Wait for the Lord, whose day is near.
Wait for the Lord: keep watch take heart!

1. Prepare the way for the Lord.
   Make a straight path for God.
   Prepare the way for the Lord.
2. Rejoice in the Lord always: God is at hand.
   Joy and gladness for all who seek the Lord.
3. The glory of the Lord shall be revealed.
   All the earth will see the Lord.
4. I waited for the Lord. God heard my cry.
5. Our eyes are fixed on the Lord our God.
   Wait for the Lord, whose day is near.
   Wait for the Lord: keep watch take heart!
6. Seek first the kingdom of God.
   Seek and you shall find.
7. O Lord show us your way.
   Guide us in your truth.

408

Margaret Rizza (b. 1929)

You are the centre, you are my life,
you are the centre, O Lord, of my life.
Come, Lord, and heal me, Lord of my life,
come, Lord, and teach me, Lord of my life.
You are the centre, Lord, of my life.
Give me your Spirit and teach me your ways,
give me your peace, Lord, and set me free. *
You are the centre, Lord, of my life.

* *Second time:*
You are the centre, you are my life,
you are the centre, O Lord, of my life.

MUSIC FOR THE EUCHARIST

409 Kyrie 1.

Jacques Berthier (1923-1994)

Ky - ri - e, Ky - ri - e, e - le - i - son.
(hum under the invocations)

410 Lord, have mercy

Friedrich Filitz (1804-1876)

1. Lord, have mer - cy on us, hear our hum - ble plea; Lord, have mer - cy on us, set our spi - rits free.

2. Christ, have mercy on us,
hear us as we pray;
Christ, have mercy on us,
take our sin away.

3. Lord, have mercy on us,
hear our humble plea;
Lord, have mercy on us,
set our spirits free.

Text: Michael Forster (b. 1946)

411 Gloria 3

Jacques Berthier (1923-1994)

This setting may be sung as a canon with entries as indicated.

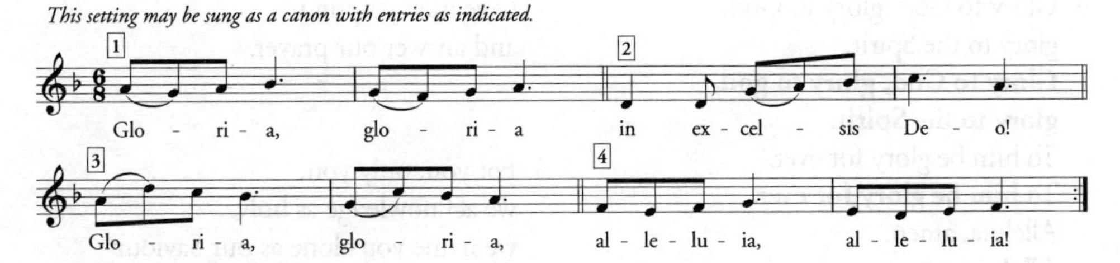
1
Glo - ri - a, glo - ri - a
2
in ex - cel - sis De - o!
3
Glo - ri - a, glo - ri - a,
4
al - le - lu - ia, al - le - lu - ia!

412 Mike Anderson (b. 1956)

Gloria, gloria, in excelsis Deo.
Gloria, gloria, in excelsis Deo.

1. Lord God, heavenly King,
peace you bring to us;
we worship you, we give you thanks,
we sing our song of praise.

2. Jesus, Saviour of all,
Lord God, Lamb of God,
you take away our sins,
O Lord, have mercy on us all.

3. At the Father's right hand,
Lord receive our prayer,
for you alone are the Holy One,
and you alone are Lord.

4. Glory, Father and Son,
glory, Holy Spirit,
to you we raise our hands up high,
we glorify your name.

413 Traditional Peruvian

1. Glory to God, glory to God,
glory to the Father.
Glory to God, glory to God,
glory to the Father.
To him be glory for ever.
To him be glory for ever.
Alleluia, amen,
alleluia, amen,
alleluia, amen,
alleluia, amen.

2. Glory to God, glory to God,
Son of the Father.
Glory to God, glory to God,
Son of the Father.
To him be glory for ever.
To him be glory for ever.
Alleluia, amen.
Alleluia, amen,
alleluia, amen,
alleluia, amen.

3. Glory to God, glory to God,
glory to the Spirit.
Glory to God, glory to god,
glory to the Spirit.
To him be glory for ever.
To him be glory for ever.
Alleluia, amen.
Alleluia, amen,
alleluia, amen,
alleluia, amen.

414 Michael Forster (b. 1946)

1. Sing glory to God
in the height of the heavens,
salvation and peace
to his people on earth;
our King and our Saviour,
our God and our Father,
we worship and praise you
and sing of your worth.

Creation unites in the power of the Spirit,
in praise of the Father,
through Jesus, the Son.
So complex, so simple,
so clear, so mysterious,
our God ever Three, yet eternally One.

2. Our Lord Jesus Christ,
only Son of the Father,
Lord God, Lamb of God,
by the nations adored,
your blood takes away
all the sin of creation:
have mercy upon us,
for whom it was poured.
For you are our Saviour,
our only Redeemer,
who came all our gladness
and sorrows to share:
you sit at the side,
the right hand of the Father,
have mercy upon us,
and answer our prayer.

3. For you, only you,
we acknowledge as holy,
we name you alone as our Saviour
and Lord;
you only, O Christ,
with the Spirit exalted,
are one with the Father,
for ever adored.
Creation unites in the power
of the Spirit,
in praise of the Father,
through Jesus the Son.
So complex, so simple,
so clear, so mysterious,
our God ever Three
yet eternally One!

415

Michael Forster (b. 1946)

1. Holy, most holy, all holy the Lord,
in power and wisdom for ever adored.
The earth and the heavens are full of your love;
our joyful hosannas re-echo above.

2. Blessèd, most blessèd is he
whose life makes us whole, and whose death sets us free:
who comes in the name of the Father of light,
let endless hosannas resound in the height.

416

Michael Forster (b. 1946)
based on the 'Agnus Dei'

1. O Lamb of God, come cleanse our hearts
and take our sin away.
O Lamb of God, your grace impart,
and let our guilty fear depart,
have mercy, Lord, we pray,
have mercy, Lord, we pray.

2. O Lamb of God, our lives restore,
our guilty souls release.
Into our lives your Spirit pour
and let us live for evermore
in perfect heav'nly peace,
in perfect heav'nly peace.

Texts For Additional Tunes

The following hymns have been included to complement the Additional Tunes in the Music Edition

417

Edward Perronet (1726-1792)
adapted by Michael Forster (b. 1946)

1. All hail the pow'r of Jesus' name,
   let angels prostrate fall;
   bring forth the royal diadem,

   and crown him, crown him, crown him,
   crown him Lord of all.
2. Crown him, all martyrs of your God,
   who from his altar call;
   praise him whose way of pain you trod,
   and crown him . . .
3. O prophets faithful to his word,
   in matters great and small,
   who made his voice of justice heard,
   now crown him . . .
4. All sinners, now redeemed by grace,
   who heard your Saviour's call,
   now robed in light before his face,
   O crown him . . .
5. Let every tribe and every race
   who heard the freedom call,
   in liberation, see Christ's face,
   and crown him . . .
6. Let every people, every tongue
   to him their heart enthral:
   lift high the universal song
   and crown him . . .

418

Caroline Maria Noel (1817-1877) alt.

1. At the name of Jesus
   ev'ry knee shall bow,
   ev'ry tongue confess him
   King of glory now;
   'tis the Father's pleasure
   we should call him Lord,
   who, from the beginning,
   was the mighty Word.
2. At his voice creation
   sprang at once to sight,
   all the angels' faces,
   all the hosts of light,
   thrones and dominations,
   stars upon their way,
   all the heav'nly orders
   in their great array.
3. Humbled for a season,
   to receive a name
   from the lips of sinners
   unto whom he came,
   faithfully he bore it,
   spotless to the last,
   brought it back victorious
   when from death he passed.
4. Bore it up triumphant
   with its human light,
   through all ranks of creatures
   to the central height,
   to the throne of Godhead,
   to the Father's breast,
   filled it with the glory
   of that perfect rest.
5. In your hearts enthrone him;
   there let him subdue
   all that is not holy,
   all that is not true;
   crown him as your captain
   in temptation's hour;
   let his will enfold you
   in its light and pow'r.
6. Truly, this Lord Jesus
   shall return again,
   with his Father's glory,
   with his angel train;
   for all wreaths of empire
   meet upon his brow,
   and our hearts confess him
   King of glory now.

419

Edwin Hatch (1835-1889), alt.

1. Breathe on me, Breath of God,
   fill me with life anew,
   that as you love, so may I love,
   and do what you would do.

2. Breathe on me, Breath of God,
until my heart is pure:
until my will is one with yours
to do and to endure.

3. Breathe on me, Breath of God,
fulfil my heart's desire,
until this earthly part of me
glows with your heav'nly fire.

4. Breathe on me, Breath of God,
so shall I never die,
but live with you the perfect life
of your eternity.

420
Reginald Heber (1783-1826)

1. Brightest and best
of the suns of the morning,
dawn on our darkness
and lend us thine aid;
star of the east,
the horizon adorning,
guide where our infant
Redeemer is laid.

2. Cold on his cradle
the dew-drops are shining;
low lies his head
with the beasts of the stall;
angels adore him
in slumber reclining,
Maker and Monarch
and Saviour of all.

3. Say, shall we yield him,
in costly devotion,
odours of Edom,
and off'rings divine,
gems of the mountain,
and pearls of the ocean,
myrrh from the forest,
or gold from the mine?

4. Vainly we offer
each humble oblation,
vainly with gifts
would his favour secure:
richer by far
is the heart's adoration,
dearer to God
are the prayers of the poor.

421
George Wallace Briggs (1875-1959)

1. Come, risen Lord,
and deign to be our guest;
nay, let us be thy guests;
the feast is thine;
thyself at thine own board
make manifest,
in thine own sacrament
of bread and wine.

2. We meet, as in
that upper room they met;
thou at thy table,
blessing, yet dost stand:
'This is my body'
– so thou givest yet;
faith still receives the cup
as from thy hand.

3. One body we,
one body who partake,
one Church united
in communion blest;
one name we bear,
one bread of life we break,
with all thy saints on earth
and saints at rest.

4. One with each other,
Lord, for one in thee,
who art one Saviour
and one living Head;
then open thou our eyes,
that we may see:
be known to us
in breaking of the bread.

422
Matthew Bridges (1800-1894)

1. Crown him with many crowns,
the Lamb upon his throne;
hark, how the heav'nly anthem drowns
all music but its own:
awake, my soul, and sing
of him who died for thee,
and hail him as thy matchless King
through all eternity.

2. Crown him the Virgin's Son,
the God incarnate born,
whose arm those crimson trophies won
which now his brow adorn;

Continued overleaf

fruit of the mystic Rose,
as of that Rose the Stem,
the Root, whence mercy ever flows,
the Babe of Bethlehem.

3. Crown him the Lord of love;
behold his hands and side,
rich wounds, yet visible above,
in beauty glorified:
no angel in the sky
can fully bear that sight,
but downward bends each burning eye
at mysteries so bright.

4. Crown him the Lord of peace,
whose pow'r a sceptre sways
from pole to pole, that wars may cease,
absorbed in prayer and praise:
his reign shall know no end,
and round his piercèd feet
fair flow'rs of paradise extend
their fragrance ever sweet.

5. Crown him the Lord of years,
the Potentate of time,
Creator of the rolling spheres,
ineffably sublime.
All hail, Redeemer, hail!
for thou hast died for me;
thy praise shall never, never fail
throughout eternity.

423

John Henry Newman (1801-1890) alt.

1. Firmly I believe and truly
God is Three and God is One;
and I next acknowledge duly
manhood taken by the Son.

2. And I trust and hope most fully
in the Saviour crucified;
and each thought and deed unruly
do to death as he has died.

3. Simply to his grace and wholly
light and life and strength belong,
and I love supremely, solely,
him the holy, him the strong.

4. And I hold in veneration,
for the love of him alone,
holy Church as his creation,
and her teachings as his own.

5. Adoration ay be given,
with and thro' th'angelic host,
to the God of earth and heaven,
Father, Son and Holy Ghost.

Last line:
Amen. Father, Son and Holy Ghost.

424

Charles Wesley (1707-1788)
Thomas Cotterill (1779-1823) and others, alt.

1. Hail the day that sees him rise, *alleluia!*
to his throne above the skies; *alleluia!*
Christ the Lamb, for sinners giv'n, *alleluia!*
enters now the highest heav'n! *alleluia!*

2. There for him high triumph waits;
lift your heads, eternal gates!
He hath conquered death and sin;
take the King of Glory in!

3. Circled round with angel-pow'rs,
their triumphant Lord and ours;
wide unfold the radiant scene,
take the King of Glory in!

4. Lo, the heav'n its Lord receives,
yet he loves the earth he leaves;
though returning to his throne,
calls the human race his own.

5. See, he lifts his hands above;
see, he shows the prints of love;
hark, his gracious lips bestow
blessings on his Church below.

6. Still for us he intercedes,
his prevailing death he pleads;
near himself prepares our place,
he the first-fruits of our race.

7. Lord, though parted from our sight,
far above the starry height,
grant our hearts may thither rise,
seeking thee above the skies.

8. Ever upward let us move,
wafted on the wings of love;
looking when our Lord shall come,
longing, sighing after home.

425 Horatius Bonar (1808-1889)

1. I heard the voice of Jesus say,
'Come unto me and rest;
lay down, thou weary one, lay down
thy head upon my breast.'
I came to Jesus as I was,
so weary, worn and sad;
I found in him a resting-place,
and he has made me glad.

2. I heard the voice of Jesus say,
'Behold, I freely give
the living water, thirsty one;
stoop down and drink and live.'
I came to Jesus, and I drank
of that life-giving stream;
my thirst was quenched, my soul revived,
and now I live in him.

3. I heard the voice of Jesus say,
'I am this dark world's light;
look unto me, thy morn shall rise,
and all thy day be bright.'
I looked to Jesus, and I found
in him my star, my sun;
and in that light of life I'll walk
till trav'lling days are done.

426 Charlotte Elliott (1789-1871)

1. Just as I am, without one plea
but that thy blood was shed for me,
and that thou bidst me come to thee,
O Lamb of God, I come.

Just as I am, just as I am,
just as I am, I come.

2. Just as I am, though tossed about
with many a conflict, many a doubt,
fightings and fears within, without,
O Lamb of God, I come.

3. Just as I am, poor, wretched, blind;
sight, riches, healing of the mind,
yea, all I need, in thee to find,
O Lamb of God, I come.

4. Just as I am, thóu wilt receive,
wilt welcome, pardon, cleanse, relieve:
because thy promise I believe,
O Lamb of God, I come.

5. Just as I am, thy love unknown
has broken ev'ry barrier down,
now to be thine, yea, thine alone,
O Lamb of God, I come.

Just as I am, just as I am,
just as I am, I come.

6. Just as I am, of that free love
the breadth, length, depth and height
to prove,
here for a season, then above,
O Lamb of God, I come.

427 George Herbert (1593-1633)

1. King of glory, King of peace,
I will love thee;
and, that love may never cease,
I will move thee.
Thou hast granted my appeal,
thou hast heard me;
thou didst note my ardent zeal,
thou hast spared me.

2. Wherefore with my utmost art,
I will sing thee,
and the cream of all my heart
I will bring thee.
Though my sins against me cried,
thou didst clear me,
and alone, when they replied,
thou didst hear me.

3. Sev'n whole days, not one in sev'n,
I will praise thee;
in my heart, though not in heav'n,
I can raise thee.
Small it is, in this poor sort
to enrol thee:
e'en eternity's too short
to extol thee.

428 John Henry Newman (1801-1890)

1. Lead, kindly light,
amid th'encircling gloom,
lead thou me on;
the night is dark,
and I am far from home;
lead thou me on.

Continued overleaf

Keep thou my feet;
I do not ask to see
the distant scene;
one step enough for me.

2. I was not ever thus,
nor prayed that thou
shouldst lead me on;
I loved to choose
and see my path; but now
lead thou me on.
I loved the garish day,
and, spite of fears,
pride ruled my will:
remember not past years.

3. So long thy pow'r
hath blest me, sure it still
will lead me on,
o'er moor and fen,
o'er crag and torrent, till
the night is gone;
and with the morn
those angel faces smile,
which I have loved long since,
and lost awhile.

429

James Edmeston (1791-1867)

1. Lead us, heav'nly Father, lead us
o'er the world's tempestuous sea;
guard us, guide us, keep us, feed us,
for we have no help but thee;
yet possessing ev'ry blessing
if our God our Father be.

2. Saviour, breathe forgiveness o'er us,
all our weakness thou dost know,
thou didst tread this earth before us,
thou didst feel its keenest woe;
lone and dreary, faint and weary,
through the desert thou didst go.

3. Spirit of our God, descending,
fill our hearts with heav'nly joy,
love with ev'ry passion blending,
pleasure that can never cloy;
thus provided, pardoned, guided,
nothing can our peace destroy.

430

George Hugh Bourne (1840-1925)

1. Lord, enthroned in heav'nly splendour,
first begotten from the dead,
thou alone, our strong defender,
liftest up thy people's head.
Alleluia, alleluia,
Jesu, true and living bread.

2. Here our humblest homage pay we,
here in loving rev'rence bow;
here for faith's discernment pray we,
lest we fail to know thee now.
Alleluia, alleluia,
thou art here, we ask not how.

3. Though the lowliest form doth veil thee
as of old in Bethlehem,
here as there thine angels hail thee,
Branch and Flow'r of Jesse's Stem.
Alleluia, alleluia,
we in worship join with them.

4. Paschal Lamb, thine off'ring, finished
once for all when thou wast slain,
in its fullness undiminished
shall for evermore remain.
Alleluia, alleluia,
cleansing souls from ev'ry stain.

5. Life-imparting heav'nly manna,
stricken rock with streaming side,
heav'n and earth with loud hosanna
worship thee, the Lamb who died.
Alleluia, alleluia,
ris'n, ascended, glorified!

431

Martin Rinkart (1586-1649)
trans. Catherine Winkworth (1827-1878)

1. Now thank we all our God,
with hearts and hands and voices,
who wondrous things hath done,
in whom his world rejoices;
who from our mother's arms
hath blessed us on our way
with countless gifts of love,
and still is ours today.

2. O may this bounteous God
through all our life be near us,
with ever joyful hearts
and blessèd peace to cheer us;
and keep us in his grace,
and guide us when perplexed,
and free us from all ills
in this world and the next.

3. All praise and thanks to God
the Father now be given,
the Son and him who reigns
with them in highest heaven,
the one eternal God,
whom earth and heav'n adore;
for thus it was, is now,
and shall be evermore.

432

John Ernest Bode (1816-1874)

1. O Jesus, I have promised
to serve thee to the end;
be thou for ever near me,
my Master and my friend:
I shall not fear the battle
if thou art by my side,
nor wander from the pathway
if thou wilt be my guide.

2. O let me feel thee near me;
the world is ever near;
I see the sights that dazzle,
the tempting sounds I hear;
my foes are ever near me,
around me and within;
but, Jesus, draw thou nearer,
and shield my soul from sin.

3. O let me hear thee speaking
in accents clear and still,
above the storms of passion,
the murmurs of self-will;
O speak to reassure me,
to hasten or control;
O speak and make me listen,
thou guardian of my soul.

4. O Jesus, thou hast promised,
to all who follow thee,
that where thou art in glory
there shall thy servant be;
and, Jesus, I have promised
to serve thee to the end:
O give me grace to follow,
my Master and my friend.

5. O let me see thy foot-marks,
and in them plant mine own;
my hope to follow duly
is in thy strength alone:
O guide me, call me, draw me,
uphold me to the end;
and then in heav'n receive me,
my Saviour and my friend.

433

Dorothy Francis Gurney (1858-1932)

1. O perfect love,
all human thought transcending,
lowly we kneel
in prayer before thy throne,
that theirs may be
the love which knows no ending,
whom thou for evermore
dost join in one.

2. O perfect life,
be thou their full assurance
of tender charity
and steadfast faith,
of patient hope
and quiet, brave endurance,
with childlike trust that fears
not pain nor death.

3. Grant them the joy
which brightens earthly sorrow,
grant them the peace
which calms all earthly strife;
and to life's day
the glorious unknown morrow
that dawns upon
eternal love and life.

434

Augustus Montague Toplady (1740-1778) alt.

1. Rock of ages, cleft for me,
let me hide myself in thee;
let the water and the blood,
from thy riven side which flowed,
be of sin the double cure:
cleanse me from its guilt and pow'r.

2. Not the labours of my hands
can fulfil thy law's demands;
could my zeal no respite know,
could my tears for ever flow,
all for sin could not atone:
thou must save, and thou alone.

3. Nothing in my hands I bring,
simply to thy cross I cling;
naked, come to thee for dress;
helpless, look to thee for grace;
tainted, to the fountain fly;
wash me, Saviour, or I die.

Continued overleaf

4. While I draw this fleeting breath,
when mine eyelids close in death,
when I soar through tracts unknown,
see thee on thy judgement throne;
Rock of ages, cleft for me,
let me hide myself in thee.

435

Charles Wesley (1707-1788)
based on Ephesians 6:10-18

1. Soldiers of Christ, arise,
and put your armour on,
strong in the strength which God supplies
through his eternal Son.
Strong in the Lord of hosts,
and in his mighty pow'r;
who in the strength of Jesus trusts
is more than conqueror.

2. Stand then in his great might,
with all his strength endued;
and take, to arm you for the fight,
the panoply of God:
to keep your armour bright,
attend with constant care,
still walking in your Captain's sight
and watching unto prayer.

3. From strength to strength go on,
wrestle and fight and pray;
tread all the pow'rs of darkness down,
and win the well-fought day;
that, having all things done,
and all your conflicts past,
ye may o'ercome, through Christ alone,
and stand entire at last.

436

St Thomas Aquinas (1227-1274)
trans. James Russell Woodford (1820-1885) alt.

1. Thee we adore,
O hidden Saviour, thee,
who in thy sacrament
art pleased to be;
both flesh and spirit
in thy presence fail,
yet here thy presence
we devoutly hail.

2. O blest memorial
of our dying Lord,
who living bread
to all doth here afford;
O may our souls
for ever feed on thee,
and thou, O Christ,
for ever precious be.

3. Fountain of goodness,
Jesus, Lord and God,
cleanse us, unclean,
with thy most cleansing blood;
increase our faith and love,
that we may know
the hope and peace
which from thy presence flow.

4. O Christ, whom now
beneath a veil we see,
may what we thirst for
soon our portion be:
to gaze on thee unveiled,
and see thy face,
the vision of thy glory
and thy grace.

437

Henry Williams Baker (1821-1877), based on Psalm 23

1. The King of love my shepherd is,
whose goodness faileth never;
I nothing lack if I am his
and he is mine for ever.

2. Where streams of living water flow
my ransomed soul he leadeth,
and where the verdant pastures grow
with food celestial feedeth.

3. Perverse and foolish oft I strayed,
but yet in love he sought me,
and on his shoulder gently laid,
and home, rejoicing, brought me.

4. In death's dark vale I fear no ill
with thee, dear Lord, beside me;
thy rod and staff my comfort still,
thy cross before to guide me.

5. Thou spread'st a table in my sight,
thy unction grace bestoweth:
and O what transport of delight
from thy pure chalice floweth!

6. And so through all the length of days
thy goodness faileth never;
good Shepherd, may I sing thy praise
within thy house for ever.

438 Psalm 23 from 'The Scottish Psalter' (1650)

1. The Lord's my shepherd, I'll not want.
   He makes me down to lie
   in pastures green.
   He leadeth me the quiet waters by.

2. My soul he doth restore again,
   and me to walk doth make
   within the paths of righteousness,
   e'en for his own name's sake.

3. Yea, though I walk in death's dark vale,
   yet will I fear no ill.
   For thou art with me, and thy rod
   and staff me comfort still.

4. My table thou hast furnishèd
   in presence of my foes,
   my head thou dost with oil anoint,
   and my cup overflows.

5. Goodness and mercy all my life
   shall surely follow me.
   And in God's house for evermore
   my dwelling-place shall be.

439 Vincent Stuckey Stratton Coles (1845-1929)

1. We pray thee, heav'nly Father,
   to hear us in thy love,
   and pour upon thy children
   the unction from above;
   that so in love abiding,
   from all defilement free,
   we may in pureness offer
   our Eucharist to thee.

2. Be thou our guide and helper,
   O Jesus Christ, we pray;
   so may we well approach thee,
   if thou wilt be the Way:
   thou, very Truth, hast promised
   to help us in our strife,
   food of the weary pilgrim,
   eternal source of life.

3. And thou, creator Spirit,
   look on us, we are thine;
   renew in us thy graces,
   upon our darkness shine;
   that, with thy benediction
   upon our souls outpoured,
   we may receive in gladness
   the body of the Lord.

4. O Trinity of Persons,
   O Unity most high,
   on thee alone relying
   thy servants would draw nigh:
   unworthy in our weakness,
   on thee our hope is stayed,
   and blessed by thy forgiveness
   we will not be afraid.

440 Isaac Watts (1674-1748)

1. When I survey the wondrous cross
   on which the Prince of Glory died,
   my richest gain I count but loss,
   and pour contempt on all my pride.

2. Forbid it, Lord, that I should boast,
   save in the death of Christ, my God:
   all the vain things that charm me most,
   I sacrifice them to his blood.

3. See from his head, his hands, his feet,
   sorrow and love flow mingling down:
   did e'er such love and sorrow meet,
   or thorns compose so rich a crown?

4. Were the whole realm of nature mine,
   that were an off'ring far too small;
   love so amazing, so divine,
   demands my soul, my life, my all.

Index of Authors, Translators and Sources of Text

Aaronic Blessing 386
Adam, David 382
Adams, Sarah Flower 235
Adkins, Donna 70
Ainger, Arthur Campbell 99
Ainger, Geoffrey 32
Alexander, Cecil Frances 141
Alstyne, Frances Jane van 28, 274, 338
Altrogge, Mark 371
Anderson, Mike 29, 57, 296, 318, 376, 412
Andrew, Diane Davis 312
Anima Christi 300
Appleford, Patrick 207, 247
Arkin, David 316
Arlott, John 104
Armstrong, Paul 302

Baker, Henry Williams 230, 259, 276, 292, 437
Bakewell, John 116
Bankhead, Dave 52
Baring-Gould, Sabine 297, 313
Barnett, John 176
Batya, Naomi 189
Baughen, Michael 298
Bell, John L. 11, 33, 42, 44, 56, 92, 123, 158, 169, 172, 174, 353, 356, 368, 390
Bennard, George 253
Berry, Jan 203
Bewes, Richard 97
Bickersteth, Edward Henry 266
Bilbrough, Dave 1, 137, 194
Birgina gazettobat zegoen 313
Bliss, Philipp 222
Boberg, Karl 248
Bode, John E. 432
Bonar, Horatius 72, 336, 425
Booth, Paul 365
Borthwick, Jane L. 26
Bourne, George Hugh 430
Bowater, Chris 62, 171, 181, 191
Bowers, John E. 40
Bowring, John 159
Brethorst, Leona von 166
Bridge, Basil 111
Bridges, Matthew 422
Bridges, Robert 2
Briggs, George Wallace 421
Brooke, Stopford Augustus 162
Bullock, Geoff 205
Burkitt, Francis Crawford 341

Caribbean traditional 263
Carter, Sydney 255, 359
Caswall, Edward 287
Chesterton, Gilbert Keith 241
Chisholm, Thomas Obadiah 113
Christmas Carols, Ancient and Modern 1833 314
Clephane,Elizabeth C. 23
Clifton, Dave 271
Cockett, Michael 8, 75
Coelho, Terrye 69
Coles, Vincent Stuckey Stratton 439
Conder, Josiah 320
Connaughton, Luke 214
Conty, Sophie 189
Cotterill, Thomas 424
Cowper, William 119
Crosby, Fanny J. 28, 274, 338
Cross, Stewart 68
Cull, Robert 261
Cullen, Tim 118
Czech Traditional 202

Daniels, John 18
Dauermann, Stuart 378
Dawn, Maggi 129
Dearmer, Percy 95, 202, 246, 339
Dix, William Chatterton 355
Doddridge, Philip 242
Doerksen, Brian 51, 280
Dudley-Smith, Timothy 73, 96, 179, 204, 208, 234, 277
Dunn, Fred 186

Edmeston, James 429
Elliott, Charlotte 426
English traditional 103, 254
Espinosa, Eddie 38
Evans, David J. 25

Faber, Frederick William 324
Farjeon, Eleanor 227
Fawcett, Nick 183
Fellingham David 20, 100, 293
Fishel, Donald 4
Fletcher, Phineas 60
Ford, Mavis 373
Forster, Michael 21, 49, 55, 83, 85, 98, 99, 102, 107, 122, 144, 148, 184, 193, 223, 224, 244, 249, 260, 279, 290, 325, 327, 340, 348, 361, 410, 414, 415, 416, 417
Fosdick, Harry Emerson 101
Founds, Rick 206
Fry, Steven 36
Fullerton, William Young 142

Gabriel, Charles H. 161
Gaelic Blessing 394
Garrett, Les 332
Gaunt, Howard Charles Adie 90, 278
Gerhardt, Paul 282
Gillard, Richard 35
Gillman, Bob 27
Glynn, John 165
Good Friday Reproaches 148
Gowans, John 322
Grafstrom, Viola 346
Green, Fred Pratt 14, 78, 360
Green, Melody 323
Grice, Edwin Le 114
Gurney, Dorothy F. 433
Gurney, John Hampden 61
Gustafson, Gerrit 257
Hart, Joseph 135
Hatch, Edwin 419
Havergal, Frances Ridley 139, 156, 309
Hawks, Annie Sherwood 154
Hayes, Pamela 215, 399
Hayford, Jack W. 219
Hayward, Rob 151
Head, Elizabeth Ann Porter 237
Hearn, Naida 178
Heber, Reginald 420
Heerman, J. 2
Herbert, George 50, 427
Hewer, Jenny 67
Hine, Stuart K. 248
Holland, Henry Scott 187
Holloway, Jean 81, 86, 211, 304, 311
Hoog, Pierre-Marie 350
Hopkins, John Henry 351
Horley, Doug 352
How, William Walsham 252, 364
Howard, Brian 145

Iona Community, The 347
Iverson, Daniel 303

Jeffery Graham 372
Jones, Keri 357

Kaan, Fred 77, 79, 105, 197, 281
Keble, John 115
Keen, Richard 134
Kelly, Robert B. 350
Ken, Thomas 272
Kendrick, Graham 19, 22, 46, 64, 66, 82, 84, 93, 180, 182, 192, 210, 221, 226, 233, 239, 250, 256, 258, 268, 285, 306, 319, 343, 345, 349, 363, 366
Kennedy, Helen 301
Kennett, John 273
King Jr. Martin Luther 348
Kirkbride, Mary 15
Kirkpatrick, William James 21
Kitchin, George William 198
Klein, Laurie 150

Lafferty, Karen 289
Langton, Stephen 405, 406
Leckebusch, Martin E. 53, 153
Leeson, Jane Elizabeth 217
Leftley, Francesca 160, 308
Locke, Mary Lou 15
Löwenstern, Matthäus Apellesvon 209
Lowry, Robert 218, 291
Lowry, Somerset Corry 9
Lucis Creator Optime 31
Lundy, Damian 3, 326, 330
Lunt, Janet 34

MacBean, Lachlan 39
MacDonald, Mary 39
Mansell, David J. 175
Maries, Andrew 344
Mark, Robin 231
Markland, Gerard 59

Marshall-Taylor, Geoffrey 312
Massey, Christopher 201
Matheson, George 251
Matthew, David 357
Maule, Graham 11, 33, 42, 44, 56, 92, 123, 158, 169, 172, 174, 353, 356, 368, 390
Mawby, Colin 392
Mayhew, Kevin 267, 386
McClellan, Sue 45
McEwan, Steve 112
Medley, Samuel 149
Miles, C. Austin 367
Mohr, Joseph 294
Morgan, Patricia 52

Nazareth, Aniceto 13, 200
Neale, John Mason 74, 108, 109
Nelson, Marc 140
New English Hymnal, The 284
Newbolt, Michael Robert 198
Newman, John Henry 423, 428
Newport, Doreen 329
Newton, John 10
Nicolai, Philipp 341
Noel, Caroline Maria 418
Noel, Richards 216, 375
Nun danket alle Gott 431
Nyberg, Anders 344
Nystrom, Martin 17

O Støre Gud 248
Oakley, Paul 177
Owens, Carol 91
Owens, Jimmy 130, 330
Owens, Priscilla Jane 369

Paculabo, John 45
Palmer, Ray 229
Pantry, John 370
Paris, Twila 124
Peacey, John Raphael 71
Pereira, Marie Lydia 94, 342
Perrin, Cathy 358
Perrin, Wayne 358
Perronet, Edward 417
Perry, Michael 199, 240, 288
Peruvian traditional 413
Piercy, Andy 271
Polish traditional 155
Pollock, Thomas Benson 63
Prayer of St Francis 220
Puer nobis nascitur 339
Pusey, Philip 209

Quinn, James 80, 331

Rawley, Francis Harold 168
Redman, Matt 167, 173, 262
Reed, Edith Margaret Gellibrand 155
Rees, Bryn A. 120, 317
Rees, John 10
Richards, Dave 76
Richards, Hubert J. 30
Richards, Noel 37, 337
Richards, Tricia 5, 37, 216
Rinkart, Martin 431
Rizza, Margaret 374, 388, 394, 399, 408
Rolinson, Chris 285
Rossetti, Christina Georgina 213
Routley, Erik 236
Rubin, Steffi Geiser 378
Ryecroft, Keith 45

Sammis, John Henry 362
Sandys, William 314
Saward, Michael 43, 295
Sayers, Susan 146, 212, 310, 335
Scheidt, Samuel 246
Schlegal, Katherina von 26
Schutte, Dan 163
Scottish Psalter, The 1650 438
Scriven, Joseph Medlicott 354
Seddon, James Edward 106, 196
Smale, Ian 65
Smith Jnr., Leonard E. 136
Smith, Henry 88
South African traditional 344
Sparrow-Simpson, William 54
Spiritual 164, 190, 305
St Patrick 141
St Teresa of Avila 395
St Thomas Aquinas 436
Stanfield, Francis 307
Strover, Christian 121
Sutton, Wes 377

Taizé Community 321, 379, 381, 384, 387, 389, 391, 396, 404, 407
Temple, Sebastian 7, 220
Timms, George Bourne 299
Toolan, Suzanne 138
Toplady, Augustus Montague 434
Townend, Stuart 133
Traditional 87, 110, 117, 128, 188, 243, 315, 334, 380, 385, 398
Turner, Roy 6
Tuttle, Carl 132, 147

Waring, Anna Laetitia 157
Watts, Isaac 89, 152, 185, 440
Wesley, Charles 12, 126, 238, 424, 435
Wesley, John 282
West Indian traditional 328
West, Peter 15
White, Estelle 228
Wilkinson, Kate Barclay 225
Wimber, John 245
Winkworth, Catherine 431
Woodford, James Russell 436
Woodward, George Ratcliffe 58, 333
Wren, Brian A. 41, 47, 127, 143, 270

Young, John Freeman 294

Zschech, Darlene 232

Scriptural Index

GENESIS

1	This world you have made	335
1:1-2	Sing glory to God the Father	295
1:1-4	Blest Creator of the light	31
	God is our strength from days of old	98
	Lord, the light of your love	210
	O Breath of Life	237
	On this day, the first of days	259
1:1-5	Lord of all life and power	208
	Morning has broken	227
	The universe was waiting	327
1:2-3	All over the world	6
1:3-25	Praise the Lord of heaven	277
1:26	For the healing of the nations	79
1:27	Dance and sing	56
	Gracious God, in adoration	111
1:28	Lord of all life and power	208
1:31	Gracious God, in adoration	111
2:1-8	Morning has broken	227
2:7	Breathe on me, Breath of God	419
	Gracious God, in adoration	111
	O Breath of Life	237
2:19-20	If I were a butterfly	145
4:7	Restore, O Lord	285
4:9	I do not know the man	144
6:4	Rise and shine	286
8:22	Great is thy faithfulness	113
9:12-17	Who put the colours in the rainbow?	365
12:1-4	One more step along the world I go	255
22:12	O Lord, my God	248
22:14	Shout for joy and sing	293
28:10-19	As Jacob with travel was weary one day	16
	Beneath the cross of Jesus	23
	Blessed assurance	28
	Nearer, my God, to thee	235
	Rise and shine	286
32:24-32	Let love be real	193
49:24	Rock of ages	434

EXODUS

3:5	Be still, for the presence of the Lord	25
3:10-11	Moses, I know you're the man	228
13-17	I give you love	148
15:2	The Lord is my song	321
15:23-25	O Lord, your tenderness	250
15:26	Shout for joy and sing	293
20:3	Make way, make way	221
23:19	Fair waved the golden corn	61
33:22	Rock of ages	434
34:26	Fair waved the golden corn	61

LEVITICUS

19:15	Beauty for brokenness	22

NUMBERS

6:1-12	Take my life, and let it be	309
6:24-26	Holy God, we place ourselves	386
	May the Lord bless you	394
20:8-11	Lord, enthroned in heavenly splendour	430

DEUTERONOMY

5:7	Make way, make way	221
8:3	Seek ye first	289
11:18-21	Take my life, and let it be	309
26:9-11	Fair waved the golden corn	61
32:3-4	Ascribe greatness	15
33:27	God is our strength and refuge	97

JOSHUA

3:14-17	This joyful Eastertide	333

2 SAMUEL

22:2	God is our strength and refuge	97
22:3	You are beneath me	372
23:5	Put thou thy trust in God	282

1 KINGS

19:12	Listen, let your heart keep seeking	200

2 CHRONICLES

3:17	Spirit of God	301
	The Spirit lives to set us free	326
3:17-18	Dance in your Spirit	57
	Lord, the light of your love	210
3:18	For the healing of the nations	79
4:6	Kindle a flame	390
	Lord, the light of your love	210
5:15	For ourselves no longer living	77
5:17	I am a new creation	137
5:21	Come and see	46
6:1-10	I bind unto myself today	141
6:10	Give thanks with a grateful heart	88
7:14	In an age of twisted values	153
8:9	Come, wounded Healer	53
	Name of all majesty	234
9:7-9	All that I am	7
9:8-11	Now thank we all our God	431

2 Chronicles

9:15	At this time of giving	19
10:4	We want to see Jesus lifted high	352
12:10	Give thanks with a grateful heart	88
13:4	Cross of Jesus	54
13:14	Sing glory to God the Father	295

NEHEMIAH

2:3	Your mercy flows	377

JOB

19:25	I know that my Redeemer lives	149

PSALMS

2:1-2	God of grace and God of glory	101
2:8	I cannot tell	142
3:3	As the deer pants for the water	17
4:1	O Lord, hear my prayer	396
4:8	My Father, for another night	230
	This joyful Eastertide	333
5:1-3	My Father, for another night	230
5:7	It's me, O Lord	164
8:1-9	O Lord, my God	248
8:3	Fill your hearts with joy and gladness	73
12	Who can sound the depths of sorrow	363
16:5	Amazing grace	10
16:9	This joyful Eastertide	333
16:11	Lord, I come to you	205
18:2	God is our strength and refuge	97
	Praise him, praise him	274
	Rock of ages	434
	Shout for joy and sing	293
18:2-:3	In you, my God	160
18:11	Put thou thy trust in God	282
18:33	God of grace and God of glory	101
18:46	Lord of our life, and God of our salvation	209
19:1	All heaven declares	5
19:1-4	Gracious God, in adoration	111
19:1-7	The ink is black	316
19:4	I love you, Lord, and I lift my voice	150
19:4-6	The holly and the ivy	315
19:8	Your love's greater	376
19:10	As the deer pants for the water	17
	Jesus, Jesus	176
20:5	We want to see Jesus lifted high	352
23	Nada te turbe	395
	The Lord's my shepherd	438
23:1-6	Faithful Shepherd, feed me	63
	Forth in the peace of Christ we go	80
	In heavenly love abiding	157
	The King of love my shepherd is	437
23:6	At this time of giving	19
24:1	For ourselves no longer living	77
24:7	Just as I am, without one plea	426
	King of glory, King of peace	427
	Make way, make way	221
24:7-10	Hail the day that sees him rise	424
25:2	Be still and know that I am God	24
25:4-5	Lord of our life, and God of our salvation	209
	Wait for the Lord	407
27	O God beyond all praising	240
27:1	God is our strength from days of old	98
	In the Lord is my joy	388
	The Lord is my light (Taizé)	402
	The Lord is my light (Rizza)	403

Psalms

27:6	Put thou thy trust in God	282
27:8	Lord, I come to you	205
	Spirit of God	301
	We bow down	346
27:11	Wait for the Lord	407
29:9	The kingdom of God	317
29:11	Lord of our life, and God of our salvation	209
31:2	God is our strength and refuge	97
31:2-3	In you, my God	160
31:3	We pray thee, heavenly Father	439
	You are beneath me	372
31:5	Father, I place into your hands	67
31:14	Be still and know that I am God	24
33:4	Faithful God	62
33:12	In an age of twisted values	153
	Lord, for the years	204
34	In the Lord I'll be ever thankful	387
34:18	Who sees it all	366
36:5	Faithful God	62
38:4	God is good	93
40:1	Wait for the Lord	407
40:2	God of grace and God of glory	101
41:1	Good King Wenceslas	109
42:1-11	As the deer pants for the water	17
42:2	Spirit of God	301
46	God is our strength and refuge	97
46:4	Your mercy flows	377
46:10	Be still and know that I am God	24
	Be still, for the presence of the Lord	25
	Be still, my soul	26
47:1-9	He is exalted	124
48:1-14	Great is the Lord and most worthy of praise	112
51:1-3	On the bloodstained ground	258
51:2	My Lord, what love is this	233
51:10	You are the centre	408
51:12	You are beneath me	372
51:14	Lord of our life, and God of our salvation	209
51:17	I will offer up my life	167
52:8	I am trusting thee, Lord Jesus	139
54:4	You are beneath me	372
55:1-2	O Lord, hear my prayer	396
55:16-17	I watch the sunrise	165
55:17	Praise him, praise him, praise him	275
55:22	You are beneath me	372
56:3	Be still and know that I am God	24
57:8	Crown him with many crowns	422
57:10	Great is thy faithfulness	113
59:16	God is our strength and refuge	97
63	God is my great desire	96
63:1	Spirit of God	301
63:8	You are beneath me	372
65	Fill your hearts with joy and gladness	73
	Praise God for the harvest	270
66:1-3	My Jesus, my Saviour	232
66:5	God is our strength and refuge	97
69	O give thanks	239
70:4	Wait for the Lord	407
71:1	I am trusting thee, Lord Jesus	139
	I'm not ashamed to own my Lord	152
	We pray thee, heavenly Father	439
71:3	God is our strength and refuge	97
	In you, my God	160
71:17	You are the light	374
72:6	The Saviour will come, resplendent in joy	325
73:1	O, how good is the Lord	243
73:21-26	Lord, when I turn my back on you	212

Psalms

78:24-25	Bread is blessed and broken	33
81:16	I, the Lord of sea and sky	163
82	Who can sound the depths of sorrow	363
84:2	Alleluia, alleluia, give thanks to the risen Lord	4
84:7	Soldiers of Christ, arise	435
85:4	Lord of our life, and God of our salvation	209
85:4-7	Your mercy flows	377
85:8-13	Fill your hearts with joy and gladness	73
85:8-14	Onward, Christian pilgrims	260
	We have a dream	348
86:1-10	O Lord, hear my prayer	396
86:11	Wait for the Lord	407
86:13	Great is thy faithfulness	113
86:16-17	O Lord, hear my prayer	396
89:14-15	We have a dream	348
89:15	The Spirit lives to set us free	326
89:15-16	We'll walk the land	349
89:26	You are beneath me	372
89:28-29	I'm not ashamed to own my Lord	152
90:1-2	Lord, for the years	204
	Lord of all life and power	208
91:1-3	Soul of my Saviour	300
91:1-6	I bind unto myself today	141
91:2	God is our strength and refuge	97
91:6	Beneath the cross of Jesus	23
91:9-16	I bind unto myself today	141
92:1-3	Thank you, Lord	312
92:4	My Jesus, my Saviour	232
92:5	O Lord, my God	248
93:1	How lovely on the mountains	136
93:3-4	Praise the Lord of heaven	277
95:1-2	Come, now is the time of worship	51
95:1-6	Sing glory to God the Father	295
95:1-7	Gracious God, in adoration	111
95:6	Come, now is the time of worship	51
96:1	My Jesus, my Saviour	232
96:7-13	Far and near	64
96:9	O sacred King	262
96:11	My Jesus, my Saviour	232
96:11-13	O give thanks	239
	Praise the Lord of heaven	277
97:1	God is working his purpose out	99
	The Lord is King!	320
97:2	Put thou thy trust in God	282
97:5	My Jesus, my Saviour	232
98	O give thanks	239
98:1-9	Joy to the world	185
	Sing to God new songs of worship	298
98:4	My Jesus, my Saviour	232
	Shout for joy and sing	293
100:1-5	Jubilate, everybody	186
	Lord, for the years	204
100:4	Christians, lift up your hearts	40
	I will enter his gates	166
	Shout for joy and sing	293
100:5	O give thanks	239
	Praise, O praise our God and King	276
	Your love's greater	376
102:25	God is our strength from days of old	98
103	Bless the Lord, my soul	381
103:1-2	Bless the Lord, my soul	29
	O, how good is the Lord	243
103:1-4	Bless the Lord, my soul	381
103:3	Be still and know that I am God	24
103:8	O Lord, your tenderness	250
103:11	Great is thy faithfulness	113

Reference	Title	No.
103:13	How deep the Father's	133
	You are beneath me	372
103:13-14	O Lord, your tenderness	250
103:20-22	Praise the Lord of heaven	277
103:21	Praise God from whom all blessings flow	271
104	Send forth your Spirit	290
104:1-30	Praise the Lord of heaven	277
104:12	If I were a butterfly	145
104:14	Fill your hearts with joy and gladness	73
104:24-25	If I were a butterfly	145
104:30	Breathe on me, Breath of God	419
	Lord of all life and power	208
	You are the centre	408
105:40	Bread is blessed and broken	33
105:41	Peace is flowing like a river	265
106:21	You are beneath me	372
107:1-9	Now thank we all our God	431
107:9	Thanks for the fellowship	311
107:23-32	Lead us, heavenly Father, lead us	429
107:23-37	Will your anchor hold	369
112:7	I am trusting thee, Lord Jesus	139
116:1-2	O God beyond all praising	240
116:12-14	I will offer up my life	167
116:12-19	O God beyond all praising	240
117	Laudate Dominum	391
	Your love's greater	376
117:1-2	Great is thy faithfulness	113
118:1	Confitemini Domino	383
118:14	Christians, lift up your hearts	40
	In the Lord is my joy	388
118:19-24	Christians, lift up your hearts	40
	I will enter his gates	166
	This is the day	332
118:25-26	Holy, most holy, all holy the Lord	415
	Hosanna, hosanna	132
119:41-42	Lord, we come to ask your healing	211
119:57	Amazing grace	10
119:105	Jesus, Jesus	176
119:105-112	When we walk with the Lord	362
121:5-6	I watch the sunrise	165
122:6	Lord of our life, and God of our salvation	209
123:2	Wait for the Lord	407
126:6	Jesus put this song	180
128:6	Lord of our life, and God of our salvation	209
129:8	Peace to you	268
130:3	Only by grace	257
130:7	There's a wideness in God's mercy	324
131	O Lord, my heart is not proud	397
133:1	Living God, your word has called us	203
135:3	God is good	93
136	Give to our God immortal praise	89
136:1	O give thanks	239
139:6	You are beautiful	371
139:9-10	He's got the whole world in his hand	128
139:10	You are beneath me	372
139:23	Lord, the light of your love	210
143:6	Spirit of God	301
143:8	Be still and know that I am God	24
145:1-7	God of glory we exalt your name	100
145:13	Faithful God	62
145:14	You are beneath me	372
145:17	Let us praise God together	196
146:6	Faithful God	62
146:7	Thanks for the fellowship	311
147:3	I cannot tell	142
147:4-18	Fill your hearts with joy and gladness	73

Psalms

Reference	Title	No.
147:18	Breathe on me, Breath of God	419
	Lord, the light of your love	210
148	All the nations of the earth	8
	New songs of celebration render	236
	Praise the Lord of heaven	277
148:13	Let us praise God together	196
149	New songs of celebration render	236
149:3	Dance in your Spirit	57
150	Bless the Lord, my soul	29
	Dance and sing	56
	New songs of celebration render	236
	Praise him on the trumpet	273

PROVERBS

Reference	Title	No.
9:5	Broken for me	34
	Gather around, for the table is spread	86
13:34	In an age of twisted values	153
14:34	Lord, for the years	204

ECCLESIASTES

Reference	Title	No.
12:1-7	Will your anchor hold	369
50:22-24	Now thank we all our God	431

SONG OF SOLOMON

Reference	Title	No.
8:6	At the name of Jesus	418
	Hark, my soul, it is the Lord	119

ISAIAH

Reference	Title	No.
1:3	What child is this	355
2:4-5	Onward, Christian pilgrims	260
	Waken, O sleeper, wake and rise	340
	We are marching	344
6:1-3	Holy, holy, holy	130
	Lord, the light of your love	210
6:2-3	Cross of Jesus	54
	Crown him with many crowns	422
	Holy, holy, holy is the Lord	131
	Holy, most holy, all holy the Lord	415
6:8-9	Inspired by love and anger	158
	I, the Lord of sea and sky	163
7:14	Hail, thou once despisèd Jesus	116
	Jesus, Name above all names	178
9:1-2	Lord, the light of your love	210
9:5-6	Crown him with many crowns	422
	Unto us a boy is born	339
	We shall stay awake	350
	You are the King of Glory	373
9:6	Drop, drop, slow tears	60
	God is working his purpose out	99
	Just as I am, without one plea	426
	King of glory, King of peace	427
	King of kings and Lord of lords	189
	Peace to you	268
11:1-2	Come, Holy Spirit, come	49
	Lord, enthroned in heavenly splendour	430
11:1-9	All over the world	6
	God is working his purpose out	99
	May the mind of Christ my Saviour	225
11:10	Crown him with many crowns	422
12:2-3	The Lord is my song	321
16:1	See, amid the winter's snow	287
25:4	God is our strength from days of old	98

35	The Saviour will come, resplendent in joy	325
40:1-11	Do not be afraid	59
	Wait for the Lord	407
	We have a dream	348
40:5	I cannot tell	142
40:8-9	Sing it in the valleys	296
40:9	Go, tell it on the mountain	110
40:11	Praise him, praise him	274
40:26	Fill your hearts with joy and gladness	73
40:31	Lord, I come to you	205
42:1	You are beneath me	372
42:1-3	How firm a foundation	134
43:1-4	Do not be afraid	59
43:3	You are beneath me	372
44:24	Shout for joy and sing	293
48:18	Peace is flowing like a river	265
49:15	Hark, my soul, it is the Lord	119
52:3	From heaven you came	82
52:7-10	Drop, drop, slow tears	60
	How lovely on the mountains	136
53	How lovely on the mountains	136
53:1-12	Christ triumphant	43
53:3	Man of sorrows	222
	My Lord, what love is this	233
	Who is this so weak and helpless	364
53:3-5	Come, wounded Healer	53
53:3-6	On the bloodstained ground	258
53:4-5	How deep the Father's love for us	133
	You are the light	374
53:4-7	Ah, holy Jesu, how hast thou offended	2
	Child in the manger	39
	Come and see	46
	Led like a lamb	192
	What a friend we have in Jesus	354
53:5	You laid aside your majesty	375
53:5-8	He was pierced	129
55:1	Spirit of God	301
55:3	Put thou thy trust in God	282
55:12	You shall go out with joy	378
57:15	O sacred King	262
58:11	You are beneath me	372
61:1	God of glory we exalt your name	100
	The kingdom of God	317
	Who sees it all	366
61:1-2	Gracious God, in adoration	111
61:1-3	God is working his purpose out	99
	I cannot tell	142
	I give you all the honour	147
	Inspired by love and anger	158
	Lord, for the years	204
	Make way, make way	221
	O for a thousand tongues to sing	238
64:8	Change my heart, O God	38
	Take me, Lord	308
66:1-2	O sacred King	262

JEREMIAH

6:13-15	O God of earth and altar	241
14:8	God is our strength from days of old	98
16:50	God is our strength and refuge	97
17:5-8	Think of a world without any flowers	329
17:13	God is our strength from days of old	98
31:3	Your love's greater	376

LAMENTATIONS

3:22-23	Morning has broken	227
	Thank you, Lord	312

EZEKIEL

10	I bind unto myself today	141
20:32-37	O God of earth and altar	241
36:25-26	All over the world	6
	I, the Lord of sea and sky	163
37	Breathe on me, Breath of God	419
47:12	For the healing of the nations	79

DANIEL

3:28	Adoramus te, Domine	379
3:52-90	Surrexit Christus	401
3:57-90	All the nations of the earth	8
7:9	Crown him with many crowns	422

JOEL

2:28	All over the world	6
	The King is among us	319

AMOS

5:24	Peace is flowing like a river	265
	The universe was waiting	327

MICAH

4:3	Onward, Christian pilgrims	260
4:3-4	Waken, O sleeper, wake and rise	340
5:2	When our God came to earth	361
6:3-5	I give you love	148

HABAKKUK

2:14	All over the world	6
3:2	Restore, O Lord	285

HAGGAI

2:6	Restore, O Lord	285

ZECHARIAH

8:4-5	In an age of twisted values	153
13:9	Purify my heart	280

MALACHI

1:11	From the sun's rising	84
3:3	Purify my heart	280
	Restore, O Lord	285
3:6	Great is thy faithfulness	113
4:2	Judge eternal, throned in splendour	187
	You are the King of Glory	373

MATTHEW

1:21	The Virgin Mary had a baby boy	328
1:23	Come, come, come to the manger	48
	Hail, thou once despisèd Jesus	116
	Jesus, Name above all names	178

Matthew

Reference	Title	No.
1:23	Let us talents and tongues employ	197
	Mary, blessèd teenage mother	224
	Morning has broken	227
	The angel Gabriel from heaven came	313
2:1-12	Brightest and best	420
	Crown him with many crowns	422
	Love came down at Christmas	213
	See him lying on a bed of straw	288
	The first Nowell	314
	The Virgin Mary had a baby boy	328
	We three kings of Orient are	351
	What child is this	355
2:2	Adoramus te, Domine	379
	When our God came to earth	361
2:13-18	Unto us a boy is born	339
3:1-3	Come on and celebrate	52
	Wait for the Lord	407
3:1-12	We shall stay awake	350
3:2	The kingdom of God	317
3:11	All over the world	6
	Come, Holy Spirit, come	49
3:13-17	I bind unto myself today	141
3:16	O let the Son of God enfold you	245
4:1-11	Forty days and forty nights in Judah's desert	81
	Lead us, heavenly Father, lead us	429
	Love is his word	214
4:4	Seek ye first	289
4:16	God is our strength from days of old	98
4:16-17	Lord, the light of your love	210
4:17-25	Jesus Christ is waiting	174
4:18-20	Follow me	75
	O happy day	242
	When God Almighty came to earth	356
	Will you come and follow me	368
5:3-12	The kingdom of heaven	318
5:5	Fill your hearts with joy and gladness	73
	Make way, make way	221
	Who sees it all	366
5:6	Jesus, the broken bread	183
5:14-16	The Spirit lives to set us free	326
5:16	This little light of mine	344
5:41	Brother, sister, let me serve you	35
5:44	O Lord, all the world belongs to you	247
6:9-13	For the fruits of his creation	78
	God forgave my sin	91
	Make me a channel of your peace	220
	Our Father (Caribbean)	263
	Our Father (Wiener)	264
	Thy way, not mine, O Lord	336
6:10	Gracious God, in adoration	111
	Jesus, the broken bread	183
	Lord, for the years	204
	Lord of creation	392
	The universe was waiting	327
6:18	Come, build the Church	47
6:20	Blest Creator of the light	31
6:24	In an age of twisted values	153
6:26	Moses, I know you're the man	228
6:28-29	There are hundreds of sparrows	322
6:31-33	Lord, for the years	204
6:33	Jesus, the broken bread	183
	Seek ye first	289
	Wait for the Lord	407
7:7	Seek ye first	289
	Wait for the Lord	407
7:10	Glory to thee, O God	90
	Thanks for the fellowship	311

Matthew

Reference	Title	No.
7:13	A new commandment	13
	Faithful Shepherd, feed me	63
	I will sing the wondrous story	168
	Loving Shepherd of thy sheep	217
7:24-37	We cannot measure	347
8:2	Will you come and follow me	368
8:11	The Spirit lives to set us free	326
8:17	What a friend we have in Jesus	354
8:20	Follow me	75
	Moses, I know you're the man	228
8:23-27	I cannot tell	142
	Inspired by love and anger	158
	Sweet sacrament divine	307
8:26	Calm me, Lord	382
	Be still, my soul	26
	You are the light	374
9:9	Follow me	75
	When God Almighty came to earth	356
	Will you come and follow me	368
9:11	The kingdom of God	317
9:17	One shall tell another	256
9:27	Spirit of God	301
9:38	From the sun's rising	84
10:8	God forgave my sin	91
10:29	There are hundreds of sparrows	322
10:29-31	There are hundreds of sparrows	322
10:38	Follow me	75
	Lift high the cross	198
	When God Almighty came to earth	356
11:5	The kingdom of God	317
11:16-19	Jesus Christ is waiting	174
11:19	Love is his word	214
11:28-29	O Love that wilt not let me go	251
11:28-30	Come, wounded Healer	53
	I cannot tell	142
	I heard the voice of Jesus say	425
	It fell upon a summer day	162
12:18	Beauty for brokenness	22
12:28-31	Love came down at Christmas	213
13:4-30	From many grains	83
13:14-15	O God of earth and altar	241
13:36-43	From many grains	83
13:41	At the name of Jesus	418
13:55	Inspired by love and anger	158
14:5	Father, Lord of all creation	68
14:13-21	Gather around, for the table is spread	86
15:1-20	Jesus Christ is waiting	174
15:32-29	Gather around, for the table is spread	86
16:16	I believe in Jesus	140
16:18	From the very depths of darkness	85
16:18-19	Firmly I believe and truly	423
16:24	Follow me	75
17:1-8	When I look into your holiness	358
18:3	It fell upon a summer day	162
18:12	Amazing grace	10
	Hark, my soul, it is the Lord	119
	I will sing the wondrous story	
	The King of love my shepherd is	437
18:21-25	O God beyond all praising	240
19:14	It fell upon a summer day	162
19:16-30	Take my life, and let it be	309
20:28	From heaven you came	82
	Jesus is Lord! Creation's voice proclaims it	175
21:8-9	Give me joy in my heart	87
	Hosanna, hosanna	132
	Lord, enthroned in heavenly splendour	430

Reference	Title	No.
	Praise him, praise him	274
	Wake, O wake! with tidings thrilling	341
	You are the King of Glory	373
21:9	Holy, most holy, all holy the Lord	415
21:12-16	Jesus Christ is waiting	174
22:34-40	Firmly I believe and truly	423
23	Jesus Christ is waiting	174
23:11	O Lord, all the world belongs to you	
24:30	Led like a lamb	192
24:30-31	O Lord, my God	248
	This joyful Eastertide	333
	We are his children	343
24:42-44	Waken, O sleeper, wake and rise	340
	We shall stay awake	350
25:1-13	Give me joy in my heart	87
	Wake, O wake! with tidings thrilling	341
	Will you come and follow me	368
25:31	At the name of Jesus	
25:31-46	When I needed a neighbour	359
25:34	As Jacob with travel was weary one day	16
25:40	The universe was waiting	327
26:26-28	Among us and before us	11
	Broken for me	34
	Come, risen Lord	421
	Jesus took a piece of bread	184
	Love is his word	214
26:26-29	God of the Passover	102
	This is my body	330
26:30	When, in our music, God is glorified	360
26:31	Praise the Lord, rise up rejoicing	278
26:36-42	Stay with me	400
26:36-46	Forty days and forty nights in Judah's desert	81
	From heaven you came	82
	Thy way, not mine, O Lord	336
26:39	Lord of creation	392
26:41	Onward, Christian pilgrims	260
26:67	Man of sorrows	222
	O Lord of our salvation	249
26:72-74	Forty days and forty nights in Judah's desert	81
	I do not know the man	144
27:22	Cross of Jesus	54
27:29	Come and see	46
	Great Son of God	114
27:32:56	Cross of Jesus	54
	Here hangs a man discarded	127
27:39-44	How deep the Father's	133
27:39-46	Ah, holy Jesu, how hast thou offended	2
	A man there lived in Galilee	9
	Great Son of God	114
27:66	Low in the grave he lay	218
28:1-10	From the very depths of darkness	85
	On this day, the first of days	259
28:9	Adoramus te, Domine	379
28:18-19	A man there lived in Galilee	9
	God forgave my sin	91
	Go forth and tell	106
28:18-20	Stand up, stand up for Jesus	304
28:19-20	From the sun's rising	84
	We are his children	343

MARK

Reference	Title	No.
1:1-4	Wait for the Lord	407
1:1-8	We shall stay awake	350
1:8	All over the world	6

Reference	Title	No.
1:10	Come. Holy Spirit, come	49
	God is our strength from days of old	98
	O let the Son of God enfold you	245
1:12	Forty days and forty nights in Judah's desert	81
	Lead us, heavenly Father, lead us	429
1:12-13	Love is his word	214
1:15	The kingdom of God	317
1:16-20	O happy day	242
	When God Almighty came to earth	356
	Will you come and follow me	368
1:17	Follow me	75
1:21-28	Firmly I believe and truly	423
	Jesus Christ is waiting	174
1:24	There is a Redeemer	323
1:29-31	When I feel the touch	357
1:40	Will you come and follow me	368
2:5	God forgave my sin	91
2:14	Follow me	75
	On Christmas night all Christians sing	254
	When God Almighty came to earth	356
	Will you come and follow me	368
2:16	The kingdom of God	317
2:22	One shall tell another	256
4:26-29	For the fruits of his creation	78
	I cannot tell	142
4:35-41	Be still, my soul	26
	I cannot tell	142
	Inspired by love and anger	158
	Sweet sacrament divine	307
4:39	Calm me, Lord	382
	You are the light	374
6:3	Inspired by love and anger	158
6:30-44	Gather around, for the table is spread	86
8	Take up your cross, he says	310
8:1-10	Gather around, for the table is spread	86
8:23	Spirit of God	301
8:34	Follow me	75
	Lift high the cross	198
8:38	At the name of Jesus	418
10:14-15	It fell upon a summer day	162
10:18	God is good	93
10:28-31	When we walk with the Lord	362
10:45	Come, wounded Healer	53
	From heaven you came	82
	Gracious God, in adoration	111
	Jesus is Lord! Creation's voice proclaims it	175
11:8-10	Give me joy in my heart	87
	Hosanna, hosanna	132
	Lord, enthroned in heavenly splendour	430
	Praise him, praise him	274
	Wake, O wake! with tidings thrilling	341
	You are the King of Glory	373
11:9-10	Holy, most holy, all holy the Lord	415
12:41-44	Take my life, and let it be	309
13:24-37	Will your anchor hold	369
13:25-26	O Lord, my God	248
	We are his children	343
13:26	Led like a lamb	192
13:33	Waken, O sleeper, wake and rise	340
	We shall stay awake	350
14:15	An upper room did our Lord prepare	14
14:22-24	Among us and before us	11
	Broken for me	34
	Come, risen Lord	421
	Jesus took a piece of bread	184

14:22-25	God of the Passover	102
	Love is his word	214
	This is my body	330
14:26	When, in our music, God is glorified	360
14:27	Praise the Lord, rise up rejoicing	278
14:32-42	Forty days and forty nights in Judah's desert	81
	From heaven you came	
	Thy way, not mine, O Lord	336
14:34-36	Lord of creation	392
	Stay with me	400
14:38	Onward, Christian pilgrims	260
14:65	Man of sorrows	222
	O Lord of our salvation	249
14:71-72	Forty days and forty nights in Judah's desert	81
	I do not know the man	144
15:13	Cross of Jesus	54
15:17-20	Come and see	46
	Great Son of God	114
15:21-41	Cross of Jesus	54
	Here hangs a man discarded	127
15:29-34	Great Son of God	114
15:33-34	How deep the Father's love for us	133
16:1-6	I bind unto myself today	141
16:1-8	From the very depths of darkness	85
	On this day, the first of days	259

LUKE

1-2	The angel Gabriel from heaven came	313
1:9	Wait for the Lord	407
1:26-38	Mary, blessèd grieving mother	223
	Mary, blessèd teenage mother	224
	The Virgin Mary had a baby boy	328
1:26-56	Shall we not love thee, Mother dear	292
1:33	Come, risen Lord	422
1:35	God is our strength from days of old	98
	There is a Redeemer	323
1:46	Magnificat	393
	Sanctum nomen Domini	398
1:46:55	Mary, blessèd teenage mother	224
	When our God came to earth	361
1:47	You are beneath me	372
1:51-52	Fill your hearts with joy and gladness	73
1:52	The universe was waiting	327
1:53	Thanks for the fellowship	311
2:1-20	Crown him with many crowns	422
	God rest you merry, gentlemen	103
	Love came down at Christmas	213
	See, amid the winter's snow	287
	See him lying on a bed of straw	288
	Silent night	294
	What child is this	355
	When our God came to earth	361
2:4-7	Shall we not love thee, Mother dear	292
2:6-7	The holly and the ivy	315
2:6-14	Sing lullaby	297
2:6-20	Cloth for the cradle	44
2:7	Away in a manger	21
	Born in the night, Mary's child	32
	Brightest and best	420
	Child in the manger	39
	Come, come, come to the manger	48
	I cannot tell	142
	Little Jesus, sleep away	201
	Little Jesus, sweetly sleep	202
	Unto us a boy is born	339
	Who is this so weak and helpless	364

2:8-14	Infant holy, infant lowly	155
	The Virgin Mary had a baby boy	
2:8-20	The first Nowell	314
2:11	My Jesus, my Saviour	232
2:13-14	Ding dong, merrily on high!	58
	Gloria 3 (Taizé)	411
	Gloria (Anderson)	412
	Glory to God (Peruvian Gloria)	413
	Sing glory to God	414
2:14	Come, come, come to the manger	48
	Gloria 3 (Taizé)	411
	On Christmas night all Christians sing	254
2:34-35	Shall we not love thee, Mother dear	292
	Sing lullaby	297
2:35	Sing we of the blessèd Mother	299
3:1-4	Wait for the Lord	407
3:1-18	We shall stay awake	350
3:2-14	Cloth for the cradle	44
3:16	All over the world	6
3:18	The kingdom of God	317
3:22	Come. Holy Spirit, come	49
	God is our strength from days of old	98
	O let the Son of God enfold you	245
4:1-13	Forty days and forty nights in Judah's desert	81
	Lead us, heavenly Father, lead us	429
	Love is his word	214
4:4	Seek ye first	289
4:18	God is working his purpose out	99
	God of glory we exalt your name	100
	I give you all the honour	147
	Make way, make way	221
	O for a thousand tongues to sing	238
	The kingdom of God	317
	Will you come and follow me	368
4:18-19	Gracious God, in adoration	111
	Lord, for the years	204
4:18-21	Christ's is the world	42
4:34	Be still, my soul	26
	There is a Redeemer	323
4:36	I believe in Jesus	140
5:1-11	O happy day	242
5:11-12	Will you come and follow me	368
5:27	Follow me	75
	When God Almighty came to earth	356
	Will you come and follow me	368
5:30	The kingdom of God	317
5:37	One shall tell another	256
6:20-23	The kingdom of heaven	318
6:21	Make way, make way	221
6:27	O Lord, all the world belongs to you	247
7:1-10	We cannot measure	347
7:16	Father, Lord of all creation	68
7:34	Jesus, Prince and Saviour	179
7:36-end	I bind unto myself today	141
7:43	Love is his word	214
7:48	God forgave my sin	91
8:1-3	I bind unto myself today	141
8:22-25	Be still, my soul	26
	Calm me, Lord	382
	I cannot tell	142
	Inspired by love and anger	158
	Sweet sacrament divine	307
	You are the light	374
9:10-17	Gather around, for the table is spread	86
9:23	Follow me	75
	Lift high the cross	198

9:26	At the name of Jesus	418
9:58	When God Almighty came to earth	356
9:58-59	Follow me	75
	Moses, I know you're the man	228
	Will you come and follow me	368
10:2	From the sun's rising	84
10:4	Moses, I know you're the man	228
10:6	God forgave my sin	91
10:27	Gracious God, in adoration	111
10:34	Hark, my soul, it is the Lord	119
	When I needed a neighbour	359
10:38-42	When we walk with the Lord	362
10:39	To be in your presence	337
11:1	Lord Jesus Christ	207
11:2-4	God forgave my sin	
	Make me a channel of your peace	220
	Our Father (Caribbean)	263
	Our Father (Wiener)	264
11:42	Beauty for brokenness	22
12:4	Moses, I know you're the man	228
12:6	There are hundreds of sparrows	322
12:6-7	There are hundreds of sparrows	322
12:24	Moses, I know you're the man	228
12:27-28	There are hundreds of sparrows	322
12:31	Wait for the Lord	407
12:35	Who is this so weak and helpless	364
13:24	Faithful Shepherd, feed me	63
	I will sing the wondrous story	168
	Loving Shepherd of thy sheep	217
14:12-24	I, the Lord of sea and sky	163
15:2	The kingdom of God	317
15:3	I will sing the wondrous story	168
15:4-6	Amazing grace	10
	Hark, my soul, it is the Lord	119
	The King of love my shepherd is	437
15:11-24	Christ's is the world	42
17:5-10	Firmly I believe and truly	423
17:11-19	Thank you, Lord	312
18:1-8	O God beyond all praising	240
18:16-17	It fell upon a summer day	162
18:19	God is good	93
19:10	Lord of all life and power	208
	The Spirit lives to set us free	326
19:37-38	You are the King of Glory	373
19:38	Holy, most holy, all holy the Lord	415
21:27	Led like a lamb	192
21:36	Onward, Christian pilgrims	260
	Waken, O sleeper, wake and rise	340
	We shall stay awake	350
22:12	An upper room did our Lord prepare	14
22:14-30	Jesus, the broken bread	183
22:19-20	Amazing grace	10
	Broken for me	34
	Come, risen Lord	421
	God of the Passover	102
	Jesus took a piece of bread	184
	Lord Jesus Christ	207
	Love is his word	214
	Thee we adore, O hidden Saviour, thee	436
	This is my body	330
22:26	O Lord, all the world belongs to you	247
22:39-44	Stay with me	400
22:40-46	Forty days and forty nights in Judah's desert	81
	From heaven you came	82
22:60-61	Forty days and forty nights in Judah's desert	81

Luke

22:63	Come and see	46
	Man of sorrows	222
	O Lord of our salvation	249
23:4	God forgave my sin	91
23:21	Cross of Jesus	54
23:26-33	Sing lullaby	297
23:26-49	Cross of Jesus	54
	Here hangs a man discarded	127
23:34	Come and see	46
	Meekness and majesty	226
23:35-37	Great Son of God	114
23:42-43	Jesus, remember me	389
23:50-56	Sing lullaby	297
24:1-8	From the very depths of darkness	85
	On this day, the first of days	259
24:13-15	When we walk with the Lord	362
24:13-35	Christians, lift up your hearts	40
	Thanks for the fellowship	311
24:35	Brightest and best	
	Gather around, for the table is spread	86
	Jesus, stand among us at the meeting of our lives	182
24:36	Among us and before us	11
24:36-43	As we are gathered	18
24:49-52	Be still, for the presence of the Lord	25
	We are his children	343

JOHN

1:1	Lord, for the years	204
1:1-5	Lord of all life and power	208
1:1-14	At the name of Jesus	418
1:4-5	Love songs from heaven	216
1:5	God is love	94
1:9-10	Lead, kindly light	428
1:11	Ah, holy Jesu, how hast thou offended	2
1:14	Christ triumphant	43
	Crown him with many crowns	422
	Father, Lord of all creation	68
	God is our strength from days of old	98
	Jesus, Name above all names	178
	What child is this	355
	You are the light	374
1:16	For ourselves no longer living	77
	O Lamb of God	244
1:29	Gloria 3 (Taizé)	411
	Gloria (Anderson)	412
	Glory to God (Peruvian Gloria)	413
	Hail the day that sees him rise	424
	Hail, thou once despisèd Jesus	116
	Just as I am, without one plea	426
	Lamb of God, Holy One	191
	Man of sorrows	222
	My faith looks up to thee	229
	O Lamb of God	244
	O Lamb of God	416
	On a hill far away	253
	Sing glory to God	414
	There is a Redeemer	323
	Who sees it all	366
1:32	O let the Son of God enfold you	245
1:37	O happy day	242
1:43	Follow me	75
	Will you come and follow me	368
1:51	As Jacob with travel was weary one day	16
	Blessed assurance	28

John

2:1-11	God in the planning	92
3:3	God forgave my sin	91
	I cannot tell	142
3:8	Breathe on me, Breath of God	419
3:14	O my Saviour, lifted from the earth	252
	We want to see Jesus lifted high	352
3:16	From heaven you came	82
	Hallelujah, my Father	118
	I stand amazed in the presence	161
	Lord of all life and power	208
	Name of all majesty	234
	Sing glory to God the Father	295
	To God be the glory!	338
3:19-21	We'll walk the land	349
4:7	Cross of Jesus	54
4:9-12	Love came down at Christmas	213
4:10	Have you heard the raindrops	121
	Spirit of God	301
	Such love	306
4:10-15	Have you heard the raindrops	121
4:14	I heard the voice of Jesus say	425
4:15	Such love	306
4:23	Father God, we worship you	66
4:24	Jesus, the broken bread	183
4:35	O Breath of Life	237
4:38	From the sun's rising	84
4:42	I cannot tell	142
	My Jesus, my Saviour	232
5:28	O for a thousand tongues to sing	238
	The Spirit lives to set us free	326
6:1-15	Gather around, for the table is spread	86
6:28	God is working his purpose out	99
6:31	Bread is blessed and broken	33
6:32-58	Eat this bread	384
6:35	Jesus, the broken bread	183
6:35-44	I am the bread of life	138
6:48	Sing we of the blessèd Mother	299
6:50	Bread is blessed and broken	33
6:51-55	Lord, enthroned in heavenly splendour	430
	Thee we adore, O hidden Saviour, thee	436
6:53-57	Jesus, the broken bread	183
6:66-68	Lord, when I turn my back on you	212
6:67-68	You are the King of Glory	373
6:68	Jesus, lover of my soul	177
	My Jesus, my Saviour	232
6:69	Be still, for the presence of the Lord	25
	Lamb of God, Holy One	191
	There is a Redeemer	323
7:37-38	Have you heard the raindrops	121
7:37-39	Breathe on me, Breath of God	419
7:38	Lord, enthroned in heavenly splendour	430
	Spirit of God	
8:1-11	Christ's is the world	42
8:12	Born in the night, Mary's child	32
	Colours of day	45
	Come, my Way, my Truth, my Life	50
	I heard the voice of Jesus say	425
	Lead, kindly light	428
	Lord, the light of your love	210
	Love songs from heaven	216
	Onward, Christian pilgrims	260
	The Lord is my light (Taizé)	402
	The Lord is my light (Rizza)	403
	The Spirit lives to set us free	326
	You are the light	374
8:36	Onward, Christian pilgrims	260

John

8:32	God is love: his the care	95
	Lord, the light of your love	210
9:1-41	Amazing grace	10
10:10	For the healing of the nations	79
10:11-16	Ah, holy Jesu, how hast thou offended	2
	I cannot tell	142
	I do not know the man	144
	Praise him, praise him	274
10:11-18	Loving Shepherd of thy sheep	217
10:28	Loving Shepherd of thy sheep	217
11:25-27	Breathe on me, Breath of God	419
	I am the bread of life	138
11:26	Christ is alive!	41
11:43	The Spirit lives to set us free	326
11:52	Ubi caritas	404
12:12-15	You are the King of Glory	373
12:13	Give me joy in my heart	87
	Holy, most holy, all holy the Lord	415
	Hosanna, hosanna	132
	Lord, enthroned in heavenly splendour	430
	Praise him, praise him	274
	Wake, O wake! with tidings thrilling	341
12:21	Open our eyes, Lord	261
12:26	O Jesus, I have promised	432
12:28	Father, we love you	70
12:31-32	Lift high the cross	198
12:35	The Spirit lives to set us free	326
13:1	An upper room did our Lord prepare	14
13:1-15	Meekness and majesty	226
13:4-11	An upper room did our Lord prepare	14
	Have you heard the raindrops	121
13:33	This is my will	331
13:34-35	A new commandment	13
	Jesus, the broken bread	183
	Living God, your word has called us	203
	Love is his word	214
	Peace, perfect peace, is the gift	267
	This is my body	330
	Ubi caritas	404
14	Take up your cross, he says	310
14:2	Hail the day that sees him rise	424
	Hail, thou once despisèd Jesus	116
	Who is this so weak and helpless	364
14:3	O Jesus, I have promised	432
14:6	Christ is alive!	41
	Come, my Way, my Truth, my Life	50
	Dance in your Spirit	57
	In an age of twisted values	153
	We pray thee, heavenly Father	439
	We want to see Jesus lifted high	352
	You are the light	374
14:8-17	Spirit of the living God (Iverson)	303
14:16	The Spirit lives to set us free	326
14:16-18	Jesus, at your name	171
14:18	Follow me	75
14:23-28	This is my body	330
14:23-29	Peace, perfect peace, in this dark world of sin	266
14:25-27	God forgave my sin	
	O Lord, all the world belongs to you	247
	Spirit of the living God (Iverson)	303
14:27	Like a mighty river flowing	199
	Peace, perfect peace, is the gift	267
	Put peace into each other's hands	281
15:1-9	This is my body	330
15:1-17	A new commandment	13

Reference	Title	No.
15:4	If we only seek peace	146
15:5	O sacred King	262
15:8	Let us talents and tongues employ	197
15:11	An upper room did our Lord prepare	14
15:12	Living God, your word has called us	203
	This is my body	330
15:13-17	This is my will	331
15:15-16	Jesus calls us	172
15:16	If we only seek peace	146
16:4-15	Spirit of the living God (Iverson)	303
16:20	Jesus put this song	180
16:22	In the Cross of Christ I glory	159
16:24	An upper room did our Lord prepare	14
16:32	Follow me	75
17:17-19	Soul of my Saviour	300
	Take my life, and let it be	309
17:21	As we are gathered	18
	Forth in the peace of Christ we go	80
	God forgave my sin	91
17:24	Cross of Jesus	54
	O Jesus, I have promised	432
17:26	Will you come and follow me	368
18:23	O Lord of our salvation	249
18:27	Forty days and forty nights in Judah's desert	81
18:37	God is love: his the care	95
19:2	Come and see	46
	Great Son of God	114
19:6	Cross of Jesus	54
19:17-37	Cross of Jesus	54
	Here hangs a man discarded	127
19:18-42	Sing lullaby	297
19:25	Mary, blessèd grieving mother	223
	Sing we of the blessèd Mother	299
19:30	Great Son of God	114
	How deep the Father's	133
	Man of sorrows	222
19:34	Lord, enthroned in heavenly splendour	430
	Rock of ages	434
	Soul of my Saviour	300
	What child is this	355
	Who is this so weak and helpless	364
20:1-18	From the very depths of darkness	85
	Led like a lamb	192
	On this day, the first of days	259
20:10-18	Morning has broken	227
20:11	Jesus, stand among us at the meeting of our lives	182
20:19	Among us and before us	11
20:19-31	As we are gathered	18
20:21	An upper room did our Lord prepare	14
	Jesus, the broken bread	183
20:21-22	Breathe on me, Breath of God	419
	O Lord, all the world belongs to you	247
20:26-28	Come, wounded Healer	53
20:26-29	Crown him with many crowns	422
	From heaven you came	82
	We will lay our burden down	353
20:27-28	Hail the day that sees him rise	424
	When I feel the touch	357
21:1-13	James and Andrew, Peter and John	169
21:15-17	Father, we adore you	69
21:16	Hark, my soul, it is the Lord	119
21:19	Follow me	75
	Will you come and follow me	368

ACTS

Reference	Title	No.
1:4-5	All over the world	6
1:6-11	Hail the day that sees him rise	424
1:8	Be still, for the presence of the Lord	25
	God forgave my sin	91
1:9-11	I bind unto myself today	141
1:11	At the name of Jesus	418
1:14-26	Sing we of the blessèd Mother	299
2	Spirit of the living God (Iverson)	303
2:1-4	Come. Holy Spirit, come	49
	Filled with the Spirit's power	71
	Lord of all life and power	208
	Lord, the light of your love	210
	O Breath of Life	237
	On this day, the first of days	259
	Rejoice, the year upon its way	284
	Sing we of the blessèd Mother	299
	Spirit of the living God (Armstrong)	302
2:5-47	Filled with the Spirit's power	71
2:17	The King is among us	319
2:18	All over the world	6
2:24	Low in the grave he lay	218
	The universe was waiting	327
2:33	Led like a lamb	192
3:1-10	Peter and John went to pray	269
3:8	O for a thousand tongues to sing	238
3:14	Ah, holy Jesu, how hast thou offended	2
3:15	From the very depths of darkness	85
	Jesus, Prince and Saviour	179
4:12	All hail the power of Jesus' name	417
	Hail, thou once despisèd Jesus	116
	Jesus, Name above all names	178
4:2	O for a thousand tongues to sing	238
4:31	Spirit of the living God (Armstrong)	302
5:32	Spirit of the living God (Armstrong)	302
8:14-17	Spirit of the living God (Iverson)	303
10:43-48	The ink is black	316
12:7	And can it be	12
13:47	We are his children	343
16:6-10	One more step along the world I go	255
17:6	O Lord, all the world belongs to you	247
18:9-10	When we walk with the Lord	362
20:28	You are the light	374
22:16	My Lord, what love is this	233
27:13-44	Will your anchor hold	369

ROMANS

Reference	Title	No.
1:20	Gracious God, in adoration	111
1:21-23	In an age of twisted values	153
3:24	Wonderful grace	370
4:5	Christ triumphant	43
4:17	Gracious God, in adoration	111
4:25	Child in the manger	39
5:1-2	I am a new creation	137
	I'm accepted, I'm forgiven	151
5:1-11	Lord, I come to you	205
5:5	Holy, holy, holy	130
5:6-11	Far and near	64
5:8	Come on and celebrate	52
	I stand amazed in the presence	161
5:10	From heaven you came	82
6:3-5	Christians, lift up your hearts	40
6:6-14	Firmly I believe and truly	423
6:9	Christ is alive!	41
6:11-23	Take my life, and let it be	309

6:18	On Christmas night all Christians sing	254
	Onward, Christian pilgrims	260
8:1	And can it be	12
	I am a new creation	137
	I'm accepted, I'm forgiven	151
8:1-3	The Spirit lives to set us free	326
8:9	Spirit of God	301
	The Spirit lives to set us free	326
8:11	Alleluia, alleluia, give thanks to the risen Lord	4
8:15	Abba, Father, let me be	1
	Alleluia (x8)	3
8:15-16	Father God, I wonder	65
8:16	If I were a butterfly	145
8:17	The kingdom of God	317
8:21-22	On Christmas night all Christians sing	254
8:31-19	Hail the day that sees him rise	424
8:31-39	Nada te turbe	395
	You are beautiful	371
8:32	O Lord, my God	248
8:35-39	O Love that wilt not let me go	251
8:37	Soldiers of Christ, arise	435
10:9	Alleluia (x8)	3
	Alleluia, alleluia, give thanks to the risen Lord	4
10:14	Go forth and tell	106
11:6	Only by grace	257
	Wonderful grace	370
11:33	I will offer up my life	167
11:33-36	Meekness and majesty	226
	You are beautiful	371
12:1	All that I am	7
	Father, we adore you	69
	I will offer up my life	167
12:1-2	Lord, for the years	204
12:1-8	Take my life, and let it be	309
12:2	Lord, I come to you	205
12:11-12	Jesus, the broken bread	183
12:15	Brother, sister, let me serve you	35
13:11-14	O God of earth and altar	241
	Wake up, O people	342
19:9	We bow down	346

1 CORINTHIANS

1:9	Faithful God	62
1:12	Lord, we come to ask your healing	211
1:18-30	How deep the Father's	133
1:18-31	Come, wounded Healer	53
	Firmly I believe and truly	423
1:25	Come. Holy Spirit, come	49
3:9	Come, build the Church	47
3:16	Spirit of God	301
3:22	The Lord is King!	320
5:7	Hail, thou once despisèd Jesus	116
	Lord, enthroned in heavenly splendour	430
6:14	By his grace	36
6:19-20	Take my life, and let it be	309
6:20	Bind us together, Lord	27
	Blessed assurance	28
9:24	May the mind of Christ my Saviour	225
10:4	Praise him, praise him	274
	Rock of ages	434
10:13	Faithful God	62
10:16-17	Come, risen Lord	421
	From many grains	83

	Ubi caritas	404
10:24	From heaven you came	82
10:31	My Father, for another night	230
11:23-25	Amazing grace	10
	Broken for me	34
	God of the Passover	102
	Jesus took a piece of bread	184
	Lord Jesus Christ	207
	Love is his word	214
	Thee we adore, O hidden Saviour, thee	436
	This is my body	330
11:23-26	I come with joy	143
12:3	Father, Lord of all creation	68
	Heaven shall not wait	123
	Jesus is Lord! Creation's voice proclaims it	175
	Lord Jesus Christ	207
12:3-4	Alleluia, alleluia, give thanks to the risen Lord	4
12:4-6	At this time of giving	19
12:4-11	Sing glory to God the Father	295
12:10	Come. Holy Spirit, come	49
12:12	Bind us together, Lord	27
12:27	Living God, your word has called us	203
	O Lord, all the world belongs to you	247
13:1-13	Come. Holy Spirit, come	49
	O perfect love	433
13:4-7	Let love be real	193
13:4-8	A new commandment	13
13:7	Father, I place into your hands	67
13:12	Loving Shepherd of thy sheep	217
13:12-13	By his grace	36
	Ubi caritas	404
14:12	Come, build the Church	47
15:3-4	Lord, I lift your name on high	206
	Lord of all life and power	208
	Sing glory to God the Father	295
15:14	This joyful Eastertide	333
15:20	Blessed assurance	28
	Hail the day that sees him rise	424
15:26-28	Going home	107
15:51-52	Steal away	305
15:52	This joyful Eastertide	333
15:54-57	Lift high the cross	198
	Stand up, stand up for Jesus	304
15:55-57	Bind us together, Lord	27
	Peace, perfect peace, in this dark world of sin	266

GALATIANS

2:19-20	Alleluia, alleluia, give thanks to the risen Lord	4
	Come on and celebrate	52
	From heaven you came	82
2:20	Alleluia, alleluia, give thanks to the risen Lord	4
	In full and glad surrender	156
	I stand amazed in the presence	161
	Lord, for the years	204
	My faith looks up to thee	229
3:13	Father, Lord of all creation	68
3:28	In an age of twisted values	153
	Living God, your word has called us	203
4:4-5	Shall we not love thee, Mother dear	292
	The holly and the ivy	315
4:4-7	At this time of giving	19

4:5-7	Blessed assurance	28
	Father God, I wonder	65
4:6	Abba, Father, let me be	1
	Alleluia (x8)	3
4:26	Jerusalem, my happy home	170
5:1	Cry 'Freedom!'	55
	From the very depths of darkness	85
5:22-23	Dance in your Spirit	57
	Lord of all life and power	208
	Sing glory to God the Father	295
6:2	Help us to help each other, Lord	126
6:14	In the Cross of Christ I glory	159
	Lord, for the years	204
6:14-15	When I survey the wondrous cross	440

EPHESIANS

1:2-10	Now thank we all our God	431
1:3	Praise God from whom all blessings flow	271
1:7	Who sees it all	366
1:13	God is working his purpose out	99
1:13-14	Dance in your Spirit	57
2:6	Lord of all life and power	208
2:8	Only by grace	257
2:14	Put peace into each other's hands	281
2:14-18	In an age of twisted values	153
2:17	Who sees it all	366
2:20	You are the light	374
2:21-22	For I'm building a people of power	76
3:6	The kingdom of God	317
3:9	By his grace	36
3:12	And can it be	12
	Blessed assurance	28
3:14	I give you all the honour	147
	In an age of twisted values	153
3:17-19	Such love	306
3:18	Just as I am, without one plea	426
3:18-19	You are beautiful	371
4:3-6	Living God, your word has called us	203
4:12	Come, build the Church	47
4:14	Lord of all life and power	208
4:15	Help us to help each other, Lord	126
4:24	And can it be	12
	For the healing of the nations	79
4:32	God forgave my sin	91
5:1-2	Come on and celebrate	52
	Lord of all life and power	208
	On Christmas night all Christians sing	254
5:2	Let love be real	193
5:8	The Spirit lives to set us free	326
	Waken, O sleeper, wake and rise	340
5:19-20	Thank you, Lord	312
5:25	In an age of twisted values	153
5:25-26	Soul of my Saviour	300
5:28	Let love be real	193
5:35	In an age of twisted values	153
6:1-4	In an age of twisted values	153
6:10-17	God of grace and God of glory	101
6:10-18	Soldiers of Christ, arise	435

PHILIPPIANS

1:9-11	I bind unto myself today	141
1:20-23	When I look into your holiness	358
2:4	From heaven you came	82
2:5	Help us to help each other, Lord	126
	May the mind of Christ my Saviour	225

2:5-11	At the name of Jesus	418
	He is Lord	125
	Jesus shall take the highest honour	181
	Meekness and majesty	226
	Name of all majesty	234
	We believe in God the Father	345
2:6-9	You laid aside your majesty	375
2:7	And can it be	12
	Christ triumphant	43
	Come, come, come to the manger	48
	God is our strength from days of old	98
	Lord, enthroned in heavenly splendour	430
	O Lord, all the world belongs to you	247
2:7-11	Jesus Christ, I think upon your sacrifice	173
2:8	I will offer up my life	167
2:9	Jesus, Name above all names	178
2:9-10	Jesus, at your name	171
2:9-11	Come, now is the time of worship	51
2:10-11	Alleluia, alleluia, give thanks to the risen Lord	4
	Holy, holy, holy is the Lord	131
	How lovely on the mountains	136
	Jesus is Lord! Creation's voice proclaims it	175
	We bow down	346
2:11	Shout for joy and sing	293
3:7-8	God of the Passover	102
	When I survey the wondrous cross	440
3:10	Come and see	46
3:10-14	Lord of all life and power	208
4:4-5	Wake up, O people	342
4:4-7	I'm accepted, I'm forgiven	151
	In the Lord I'll be ever thankful	387
	Rejoice in the Lord always	283
	Wait for the Lord	407
4:7	God is love	94
	Like a mighty river flowing	199

COLOSSIANS

1:5	God is working his purpose out	99
1:15	Meekness and majesty	226
1:15-28	Peace, perfect peace, in this dark world of sin	266
1:16	At the name of Jesus	418
1:27	Come, risen Lord	421
	Hail the day that sees him rise	424
	Lord, for the years	204
2:10	O Lamb of God	244
2:13	God forgave my sin	91
2:13-15	I will offer up my life	167
3:1	Glory to God (Peruvian Gloria)	413
3:1-4	Dance in your Spirit	57
3:4	Thee we adore, O hidden Saviour, thee	436
3:14	Bind us together, Lord	27
	Lord, we come to ask your healing	211
3:15-16	Forth in the peace of Christ we go	80
3:17	My Father, for another night	230

1 THESSALONIANS

4:9-10	Let there be love	194
4:16	This joyful Eastertide	333
5:24	Faithful God	62

2 THESSALONIANS

1:7	At the name of Jesus	418
2:10	God is love: his the care	95

1 TIMOTHY

1:17	Cross of Jesus	54
	Meekness and majesty	226
	Name of all majesty	234
3:16	Name of all majesty	234
4:9-10	I am trusting thee, Lord Jesus	139
6:10	In an age of twisted values	153

2 TIMOTHY

1:10	Jesus, the broken bread	183
	My Jesus, my Saviour	232
	Name of all majesty	234
1:14	Spirit of God	301
3:14-17	Lord, for the years	204

TITUS

3:4	The Spirit lives to set us free	326

HEBREWS

1:3	Meekness and majesty	226
2:9	All hail the power of Jesus' name	417
	Be still, for the presence of the Lord	25
2:9-10	How deep the Father's	133
2:14	A man there lived in Galilee	9
4:16	Blessed assurance	28
5:2	Cross of Jesus	54
5:8	Meekness and majesty	226
7:25	Hail the day that sees him rise	424
	I know that my Redeemer lives	149
9:5	Hail the day that sees him rise	424
	Hail, thou once despisèd Jesus	116
9:11	Father, Lord of all creation	68
9:12	Who sees it all	366
10:19-20	Lord, the light of your love	210
11:1	Blessed assurance	28
11:1-3	One more step along the world I go	255
11:8-16	One more step along the world I go	255
12:5-6	O sacred King	262
12:22	Jerusalem, my happy home	170

JAMES

1:17	Be still, my soul	26
	Great is thy faithfulness	113
1:22-25	In an age of twisted values	153
2:5	The kingdom of God	317

1 PETER

1:1-5	Peace, perfect peace, in this dark world of sin	266
1:3	God forgave my sin	91
1:6	What a friend we have in Jesus	354
1:10	All hail the power of Jesus' name	417
1:18-19	Blessed assurance	28
	I believe in Jesus	140
	You are the light	374
1:19	Bind us together, Lord	27
	Man of sorrows	222
2:21	Come, build the Church	47
2:21-22	All hail the power of Jesus' name	417
	A man there lived in Galilee	9
2:24	Ah, holy Jesu, how hast thou offended	2
2:25	O Jesus, I have promised	432
3:18-19	Finished the strife	74

2 PETER

3:4	Inspired by love and anger	158
3:13	The universe was waiting	327

1 JOHN

1:1	God is our strength from days of old	98
	Jesus calls us	172
1:5	Lead, kindly light	428
1:6-9	On the bloodstained ground	258
1:7	The Spirit lives to set us free	326
1:9	In an age of twisted values	153
1:14	For ourselves no longer living	77
2:2	Sing glory to God the Father	295
2:14	May the mind of Christ my Saviour	225
3:1	How deep the Father's	133
3:2	Thee we adore, O hidden Saviour, thee	436
3:3-20	Let love be real	193
3:5	Be still, for the presence of the Lord	25
4:7	Ubi caritas	404
4:8	God is love	94
4:9	From heaven you came	82
4:10	Come, wounded Healer	53
4:16	God is love	94
	God is love: his the care	95
	Ubi caritas	404
4:18	Dance in your Spirit	57
	Gracious God, in adoration	111

2 JOHN

1:12	Let there be love	194

3 JOHN

1:14	Let there be love	194

REVELATION

1:5	Lord, enthroned in heavenly splendour	430
1:6	From the sun's rising	84
1:8	God is our strength from days of old	98
	Jesus, lover of my soul	177
	Unto us a boy is born	339
1:14-18	At your feet we fall	20
1:17-18	Heaven is open wide	122
1:18	Christ is alive!	41
	Jesus, the broken bread	183
3:12	God is our strength and refuge	97
4 -5	Shall we gather at the river	291
4:6	I will sing the wondrous story	168
4:8	Holy, holy, holy	130
	Holy, holy, holy is the Lord	131
4:12	Holy, holy, holy is the Lord	131
5:5	Hail the day that sees him rise	424
5:6	Come, wounded Healer	53
5:6-14	Crown him with many crowns	422
5:8-10	All hail the power of Jesus' name	417
	All heaven declares	5
	From the sun's rising	84
	Man of sorrows	222
5:9	Holy, holy, holy	130
	Lift high the cross	198
5:11	Praise God from whom all blessings flow	271
5:11-14	I cannot tell	142
	Majesty, worship his majesty	219

Revelation

5:12	Come and see	46
5:12-13	Hail the day that sees him rise	424
	Lamb of God, Holy One	191
5:13	All heaven declares	5
6:9-10	All hail the power of Jesus' name	417
	Inspired by love and anger	158
	Love songs from heaven	216
7:3	Lift high the cross	198
7:13	Shall we gather at the river	291
7:14	As we are gathered	18
	Blessed assurance	28
	Only by grace	257
7:14-15	Blessed assurance	28
	By his grace	36
7:17	All heaven declares	5
	Be still, my soul	26
	Have you heard the raindrops	121
11:15	Crown him with many crowns	422
	Praise him, praise him	274
14	Jesus, lover of my soul	177
14:6	From the sun's rising	84
15:4	Adoramus te, Domine	379
19:11	Faithful God	62
19:16	Hosanna, hosanna	132
	Jesus, the broken bread	183
	Judge eternal, throned in splendour	187

Revelation

	King of kings and Lord of lords	189
	Majesty, worship his majesty	219
	Sing it in the valleys	296
21:2	God is our strength and refuge	97
	I'm not ashamed to own my Lord	152
21:3-5	Be still, my soul	26
	O Lord, all the world belongs to you	247
21:3-10	Wake, O wake! with tidings thrilling	341
21:6	God is our strength from days of old	98
	Have you heard the raindrops	121
	Jesus, lover of my soul	177
21:18	Who is this so weak and helpless	364
21:21	Wake, O wake! with tidings thrilling	341
22:1	God is our strength and refuge	97
	Have you heard the raindrops	121
	Shall we gather at the river	291
22:1-3	Crown him with many crowns	422
22:1-4	All heaven declares	5
	For the healing of the nations	79
22:13	God is our strength from days of old	98
	How good is the God we adore	135
	Jesus, lover of my soul	177
	You are beneath me	372
22:16-17	Heaven is open wide	122
22:17	Have you heard the raindrops	121
22:20	Alleluia (x8)	3

Index of Uses

THE GOSPEL

Grace and Providence

All the nations of the earth 8
Amazing grace 10
And can it be 12
Be still and know that I am God 24
Be still, for the presence of the Lord 25
Breathe on me, Breath of God 419
Christ's is the world 42
Come, Holy Spirit, come 49
Dance and sing 56
Do not be afraid 59
Faithful Shepherd, feed me 63
Father, Lord of all creation 68
For I'm building a people of power 76
God is love: his the care 95
God is our strength from days of old 98
God is working his purpose out 99
God of grace and God of glory 101
God whose love is all around us 105
Great is thy faithfulness 113
Have you heard the raindrops 121
He's got the whole world in his hand 128
How firm a foundation 134
I am a new creation 137
I am the bread of life 138
I bind unto myself today 141
I heard the voice of Jesus say 425
I know that my Redeemer lives 149
I need thee every hour 154
I stand amazed in the presence 161
James and Andrew, Peter and John 169
Lead us, heavenly Father, lead us 429
Lord Jesus Christ 207
Lord of our life, and God of our salvation 209
Lord, the light of your love 210
Mary, blessèd teenage mother 224
Meekness and majesty 226
Morning has broken 227
My faith looks up to thee 229
O happy day 242
O Lord, your tenderness 250
One more step along the world I go 255
Only by grace 257
O sacred king 262
Peace, perfect peace, in this dark world of sin 266
Peace, perfect peace, is the gift 267
Purify my heart 280
Put thou thy trust in God 282
Rise and shine 286
Rock of ages 434
Seek ye first 289
Soldiers of Christ, arise 435
Such love 305
The King of love my shepherd is 437
The Lord is my song 321
The Lord's my shepherd 438
There are hundreds of sparrows 322
There's a wideness in God's mercy 324
Think of a world without any flowers 329
This little light of mine 334
We cannot measure 347
What a friend we have in Jesus 354
When I feel the touch 357
Who put the colours in the rainbow? 365
Wide, wide as the ocean 367
Will your anchor hold 369
Wonderful grace 370

Grace and Providence
Chants

Nada te turbe 395
The Lord is my light (Taizé) 402

Joy, Praise and Thanksgiving

Alleluia (x8) 3
All hail the power of Jesus' name 417
All heaven declares 5
All the nations of the earth 8
Ascribe greatness 15
As the deer pants for the water 17
At the name of Jesus 418
At your feet we fall 20
Blessed assurance 28
Bless the Lord, my soul 29
Christ is alive! 41
Christ triumphant 43
Come, now is the time to worship 51
Crown him with many crowns 422
Dance and sing 56
Dance in your Spirit 57
Faithful God 62
Far and near 64

Father God, I wonder 65
Father God, we worship you 66
Father, we adore you 69
Father, we love you 70
Fill thou my life, O Lord my God 72
Fill your hearts with joy and gladness 73
For the fruits of his creation 78
From the sun's rising 84
Give me joy in my heart 87
Give thanks with a grateful heart 88
Give to our God immortal praise 89
God is good 93
God of glory we exalt your name 100
God whose love is all around us 105
Gracious God, in adoration 111
Great is the Lord and most worthy of praise 112
Great is thy faithfulness 113
Hail, thou once despisèd Jesus 116
Hallelujah, my Father 118
He is exalted 124
He's got the whole world in his hand 128
Hosanna, hosanna 132
How deep the Father's love 133
How good is the God we adore 135
If I were a butterfly 145
I give you all the honour 147
I love you, Lord, and I lift my voice 150
I'm accepted, I'm forgiven 151
I will enter his gates 166
I will offer up my life 167
Jesus calls us 172
Jesus is Lord! Creation's voice proclaims it 175
Jesus, Jesus 176
Jesus, Name above all names 178
Jesus put this song 180
Jesus shall take the highest honour 181
Jubilate, everybody 186
King of glory, King of peace 427
King of kings and Lord of lords 189
Lamb of God, Holy One 191
Let us praise God together 196
Lift high the cross 198
Living God, your word has called us 203
Lord, enthroned in heavenly splendour 430
Lord, for the years 204
Lord, I lift your name on high 206
Lord of all life and power 208
Lovely in your littleness 215
Love songs from heaven 216
Majesty, worship his majesty 219
Man of sorrows 222
Meekness and majesty 226
Morning has broken 227
My heart will sing to you 231
My Jesus, my Saviour 232
Name of all majesty 234
New songs of celebration render 236
Now thank we all our God 431
O for a thousand tongues to sing 238
O give thanks 239
O God beyond all praising 240
O happy day 242
O Lord, my God 248
On the bloodstained ground 258
On this day, the first of days 259
O sacred king 262
Peter and John went to pray 269
Praise God for the harvest 270
Praise God from whom all blessings flow 271
Praise God from whom all blessings flow 272
Praise him, praise him 274
Praise him, praise him, praise him 275
Praise the Lord of heaven 277
Praise to God for saints and martyrs 279
Rejoice in the Lord always 283
Rise and shine 286
Send forth your spirit, Lord 290
Shout for joy and sing 292
Sing glory to God the Father 295
Sing to God new songs of worship 298
Thank you, Lord 312
The kingdom of God 317
The Lord is King! 320
The Lord is my song 321
There are hundreds of sparrows 322
There is a Redeemer 323
Think of a world without any flowers 329
This is the day 332
This little light of mine 334
This world you have made 335
To God be the glory! 338
We want to see Jesus lifted high 352
When I feel the touch 357
When I look into your holiness 358
When, in our music, God is glorified 360
You are beautiful 371
You are the King of Glory 373
You laid aside your majesty 375
Your love's greater 376
You shall go out with joy 378

Joy, Praise and Thanksgiving
Chants

Adoramus te, Domine 379
Adoramus te, Domine Deus 380
Confitemini Domino 383
In the Lord I'll be ever thankful 387
In the Lord is my joy 388
Laudate Dominum 391
Lord of creation 392
Magnificat 393
Sanctum nomen Domini 398

Faith, Trust and Commitment

All that I am 7
A new commandment 13
As Jacob with travel was weary one day 16
Be still and know that I am God 24
Be still, my soul 26
Come, Holy Spirit, come 49
Come, my Way, my Truth, my Life 50
Cry 'Freedom!' 55
Faithful God 62
Father, I place into your hands 67
Filled with the Spirit's power 71
Firmly I believe and truly 423
For the healing of the nations 79
Forth in the peace of Christ we go 80
God is love 94
God is my great desire 96
God is our strength and refuge 97
God is working his purpose out 99
God of grace and God of glory 101
Hark, my soul, it is the Lord 119
Have faith in God, my heart 120
Help us to help each other, Lord 126
How good is the God we adore 135
I am trusting thee, Lord Jesus 139
I believe in Jesus 140
I bind unto myself today 141
I'm not ashamed to own my Lord 152
In full and glad surrender 156
In heavenly love abiding 157
It fell upon a summer day 162
I, the Lord of sea and sky 163
James and Andrew, Peter and John 169
Jesus Christ is waiting 174
Jesus lover of my soul 177
Just as I am, without one plea 426
Lead, kindly light 428
Lift high the cross 198
Lord, for the years 204
Lord I come to you 205
Lord Jesus Christ 207
Make me a channel of your peace 220
Moses, I know you're the man 228
Nearer, my God, to thee 235
O happy day 242
O Jesus, I have promised 432
One more step along the world I go 255
Onward, Christian pilgrims 260
Peace, perfect peace, is the gift 267
Put thou thy trust in God 282
Rise and shine 286
Seek ye first 289
Soldiers of Christ, arise 435
Stand up, stand up for Jesus 304
Take me, Lord 308
Take my life, and let it be 309
Take up your cross, he says 310
The king is among us 319
The King of love my shepherd is 437
The Lord's my shepherd 438
This little light of mine 334
Thy way, not mine, O Lord 336
We believe in God the Father 345
We bow down 319
We cannot measure 342
We will lay our burden down 353
When God Almighty came to earth 356
When we walk with the Lord 362
Will you come and follow me 368
Will your anchor hold 369
Wonderful grace 370

Faith, Trust and Commitment
Chants

The Lord is my light (Taizé) 402

Temptation, Penitence and Forgiveness

Beauty for brokenness 22
Blest Creator of the light 31
Change my heart, O God 38

Come and see 46
Drop, drop, slow tears 60
God forgave my sin 91
Great Son of God 114
I do not know the man 144
I'm accepted, I'm forgiven 151
It's me, O Lord 164
Just as I am, without one plea 426
Man of sorrows 222
O God of earth and altar 241
Spirit of God 301
The kingdom of God 317
There's a wideness in God's mercy 324
Who can sound the depths of sorrow 363
Who sees it all 366
Will your anchor hold 369
You laid aside your majesty 375

Hope and Consolation

Amazing grace 10
Be still and know that I am God 24
Be still, my soul 26
Blessed assurance 28
Christ's is the world 42
Come, build the Church 47
Come, my Way, my Truth, my Life 50
Come, wounded Healer 53
Do not be afraid 59
Heaven shall not wait 123
How lovely on the mountains 136
I cannot tell 142
In the Cross of Christ I glory 159
Jerusalem, my happy home 170
Let love be real 193
Like a mighty river flowing 199
Living God, your word has called us 203
Man of sorrows 222
Mary, blessèd grieving mother 223
Mary, blessèd teenage mother 224
My faith looks up to thee 229
O Love that wilt not let me go 251
Onward, Christian pilgrims 260
Peace, perfect peace, in this dark world of sin 266
Peace, perfect peace, is the gift 267
Take up your cross, he says 310
The kingdom of God 317
The kingdom of heaven 318
The Saviour will come, resplendent in joy 325
The universe was waiting 327
To be in your presence 337
We will lay our burden down 353
You are beneath me 372

Hope and Consolation
Chants

Stay with me 400

Healing

Beauty for brokenness 22
Be still and know that I am God 24
Brother, sister, let me serve you 35
Christ's is the world 42
For the healing of the nations 79
In an age of twisted values 153
Let love be real 193
Like a mighty river flowing 199
Lord, we come to ask your healing 211
O, how good is the Lord 243
Peter and John went to pray 269
Put peace into each other's hands 281
Sing it in the valleys 296
The Saviour will come, resplendent in joy 325
To be in your presence 337
We cannot measure 347
Who sees it all 366

Healing
Chants

Bless the Lord, my soul 381
Silent, surrendered 399
You are the centre 408

Suffering and Sorrow

Be still and know that I am God 24
Be still, for the presence of the Lord 25
Be still, my soul 26
Christ's is the world 42
Come, wounded Healer 53
Do not be afraid 59
Father, I place into your hands 67
Have faith in God, my heart 120
Heaven shall not wait 123
He was pierced 129
How deep the Father's love 133
How firm a foundation 134
Inspired by love and anger 158
In the Cross of Christ I glory 159
I will offer up my life 167
Kindle a flame 390
Kum ba yah 190
Lord, I lift your name on high 206
Mary, blessèd grieving mother 223
On the bloodstained ground 258
Peace, perfect peace, in this dark world of sin 266
Peace, perfect peace, is the gift 267
We will lay our burden down 353
You laid aside your majesty 375

Suffering and Sorrow
Chants

O Lord, hear my prayer 396
Stay with me 400
The Lord is my light (Taizé) 402

Protection

Amazing grace 10
Beneath the cross of Jesus 23
Be still and know that I am God 24
Do not be afraid 59
Follow me 75
I bind unto myself today 141
I need thee every hour 154
In the Cross of Christ I glory 159
In you, my God 160
I stand amazed in the presence 161
I watch the sunrise 165
Like a mighty river flowing 199
Lord of our life, and God of our salvation 209
Lord, when I turn my back on you 212
Loving Shepherd of thy sheep 217
My heart will sing to you 231
Rock of ages 434
To be in your presence 337
Will your anchor hold 369
You are beneath me 372
You are the light 374

Protection
Chants

Nada te turbe 395

Redemption and Salvation

Amazing grace 10
And can it be 12
At the name of Jesus 418
Beneath the cross of Jesus 23
Be still, my soul 26
Blessed assurance 28
By his grace 36
Christ is alive! 41
Christ triumphant 43
Come, my Way, my Truth, my Life 50
Crown him with many crowns 422
Dance in your Spirit 57
Do not be afraid 59
Follow me 75
For ourselves no longer living 77
From heaven you came 82
God is our strength from days of old 98
Great Son of God 114
Hallelujah, my Father 118
He was pierced 129
How lovely on the mountains 136
I am a new creation 137
I bind unto myself today 141
I cannot tell 142
In you, my God 160
I stand amazed in the presence 161
I will offer up my life 167
I will sing the wondrous story 168
Lift high the cross 198
Lord, when I turn my back on you 212
Man of sorrows 222
Mary, blessèd teenage mother 224
Meekness and majesty 226
Moses, I know you're the man 228
My faith looks up to thee 229
Nearer, my God, to thee 235
O God of earth and altar 241
O, how good is the Lord 243
O Lord, all the world belongs to you 247
Only by grace 257
Rock of ages 434
Send forth your Spirit, Lord 290
Sing it in the valleys 296
Spirit of God 301
There is a Redeemer 323
There's a wideness in God's mercy 324
We are his children 343
When God Almighty came to earth 356

Who can sound the depths of sorrow 363
Who sees it all 366
You are the light 374

The Journey of Life

(Hymns which, being singular, do not fit under The Pilgrim Community)

Amazing grace 10
Faithful Shepherd, feed me 63
I watch the sunrise 165
Lead, kindly light 428
Nearer, my God, to thee 235
One more step along the world I go 255
Put thou thy trust in God 282
Shall we gather at the river 291
Thy way, not mine, O Lord 336
Will you come and follow me 368

THE CHURCH THE PEOPLE OF GOD

The Communion of Saints

All hail the power of Jesus' name 417
Follow me 75
Glory to thee, O God 90
Jerusalem, my happy home 170

The Body of Christ

A new commandment 13
As we are gathered 18
Bind us together, Lord 27
Christ's is the world 42
Come, Holy Spirit, come 49
Follow me 75
For I'm building a people of power 76
Help us to help each other, Lord 126
Love is his word 214
O Lord, all the world belongs to you 247

The Serving Community

Christ's is the world 42
Come, Holy Spirit, come 49
God whose love is all around us 105
For ourselves no longer living 77
For the healing of the nations 79
From heaven you came 82
God of grace and God of glory 101
Gracious God, in adoration 111
Help us to help each other, Lord 126
If we only seek peace 146
James and Andrew, Peter and John 169
Jesus, at your name 171
Let love be real 193
Love is his word 214
My Jesus, my Saviour 232
O Lord, all the world belongs to you 247
Take me, Lord 308

The Suffering Community

Beauty for brokenness 22
Christ's is the world 42
Come, Holy Spirit, come 49
Come, wounded Healer 53
From heaven you came 82
Inspired by love and anger 158
Jesus Christ, I think upon your sacrifice 173
Mary, blessèd grieving mother 223
When I needed a neighbour 359

The Pilgrim Community

As Jacob with travel was weary one day 16
Brother, sister, let me serve you 35
Do not be afraid 59
Follow me 75
Lead us, heavenly Father, lead us 429
Moses, I know you're the man 228
Onward, Christian pilgrims 260
The Spirit lives to set us free 326
We will lay our burden down 353
When we walk with the Lord 362

Christian Unity

As we are gathered 18
Bind us together, Lord 27
Brother, sister, let me serve you 35
Father, Lord of all creation 68
Filled with the Spirit's power 71
For I'm building a people of power 76
From many grains 83
From the sun's rising 84
God of grace and God of glory 101
Heaven is open wide 122
I come with joy 143
Jesus Christ, I think upon your sacrifice 173
Jesus lover of my soul 177
Jesus put this song 180
Jesus, stand among us at the meeting of our lives 182
Lord, we come to ask your healing 211
Love is his word 214
Seek ye first 289
We believe in God the Father 345
We have a dream 348

THE WORLD

Home and Family

Brother, sister, let me serve you 35
He's got the whole world in his hand 128
In an age of twisted values 153
It's me, O Lord 164
Jesus put this song 180

The Local Community

Christ's is the world 42
Come, Holy Spirit, come 49
In an age of twisted values 153
Inspired by love and anger 158
It's me, O Lord 164
James and Andrew, Peter and John 169
Jesus Christ is waiting 174

The Nation

In an age of twisted values 153
Judge eternal, throned in splendour 187
Let there be love 194
Lord, for the years 204
O God of earth and altar 241

International Relations

For the healing of the nations 79
God is working his purpose out 99
Gracious God, in adoration 111
He's got the whole world in his hand 128
Mary, blessèd teenage mother 224
The ink is black 316
Waken, O sleeper, wake and rise 340
We have a dream 348

The Wholeness of Creation

All the nations of the earth 8
Dance and sing 56
For the fruits of his creation 78
For the healing of the nations 79
God of grace and God of glory 101
Inspired by love and anger 158
James and Andrew, Peter and John 169
Lord of all life and power 208
O God of earth and altar 241
O Lord, all the world belongs to you 247
Onward, Christian pilgrims 260
Praise the Lord of heaven 277
Sing glory to God the Father 295
The ink is black 316
The universe was waiting 327
Think of a world without any flowers 329
This world you have made 335
When God Almighty came to earth 356
Who put the colours in the rainbow? 365
Will you come and follow me 368
Your love's greater 376

Human Rights

Beauty for brokenness 22
Christ's is the world 42
Come, Holy Spirit, come 49
Cry 'Freedom!' 55
For ourselves no longer living 77
From the very depths of darkness 85
Heaven shall not wait 123
Inspired by love and anger 158
Jesus Christ is waiting 174
Mary, blessèd grieving mother 223
Mary, blessèd teenage mother 224
Stand up, stand up for Jesus 304
The ink is black 316
We have a dream 348
When God Almighty came to earth 356

Aid and Development

Beauty for brokenness 22
Cry 'Freedom!' 55
Have you heard the raindrops 121
Inspired by love and anger 158
I, the Lord of sea and sky 163
Jesus Christ is waiting 174
O Lord, all the world belongs to you 247
The ink is black 316
Will you come and follow me 368

Evangelism

All over the world 6
At the name of Jesus 418
Christians, lift up your hearts 40
Colours of day 45
Come, now is the time to worship 51
Far and near 64
Filled with the Spirit's power 71
For I'm building a people of power 76
Forth in the peace of Christ we go 80
From the sun's rising 84
From the very depths of darkness 85
God is working his purpose out 99
Go forth and tell 106
Have you heard the raindrops 121
How lovely on the mountains 136
I, the Lord of sea and sky 163
It's me, O Lord 164
James and Andrew, Peter and John 169
Jesus calls us 172
Lift high the cross 198
Lord, for the years 204
Lord, the light of your love 210
Make way, make way 221
O Breath of Life 237
O give thanks 239
One shall tell another 256
Restore, O Lord 285
Sing it in the valleys 296
Stand up, stand up for Jesus 304
We are his children 343
We are marching 344
We believe in God the Father 345
We'll walk the land 349
Will you come and follow me 368

TIMES AND SEASONS

Hymns generally applicable to the main seasons are included here. For suggestions more specifically related to the Lectionary, see the Common Worship Lectionary Index.

Morning

Colours of day 45
Give me joy in my heart 87
I watch the sunrise 165
Lord, the light of your love 210
Morning has broken 227
My Father, for another night 230
Thank you, Lord 312

Evening

Blest Creator of the light 31
Hail, gladdening light 115
Lead, kindly light 428

Advent

Be still, for the presence of the Lord 25
Come, my Way, my Truth, my Life 50
Heaven shall not wait 123
How lovely on the mountains 136
Kum ba yah 190
Make way, make way 221
Restore, O Lord 285
Sing to God new songs of worship 298
The Saviour will come, resplendent in joy 325
The universe was waiting 327
Waken, O sleeper, wake and rise 340
Wake, O wake! with tidings thrilling 341
Wake up, O people 342
We shall stay awake 350

Advent
Chants

In the Lord I'll be ever thankful 387
Wait for the Lord 407

Christmas

At this time of giving 19
Away in a manger 21
Born in the night, Mary's child 32
Child in the manger 35
Cloth for the cradle 44
Come, come, come to the manger 48
Ding dong, merrily on high! 58
God rest you merry, gentlemen 103
Good Christians all, rejoice 108
Good King Wenceslas 109
Go, tell it on the mountain 110
Infant holy, infant lowly 155
Joy to the world 185
Little Jesus, sleep away 201
Little Jesus, sweetly sleep 202
Lord Jesus Christ 207
Love came down at Christmas 213
Lovely in your littleness 215
Mary, blessèd teenage mother 224
O little one sweet, O little one mild 246
On Christmas night all Christians sing 254
See amid the winter's snow 287
See him lying on a bed of straw 288
Silent night 294
Sing lullaby 297
The angel Gabriel from heaven came 313
The first Nowell 314
The holly and the ivy 315
The Virgin Mary had a baby boy 328
Unto us a boy is born 339
What child is this 355
When our God came to earth 361
Who is this so weak and helpless 364

New Year and Anniversaries

A new commandment 13
Breathe on me, Breath of God 419
God is working his purpose out 99
It's me, O Lord 164
Lord, for the years 204

Epiphany

Brightest and best 420
Lord, the light of your love 210
We three kings of Orient are 351
What child is this 355

Lent

Be still, for the presence of the Lord 25
Cross of Jesus 54
Drop, drop, slow tears 60
Forty days and forty nights in Judah's desert 81
I give you love 148
I need thee every hour 154
Inspired by love and anger 158
It's me, O Lord 164
Just as I am, without one plea 426
Lord of our life, and God of our salvation 209
Put thou thy trust in God 282
Rock of ages 434
Seek ye first 289
When God Almighty came to earth 356
Will your anchor hold 369

Lent
Chants

Stay with me 400

Passiontide

Ah, holy Jesu, how hast though offended 2
An upper room did our Lord prepare 14
Beneath the cross of Jesus 23
Come and see 46
Come, wounded Healer 53
Cross of Jesus 54
Forty days and forty nights in Judah's desert 81
From heaven you came 82
Great Son of God 114
Here hangs a man discarded 127
I do not know the man 144
I give you love 148
In the Cross of Christ I glory 159
Lamb of God, Holy One 191
Lift high the Cross 198
Mary, blessèd grieving mother 223
My faith looks up to thee 229
My Lord, what love is this 233
O Lord of our salvation 249
O my Saviour, lifted from the earth 252
On a hill far away 253
Rock of ages 434
Soul of my Saviour 300
When I survey the wondrous cross 440
You are the King of Glory 373

Passiontide
Chants

Jesus, remember me 389
Stay with me 400

Easter

Alleluia, alleluia, give thanks to the risen Lord 4
All heaven declares 5
A man there lived in Galilee 9
Christ is alive! 41
Colours of day 45

Finished the strife 74
From the very depths of darkness 85
Heaven is open wide 122
He is Lord 125
He was pierced 129
How deep the Father's love 133
I know that my Redeemer lives 149
Jesus is Lord! Creation's voice proclaims it 175
Jesus, Prince and Saviour 179
Led like a lamb 192
Low in the grave he lay 218
Morning has broken 227
Name of all majesty 234
On the bloodstained ground 258
This joyful Eastertide 333
You laid aside your majesty 375

Easter
Chants

Surrexit Christus 401

Ascensiontide

All hail the power of Jesus' name 417
All heaven declares 5
As Jacob with travel was weary one day 16
At the name of Jesus 418
Christ triumphant 43
Crown him with many crowns 422
Forth in the peace of Christ we go 80
Hail the day that sees him rise 424
Hail, thou once despisèd Jesus 116
He is exalted 124
Jesus shall take the highest honour 181
Lord, I lift your name on high 206
Majesty, worship his majesty 219
Name of all majesty 234
Praise him, praise him 274
Stand up, stand up for Jesus 304
The Lord is King! 320

Pentecost

Alleluia (x8) 3
Breathe on me, Breath of God 419
Christians, lift up your hearts 40
Come, Holy Spirit, come 49
Dance in your Spirit 57
Filled with the Spirit's power 71
For I'm building a people of power 76
God of grace and God of glory 101
Go forth and tell 106
Listen, let your heart keep seeking 200
Lord of all life and power 208
Rejoice, the year upon its way 284
Send forth your Spirit, Lord 290
Spirit of God 301
Spirit of the living God (Armstrong) 302
Spirit of the living God (Iverson) 303
The Spirit lives to set us free 326

Pentecost
Chants

Silent, surrendered 399
Veni, Sancte Spiritus 406

You are the centre 408

The Holy Trinity

Father God, we worship you 66
Firmly I believe and truly 423
God is our strength from days of old 98
I bind unto myself today 141
Sing glory to God the Father 295
We believe in God the Father 345
We pray thee, heavenly Father 439

Harvest Festival

All that I am 7
Dance and sing 56
Fair waved the golden corn 61
Fill your hearts with joy and gladness 73
For the fruits of his creation 78
For the healing of the nations 79
God, whose farm is all creation 104
Inspired by love and anger 158
James and Andrew, Peter and John 169
O give thanks 239
Praise God for the harvest 270
Praise, O praise our God and King 276
Think of a world without any flowers 329
This world you have made 335
Who put the colours in the rainbow? 365

All Saints

All hail the power of Jesus' name 417
All heaven declares 5
Bind us together, Lord 27
Glory to thee, O God 90
Praise to God for saints and martyrs 279
Shall we gather at the river 291

Remembrance

For the healing of the nations 79
Mary, blessèd grieving mother 223
O God of earth and altar 241
Peace is flowing like a river 263
We will lay our burden down 353

Patronal Festivals

Glory to thee, O God 90
Praise to God for saints and martyrs 279

Patronal Festivals
Chants

Adoramus te, Domine 379

THE SACRAMENTS

Baptism

Do not be afraid 59
Father God, I wonder 65
Firmly I believe and truly 423
For I'm building a people of power 76
Have you heard the raindrops 121
He's got the whole world in his hand 128
I'm accepted, I'm forgiven 151
Loving Shepherd of thy sheep 217
Morning has broken 227
O let the Son of God enfold you 245
Only by grace 257
There are hundreds of sparrows 322

Confirmation

Amazing grace 10
As Jacob with travel was weary one day 16
Be still and know that I am God 24
Be still, for the presence of the Lord 25
Breathe on me, Breath of God 419
Come, Holy Spirit, come 49
Father God, I wonder 65
Fill thou my life, O Lord my God 72
Firmly I believe and truly 423
God forgave my sin 91
God is our strength from days of old 98
God of grace and God of glory 101
In full and glad surrender 156
Lord, the light of your love 210
O Breath of Life 237
O happy day 242
O Jesus, I have promised 432
One more step along the world I go 255
Spirit of God 301
Spirit of the living God (Armstrong) 302
Spirit of the living God (Iverson) 303
Stand up, stand up for Jesus 304
This little light of mine 334
We believe in God the Father 345
When I feel the touch 357
Will you come and follow me 368

Confirmation
Chants

Calm me, Lord 382
May the Lord bless you 394
Nada te turbe 395
O Lord, my heart is not proud 397
Silent, surrendered 399

Holy Communion
(See also Music for the Eucharist nos 409-416)

Among us and before us 11
An upper room did our Lord prepare 14
Be still and know that I am God 24
Be still, for the presence of the Lord 25
Bread is blessed and broken 33
Broken for me 34
Brother, sister, let me serve you 35
Come, risen Lord 421
God whose love is all around us 105
From many grains 83
Gather around, for the table is spread 86
God of the Passover 102
I am the bread of life 138
I come with joy 143
Jesus calls us 172
Jesus, stand among us at the meeting of our lives 182
Jesus, the broken bread 183
Jesus took a piece of bread 184

Let us break bread together 195
Let us talents and tongues employ 197
Lord, enthroned in heavenly splendour 430
Lord Jesus Christ 207
Lord, we come to ask your healing 211
Love is his word 214
O let the Son of God enfold you 245
Praise the Lord, rise up rejoicing 278
Put peace into each other's hands 281
Soul of my Saviour 300
Sweet sacrament divine 307
Thanks for the fellowship 311
Thee we adore, O hidden Saviour, thee 436
This is my body 330
We believe in God the Father 345
We pray thee, heavenly Father 439

Holy Communion
Chants

Eat this bread 384
Jesus, remember me 389
May the Lord bless you 394
The Lord is my light (Taizé) 402
The Lord is my light (Rizza) 403
Ubi caritas 404

Marriage

A new commandment 13
God, in the planning 92
Lead us, heavenly Father, lead us 429
Lord, for the years 204
O perfect love 433

Funerals
(See also The Communion of Saints)

Be still and know that I am God 24
Going home 107
I know that my Redeemer lives 149
In heavenly love abiding 157
O Lamb of God 244
O Love that wilt not let me go 251
Rock of ages 434
There's a wideness in God's mercy 324

Funerals
Chants

Jesus, remember me 389
May the Lord bless you 394
Nada te turbe 395
The Lord is my light (Taizé) 402
The Lord is my light (Rizza) 403

Ordination/Commissioning
(See also Baptism and Confirmation)

Come, Holy Spirit, come 49
Firmly I believe and truly 423
Listen, let your heart keep seeking 200
Lord, for the years 204
Spirit of God 301
Take me, Lord 308
We are his children 343
When God Almighty came to earth 356

THE ORDER FOR HOLY COMMUNION
(See also the Music for the Eucharist section nos 952 - 978)

Opening Hymn

As we are gathered 18
Give to our God immortal praise 89
I will enter his gates 166
Jesus, stand among us at the meeting of our lives 182
Jubilate, everybody 186
Living God, your word has called us 203
Lord, the light of your love 210
Lord, we come to ask your healing 211
Morning has broken 227
O Breath of Life 237
O God beyond all praising 240
Only by grace 257
This is the day 332
To God be the glory! 338

Opening Hymn
Chants

Laudate Dominum 391

Gradual Hymn

God is working his purpose out 99
Lord, for the years 204
Lord, the light of your love 210
Love is his word 214
May the mind of Christ my Saviour 225
Open our eyes, Lord 261
Praise the Lord, rise up rejoicing 278
Seek ye first 289

Gradual Hymn
Chants

Adoramus te, Domine 379

Offertory Hymn

Abba, Father, let me be 1
All that I am 7
I am the bread of life 138
Peter and John went to pray 269
Take my life, and let it be 309

Communion

Among us and before us 11
An upper room did our Lord prepare 14
As we are gathered 18
Be still and know that I am God 24
Be still, for the presence of the Lord 25
Blest are you, Lord of creation 30
Bread is blessed and broken 33
Broken for me 34
Come, risen Lord 421
From many grains 83
Gather around, for the table is spread 86
Let us break bread together 195
Lord, we come to ask your healing 211
Only by grace 257
Open our eyes, Lord 261
Our Father (Caribbean) 263
Our Father (Wiener) 264
Peace, perfect peace, is the gift 267
Thee we adore, O hidden Saviour, thee 436
This is my body 330

Communion
Chants

Adoramus te, Domine 271
Nada te turbe 395
Ubi caritas 404

Final Hymn

God whose love is all around us 105
Forth in the peace of Christ we go 80
Go forth and tell 106
Jesus Christ is waiting 174
Lead us, heavenly Father, lead us 429
Peace to you 268
Shall we not love thee, Mother dear 292
Sing we of the blessèd Mother 299
Thanks for the fellowship 311
The angel Gabriel from heaven came 313
You shall go out with joy 378

Index of Hymns for the Common Worship Lectionary

YEAR A

ADVENT

FIRST SUNDAY OF ADVENT - A

Lord of our life, and God of our salvation 209
O God of earth and altar 241
Onward, Christian pilgrims 260
Waken, O sleeper, wake and rise 340
Wake up, O people 342
We are marching 344

SECOND SUNDAY OF ADVENT - A

All over the world 6
Come, Holy Spirit, come 49
Come on and celebrate 52
Crown him with many crowns 422
God is working his purpose out 99
Lord, enthroned in heavenly splendour 430
May the mind of Christ my Saviour 225
The kingdom of God 317
The Saviour will come, resplendent in joy 325
We shall stay awake 350
Chants
Wait for the Lord 407

THIRD SUNDAY OF ADVENT -A

Faithful God 62
Mary, blessèd teenage mother 224
Thanks for the fellowship 311
The angel Gabriel from heaven came 313
The kingdom of God 317
The Saviour will come, resplendent in joy 325
When our God came to earth 361

FOURTH SUNDAY OF ADVENT - A

Jesus, Name above all names 178
Mary, blessèd teenage mother 224
The angel Gabriel from heaven came 313

CHRISTMAS

CHRISTMAS EVE - FOR YEARS A, B and C
Any of the following Sets may be used on the evening of Christmas Eve

CHRISTMAS DAY - FOR YEARS A, B and C

Set I

Away in a manger 21
Born in the night, Mary's child 32
Brightest and best 420
Child in the manger 39
Crown him with many crowns 422
Ding dong, merrily on high! 58
Far and near 64
God is working his purpose out 99
God rest you merry, gentlemen 103
Go, tell it on the mountain 110
I cannot tell 142
Infant holy, infant lowly 155
King of glory, King of peace 427
King of kings and Lord of lords 189
Let there be love 194
My Jesus, my Saviour 232
O give thanks 239
On Christmas night all Christians sing 254
Peace to you 268
Praise the Lord of heaven 277
See amid the winter's snow 287
See him lying on a bed of straw 288
The angel Gabriel from heaven came 313
The first Nowell 314
The Virgin Mary had a baby boy 328
Unto us a boy is born 339
We shall stay awake 350
What child is this 355
When our God came to earth 361
You are the King of Glory 373
Chants
Wait for the Lord 407

Set II

Away in a manger 21
Born in the night, Mary's child 32
Brightest and best 420
Child in the manger 39
Cloth for the cradle 44
Come, come, come to the manger 48
Crown him with many crowns 422
Ding dong, merrily on high! 58
God is working his purpose out 99
God rest you merry, gentlemen 103
Go, tell it on the mountain 110
I cannot tell 142
Infant holy, infant lowly 155
Little Jesus, sleep away 201
Little Jesus, sweetly sleep 202
Love came down at Christmas 213
My Jesus, my Saviour 232
On Christmas night all Christians sing 254
See amid the winter's snow 287
Shall we not love thee, Mother dear 292
See him lying on a bed of straw 288
Silent night 294
Sing lullaby 297
The first Nowell 314
The holly and the ivy 315
The Virgin Mary had a baby boy 328
Unto us a boy is born 339
What child is this 355
When our God came to earth 361
Who is this so weak and helpless 364

Set III

At the name of Jesus 418
How lovely on the mountains 136
Jesus, Name above all names 178
Joy to the world 185
Meekness and majesty 226
O give thanks 239
Shout for joy and sing 293
Sing to God new songs of worship 298
What child is this 355
Chants
You are the light 374

FIRST SUNDAY OF CHRISTMAS - A

All the nations of the earth 8
A man there lived in Galilee 9
Dance in your Spirit 57
Father, Lord of all creation 68
God is love 94
Lead, kindly light 428
Let us praise God together 196
Lord for the years 204
Love songs from heaven 216
New songs of celebration render 236
Praise the Lord of heaven 277
Unto us a boy is born 339
Who sees it all 366
Chants
You are the light 374

SECOND SUNDAY OF CHRISTMAS - FOR YEARS A, B and C

At the name of Jesus 418
Breathe on me, Breath of God 419
Christ triumphant 43
Crown him with many crowns 422
Fill your hearts with joy and gladness 73
God is our strength from days of old 98
God is working his purpose out 99
Jesus, Name above all names 178
Lord, the light of your love 210
What child is this 355

EPIPHANY

THE EPIPHANY - FOR YEARS A, B and C

And can it be 12
Blessed assurance 28
Brightest and best 420
By his grace 36
Have you heard the raindrops 121
Love came down at Christmas 213
See him lying on a bed of straw 288
The Saviour will come, resplendent in joy 325
We three kings of Orient are 351
What child is this 355

THE BAPTISM OF CHRIST - A

How firm a foundation 134
I bind unto myself today 141
Lord of our life, and God of our salvation 209
O let the Son of God enfold you 245
The kingdom of God 317
You are beneath me 372

SECOND SUNDAY OF EPIPHANY - A

Faithful God 62
God of grace and God of glory 101
Just as I am, without one plea 426
Lamb of God, Holy One 191
O happy day 242
O let the Son of God enfold you 245
There is a Redeemer 323
Chants
Wait for the Lord 407

THIRD SUNDAY OF EPIPHANY - A

Follow me 75
God is our strength from days of old 98
Jesus is waiting 174
Lord I come to you 205
Lord, the light of your love 210
Lord, we come to ask your healing 211
O happy day 242
Put thou thy trust in God 282
Spirit of God 301
We bow down 346
When God Almighty came to earth 356
Will you come and follow me 368
Chants
In the Lord is my joy 388
The Lord is my light (Taizé) 402
The Lord if my light (Rizza) 403

FOURTH SUNDAY OF EPIPHANY - A

Come, Holy Spirit, come 49
Come, wounded healer 53
Faithful God 62
Firmly I believe and truly 423
God, in the planning 92
Your love's greater 376

THE PRESENTATION OF CHRIST IN THE TEMPLE - FOR YEARS A, B and C Candlemass

A man there lived in Galilee 9
For ourselves no longer living 77
Just as I am without one plea 426
King of glory, King of peace 427
Make way, make way 221
Purify my heart 280
Restore, O Lord 285
Sing we of the blessèd Mother 299

ORDINARY TIME

PROPER 1 - A

I am trusting thee, Lord Jesus 139
Lord, the light of your love 210
The Spirit lives to set us free 326
This little light of mine 334
You are beneath me 372

PROPER 2 - A

Bind us together, Lord 27
Come, build the Church 47
Father, Lord of all creation 68
God of grace and God of glory 101
Let there be love 194
Lord of our life, and God of our salvation 209

PROPER 3 - A

Beauty for brokenness 22
Brother, sister, let me serve you 35
Come, build the Church 47
O Lord, all the world belongs to you 247
Spirit of God 301
The Lord is King! 320

SECOND SUNDAY BEFORE LENT - A

All over the world 6
Blest Creator of the light 31
Dance and sing 56
For the healing of the nations 79
Give to our God immortal praise 89
God is our strength from days of old 98
Gracious God, in adoration 111
He's got the whole world in his hand 128
Jesus, the broken bread 183
Lord of all live and power 208
Lord, the light of your love 210
Morning has broken 227
Moses, I know you're the man 228
O Breath of Life 237
O give thanks 239
On this day, the first of days 259
Seek ye first 289
There are hundreds of sparrows 322
The universe was waiting 327
This world you have made 335
Chants
Wait for the Lord 407

SUNDAY NEXT BEFORE LENT - A

God of grace and God of glory 101
I cannot tell 142
When I look into your holiness 358

LENT

ASH WEDNESDAY - FOR YEARS A, B and C

Blest Creator of the light 31
Christ's is the world 42
Come, build the Church 47
Give thanks with a grateful heart 88
I will offer up my life 167
Lord of our life, and God of our salvation 209
My Lord, what love is this 233
On the bloodstained ground 258
You are beneath me 372
Chants
You are the centre 408

FIRST SUNDAY OF LENT - A

Forty days and forty nights in Judah's desert 81
Lead us, heavenly Father, lead us 429
Love is his word 214
Seek ye first 289

SECOND SUNDAY OF LENT - A

Breathe on me, Breathe of God 419
Christ triumphant 43
From heaven you came 82
God forgave my sin 91
Gracious God, in adoration 111
Hallelujah, my Father 118
I cannot tell 142
I stand amazed in the presence 161
I watch the sunrise 165
Lord of all life and power 208
Name of all majesty 234
O my Saviour, lifted from the earth 252
One more step along the world I go 255
Sing glory to God the Father 295
To God be the glory! 338
We want to see Jesus lifted high 352

THIRD SUNDAY OF LENT - A

Come, now is the time to worship 51
Far and near 64
Father God, we worship you 66
From the sun's rising 84
Gracious God, in adoration 111
Have you heard the raindrops 121
Holy, holy, holy 130
I am a new creation 137
I cannot tell 142
I heard the voice of Jesus say 425
I'm accepted, I'm forgiven 151
I stand amazed in the presence 161
Lord I come to you 205
O Breath of Life 237
Spirit of God 301
Such love 306

FOURTH SUNDAY OF LENT - A

Amazing grace 10
At this time of giving 19
Faithful Shepherd, feed me 63
Forth in the peace of Christ we go 80
In heavenly love abiding 157
New songs of celebration render 236
The King of love my shepherd is 437
The Lord's my shepherd 438
Waken, O sleeper, wake and rise 340
Chants
Nada te turbe 395

Or: MOTHERING SUNDAY - FOR YEARS A, B and C

Bind us together, Lord 27
Forth in the peace of Christ we go 80

Lord, we come to ask your healing 211
Mary, blessèd grieving mother 223
Shall we not love thee, Mother dear 292
Sing we of the blessèd Mother 299
Chants
In the Lord I'll be ever thankful 387

FIFTH SUNDAY OF LENT - A

Breathe on me, Breath of God 419
I am the bread of life 138
O Breath of Life 237
Only by grace 257
Spirit of God 301
There's a wideness in God's mercy 324
The Spirit lives to set us free 326

PALM SUNDAY - A

Liturgy of the Palms

Christians, lift up your hearts 40
Give me joy in my heart 87
Hosanna, hosanna 132
I will enter his gates 166
Lord, enthroned in heavenly splendour 430
Praise him, praise him 274
This is the day 332
Wake, O wake! with tidings thrilling 341
You are the King of Glory 373
Chants
Confitemini Domino 383

Liturgy of the Passion

Ah, holy Jesu, how hast thou offended 2
A man there lived in Galilee 9
And can it be 12
At the name of Jesus 418
Be still and know that I am God 24
Broken for me 34
Christ triumphant 43
Come and see 46
Come, now is the time to worship 51
Forty days and forty nights in Judah's desert 81
From heaven you came 82
God is our strength from days of old 98
Great Son of God 114
Help us to help each other, Lord 126
Holy, holy, holy is the Lord 131
I do not know the man 144
I will offer up my life 167
Jesus, at your name 171
Jesus Christ, I think upon your sacrifice 173
Jesus, Name above all names 178
Jesus shall take the highest honour 181
Love is his word 214
May the mind of Christ my Saviour 225
Meekness and majesty 226
Name of all majesty 234
O Lord of our salvation 249
Thy way, not mine, O Lord 336
We believe in God the Father 345
We bow down 346
You laid aside your majesty 375

Chants
Stay with me 400

MONDAY OF HOLY WEEK - FOR YEARS A, B and C

Faithful God 62
How firm a foundation 134
Your love's greater 376

TUESDAY OF HOLY WEEK - FOR YEARS A, B and C

Come, Holy Spirit, come 49
Come, wounded Healer 53
Father, we love you 70
Firmly I believe and truly 423
I am trusting thee, Lord Jesus 139
I'm not ashamed to own my Lord 152
Lift high the cross 198
O Jesus, I have promised 432
Open our eyes, Lord 261
The Spirit lives to set us free 326
We pray thee, heavenly Father 439

WEDNESDAY OF HOLY WEEK - FOR YEARS A, B and C

Christ triumphant 43
Glory to thee, O God 90
Chants
Wait for the Lord 407

MAUNDY THURSDAY - FOR YEARS A, B and C

Amazing grace 10
A new commandment 13
An upper room did our Lord prepare 14
Broken for me 34
God of the Passover 102
Have you heard the raindrops 121
I come with joy 143
I will offer up my life 167
Jesus took a piece of bread 184
Lord Jesus Christ 207
Love is his word 214
Meekness and majesty 226
O God beyond all praising 240
Peace, perfect peace, is the gift 267
Thee we adore, O hidden Saviour, thee 436
This is my body 330
Chants
Ubi Caritas 404

GOOD FRIDAY - FOR YEARS A, B and C

Ah, holy Jesu, how hast thou offended 2
Come and see 46
Cross of Jesus 54
Forty days and forty nights in Judah's desert 81
Great Son of God 114
Here hangs a man discarded 127
He was pierced 129
How deep the Father's love 133

Man of sorrows 210
Mary, blessèd grieving mother 223
Meekness and majesty 226
My Lord, what love is this 233
O Lord of our salvation 249
Rock of ages 434
Sing we of the blessèd Mother 299
Soul of my Saviour 300
What a friend we have in Jesus 354
Who can sound the depths of sorrow 363
You laid aside your majesty 375

EASTER EVE - FOR YEARS A, B and C

Services other than the Easter Vigil

Father, I place into your hands 67
In you my God 160
Low in the grave he lay 218
We pray thee, heavenly Father 439

EASTER

EASTER VIGIL - FOR YEARS A, B and C

All heaven declares 5
Be still and know that I am God 24
Be still, for the presence of the Lord 25
Blest Creator of the light 31
Breathe on me, Breath of God 419
Christ is alive! 41
From the very depths of darkness 85
Gather around, for the table is spread 86
Give to our God immortal praise 89
God is our strength and refuge 97
I, the Lord of sea and sky 163
Jesus, Jesus 176
Lord, the light of your love 210
My Jesus, my Saviour 232
On this day, the first of days 259
Put thou thy trust in God 282
Sing to God new songs of worship 298
The Lord is my song 321
This joyful Eastertide 333

EASTER DAY - A

Christians, lift up your hearts 40
Dance in your Spirit 57
From the very depths of darkness 85
I will enter his gates 166
Jesus, stand among us at the meeting of our lives 182
Led like a lamb 192
Morning has broken 227
On this day, the first of days 259
Shout for joy and sing 293
Thee we adore, O hidden Saviour, thee 436
This is the day 332
Chants
Adoramus te, Domine 379
Confitemini Domino 383
In the Lord is my joy 388

SECOND SUNDAY OF EASTER - A

All hail the power of Jesus' name 417
Crown him with many crowns 422
Lord I come to you 205
Low in the grave he lay 218
This joyful Eastertide 333
We will lay our burden down 353
What a friend we have in Jesus 354

THIRD SUNDAY OF EASTER - A

All hail the power of Jesus' name 417
A man there lived in Galilee 9
Bind us together, Lord 27
Christians, lift up your hearts 40
Come, build the Church 47
Come, risen Lord 421
I believe in Jesus 140
I will offer up my life 167
Jesus, stand among us at the meeting of our lives 182
Man of sorrows 222
O God beyond all praising 240
Thank you, Lord 312

FOURTH SUNDAY OF EASTER - A

All hail the power of Jesus' name 417
A man there lived in Galilee 9
Come, build the Church 47
For the healing of the nations 79
Forth in the peace of Christ we go 80
In heavenly love abiding 157
O Jesus, I have promised 432
The King of love my shepherd is 437
The Lord's my shepherd 438
Chants
Nada te turbe 395

FIFTH SUNDAY OF EASTER - A

Christ is alive! 41
Come, my Way, my Truth, my Life 50
Dance in your Spirit 57
Faithful Shepherd, feed me 63
Father, I place into your hands 67
Hail, thou once despisèd Jesus 116
In an age of twisted values 153
In you, my God 160
O Jesus, I have promised 432
Take up your cross, he says 310
We pray thee, heavenly Father 439
Who is this so weak and helpless 364
You are the light 374

SIXTH SUNDAY OF EASTER - A

Finished the strife 74
Great is thy faithfulness 113

ASCENSION DAY - FOR YEARS A, B and C

All over the world 6
At the name of Jesus 418
Crown him with many crowns 422
God forgave my sin 91
Hail the day that sees him rise 424
He is exalted 124
I bind unto myself today 141
My Jesus, my Saviour 232
We are his children 343

SEVENTH SUNDAY OF EASTER - A

At the name of Jesus 418
God forgave my sin 91
I bind unto myself today 141

PENTECOST (Whit Sunday) - A

All over the world 6
Among us and before us 11
At this time of giving 19
Bind us together, Lord 27
Breathe on me, Breath of God 419
Come, Holy Spirit, come 49
Father, Lord of all creation 68
Filled with the Spirit's power 71
Have you heard the raindrops 121
Heaven shall not wait 123
If I were a butterfly 145
Jesus is Lord! Creation's voice proclaims it 175
Lord, enthroned in heavenly splendour 430
Lord, the light of your love 210
O Breath of Life 237
Rejoice, the year upon its way 284
Send forth your spirit, Lord 290
Spirit of the living God (Armstrong) 302
Spirit of the living God (Iverson) 303
The King is among us 319
Chants
You are the centre 408

ORDINARY TIME

TRINITY SUNDAY - A

A man there lived in Galilee 9
Come, Holy Spirit, come 49
From the sun's rising 84
God forgave my sin 91
Go forth and tell 106
Lord I come to you 205
Loving Shepherd of thy sheep 217
O Lord, my God 248
We are his children 343

DAY OF THANKSGIVING FOR HOLY COMMUNION
Thursday after Trinity Sunday (Corpus Christi) FOR YEARS A, B and C

Amazing grace 10
Broken for me 34
God of the Passover 102
I come with joy 143
Jesus, the broken bread 183
Jesus took a piece of bread 184
Lord, enthroned in heavenly splendour 430
Lord Jesus Christ 207
Love is his word 214
O God beyond all praising 240
Thee we adore, O hidden Saviour, thee 436
This is my body 330
Chants
Eat this bread 384

PROPER 4 - A

Be still and know that I am God 24
Be still, for the presence of the Lord 25
God is our strength and refuge 97
My Jesus, my Saviour 232
Rise and shine 286
We pray thee, heavenly Father 439
Wonderful grace 370
Your mercy flows 377

PROPER 5 - A

In an age of twisted values 153
One more step along the world I go 255
The kingdom of God 317
When God Almighty came to earth 356
Will you come and follow me 368

PROPER 6 - A

God forgave my sin 91
Holy, holy, holy 130
I am a new creation 137
I'm accepted, I'm forgiven 151
I stand amazed in the presence 161
I will enter his gates 166
Jubilate, everybody 186
O God beyond all praising 240
Praise, O praise our God and King 276

PROPER 7 - A

Christians, lift up your hearts 40
Christ is alive! 41
Great is thy faithfulness 113
Lift high the cross 198
My Jesus, my Saviour 232
There are hundreds of sparrows 322
When God Almighty came to earth 356
Chants
O Lord, hear my prayer 396

PROPER 8 - A

Amazing grace 10
O Lord, my God 248
Shout for joy and sing 293

PROPER 9 - A

I cannot tell 142
I heard the voice of Jesus say 425
It fell upon a summer day 162
Jesus Christ is waiting 174
Love is his word 214
O Love that wilt not let me go 251

PROPER 10 - A

And can it be 12

I am a new creation 137
I'm accepted, I'm forgiven, 151
Jesus, Jesus 176
Spirit of God 301
The Spirit lives to set us free 326
You shall go out with joy 378

PROPER 11 - A

Abba, Father, let me be 1
Alleluia (x8) 3
As Jacob with travel was weary one day 16
Beneath the cross of Jesus 23
Blessed assurance 28
Great is thy faithfulness 113
He's got the whole world in his hand 128
Lord, the light of your love 210
Nearer, my God, to thee 235
Rise and shine 286
You are beautiful 371
Chants
Wait for the Lord 407

PROPER 12 - A

Lord of our life, and God of our salvation 209
O Lord, my God 248
O Love that wilt not let me go 251
Soldiers of Christ, arise 435
You are beautiful 371
Chants
Nada te turbe 395

PROPER 13 - A

Gather around, for the table is spread 86
Let love be real 193
Let us praise God together 196
Put thou thy trust in God 282

PROPER 14 - A

Alleluia (x8) 3
Alleluia, alleluia, give thanks to the risen Lord 4
Fill your hearts with joy and gladness 73
Go forth and tell 106
Listen, let your heart keep seeking 200

PROPER 15 - A

Jesus Christ is waiting 174
Living God, your word has called us 203
O Lord, all the world belongs to you 247

PROPER 16 - A

Brother, sister, let me serve you 35
Cry 'Freedom!' 55
Father, we adore you 69
Firmly I believe and truly 423
I believe in Jesus 140
I will offer up my life 167
Lord I come to you 205

PROPER 17 - A

Be still, for the presence of the Lord 25
Moses, I know you're the man 228

PROPER 18 - A

Dance in your Spirit 57
I give you love 148
Lord, the light of your love 210
New songs of celebration render 236
O God of earth and altar 241
Wake up, O people 342

PROPER 19 - A

Be still and know that I am God 24
Great is thy faithfulness 113
O God beyond all praising 240
Chants
Bless the Lord, my soul (Taizé) 381

PROPER 20 - A

Bread is blessed and broken 33
Peace is flowing like a river 265
When I look into your holiness 358

PROPER 21 - A

And can it be 12
At the name of Jesus 418
Be still and know that I am God 24
Christ triumphant 43
Come, now is the time to worship 51
God is our strength from days of old 98
He is Lord 125
Help us to help each other, Lord 126
Holy, holy, holy is the Lord 131
I will offer up my life 167
Jesus, at your name 171
Jesus Christ, I think upon your sacrifice 173
Jesus, Name above all names 178
Jesus shall take the highest honour 181
Lord, enthroned in heavenly splendour 430
Lord of our life, and God of our salvation 209
May the mind of Christ my Saviour 225
Meekness and majesty 226
Name of all majesty 234
We believe in God the Father 345
We bow down 346
You laid aside your majesty 375
Chants
Wait for the Lord 407

PROPER 22 - A

All heaven declares 5
As the deer pants for the water 17
Come and see 46
Going home 107
I love you, Lord, and I lift my voice 150
Jesus, Jesus 176
Make way, make way 221
The ink is black 316

PROPER 23 - A

Faithful Shepherd, feed me 63
Forth in the peace of Christ we go 80
God is love 94
God is our strength from days of old 98
I'm accepted, I'm forgiven 151
In heavenly love abiding 157
Like a mighty river flowing 199
Rejoice in the Lord always 283
The King of love my shepherd is 437
The Lord's my shepherd 438
Chants
In the Lord I'll be ever thankful 387
Wait for the Lord 407

PROPER 24 - A

God is our strength from days of old 98
Rock of ages, cleft for me 434

PROPER 25 - A

Love is his word 214

Or: BIBLE SUNDAY - A

Bind us together, Lord 27
Forth in the peace of Christ we go 80
Led like a lamb 192
Lord, we come to ask your healing 211
My Father, for another night 230
We are his children 343

DEDICATION FESTIVAL - A

Give me joy in my heart 87
Hosanna, hosanna 132
Jerusalem, my happy home 170
Jesus Christ is waiting 174
Lord, enthroned in heavenly splendour 430
Lord of our life, and God of our salvation 209
Praise him, praise him 274
You are the King of Glory 373

ALL SAINTS' DAY - A

All heaven declares 5
As we are gathered 18
Blessed assurance 28
By his grace 36
Fill your hearts with joy and gladness 73
Have you heard the raindrops 121
How deep the Father's love 133
Make way, make way 221
Only by grace 257
Thee we adore, O hidden Saviour, thee 436
The kingdom of heaven 317
Chants
In the Lord I'll be ever thankful 387

FOURTH SUNDAY BEFORE ADVENT - A

O Jesus, I have promised 432

THIRD SUNDAY BEFORE ADVENT - A

Give me joy in my heart 87
Peace is flowing like a river 265

The universe was waiting 327
Waken, O sleeper, wake and rise 340
Wake, O wake! with tidings thrilling 341
Will you come and follow me 368
Chants
Wait for the Lord 407

SECOND SUNDAY BEFORE ADVENT - A

Lord of all life and power 208

CHRIST THE KING - A

As Jacob with travel was weary one day 16
At the name of Jesus 418
Come, now is the time to worship 51
Gracious God, in adoration 111
Sing glory to God the Father 295
The universe was waiting 327
When I needed a neighbour 359

YEAR B

ADVENT

FIRST SUNDAY OF ADVENT - B

Change my heart, O God 38
Take me, Lord 308
We shall stay awake 350

SECOND SUNDAY OF ADVENT - B

All over the world 6
Fill your hearts with joy and gladness 73
I cannot tell 142
Onward, Christian pilgrims 260
Praise him, praise him 274
Sing it in the valleys 296
We have a dream 348
We shall stay awake 350
Chants
Wait for the Lord 407

THIRD SUNDAY OF ADVENT - B

Faithful God 62
God is working his purpose out 99
God of glory we exalt your name 100
I cannot tell 142
I give you all the honour 147
Inspired by love and anger 158
Jesus put this song 180
Make way, make way 221
Mary, blessèd teenage mother 224
O for a thousand tongues to sing 238
The kingdom of God 317
When our God came to earth 361

FOURTH SUNDAY OF ADVENT - B

Crown him with many crowns 422
Mary, blessèd teenage mother 224
The angel Gabriel from heaven came 313
When our God came to earth 361

Chants
Magnificat 393

CHRISTMAS

CHRISTMAS EVE - See Year A

CHRISTMAS DAY - See Year A

FIRST SUNDAY OF CHRISTMAS - B

Abba, Father, let me be 1
Alleluia (x8) 3
All the nations of the earth 8
At this time of giving 19
Father God, I wonder 65
Let us praise God together 196
New songs of celebration render 236
Praise the Lord of heaven 277
Shall we not love thee, Mother dear 292
The holly and the ivy 315

SECOND SUNDAY OF CHRISTMAS - See Year A

EPIPHANY

THE EPIPHANY - See YEAR A

THE BAPTISM OF CHRIST - B

Blest Creator of the light 31
God is our strength from days of old 98
Lord of our life, and God of our salvation 209
Lord, the light of your love 210
Morning has broken 227
O Breath of Life 237
On this day, the first of days 259
Sweet sacrament divine 307
This is the world you have made 335
Chants
Wait for the Lord 407

SECOND SUNDAY OF EPIPHANY - B

All hail the power of Jesus' name 417
As Jacob with travel was weary one day 16
From the sun's rising 84
Will you come and follow me 368
You are beautiful 371

THIRD SUNDAY OF EPIPHANY - B

God, in the planning 92
Lord of our life, and God of our salvation 209

FOURTH SUNDAY OF EPIPHANY - B

Firmly I believe and truly 423
Give thanks with a grateful heart 88
I give you all the honour 147
Jesus Christ is waiting 174
There is a Redeemer 323

THE PRESENTATION OF CHRIST IN THE TEMPLE - See YEAR A

ORDINARY TIME

PROPER 1 - B

Fill your hearts with joy and gladness 73
I cannot tell 142
Lord I come to you 205
When I feel the touch 357

PROPER 2 - B

May the mind of Christ my Saviour 225
Will you come and follow me 368

PROPER 3 - B

God forgave my sin 91

SECOND SUNDAY BEFORE LENT - B

At the name of Jesus 418
Breathe on me, Breath of God 419
Christ triumphant 43
Come, risen Lord 421
Crown him with many crowns 422
God is our strength from days of old 98
If I were a butterfly 145
Jesus, Name above all names 178
Jesus, stand among us at the meeting of our lives 182
Send forth your spirit, Lord 290

SUNDAY NEXT BEFORE LENT - B

Beauty for brokenness 22
Be still, for the presence of the Lord 25
He is exalted 124
Lord, the light of your love 210

LENT

ASH WEDNESDAY - See YEAR A

FIRST SUNDAY OF LENT - B

Be still and know that I am God 24
Come, Holy Spirit, come 49
Forty days and forty nights in Judah's desert 81
God is our strength from days of old 98
Lead us, heavenly Father, lead us 429
Lord of our life, and God of our salvation 209
O let the Son of God enfold you 245
The kingdom of God 317
Who put the colours in the rainbow? 365
Chants
Wait for the Lord 407

SECOND SUNDAY OF LENT - B

At the name of Jesus 418
Lift high the cross 198
Take up your cross, he says 310

THIRD SUNDAY OF LENT - B

All heaven declares 5
As the deer pants for the water 17
Come, Holy Spirit, come 49
Firmly I believe and truly 423
I love you, Lord, and I lift my voice 150
Jesus, Jesus 176
The ink is black 316

FOURTH SUNDAY OF LENT - B

From heaven you came 82
I stand amazed in the presence 161
Name of all majesty 234
O my Saviour, lifted from the earth 252
Only by grace 257
To God be the glory! 338
We want to see Jesus lifted high 352

Or: MOTHERING SUNDAY - See YEAR A

FIFTH SUNDAY OF LENT - B

Father, we love you 70
Lord, teach us how to pray aright 418
My Lord, what love is this 233
O Jesus I have promised 432
On the bloodstained ground 258
Open our eyes, Lord 261
Chants
You are the centre 408

PALM SUNDAY - B

Liturgy of the Palms

Christians, lift up your hearts 40
Hosanna, hosanna 132
I will enter his gates 166
Praise him, praise him 274
This is the day 332
You are the King of Glory 373
Chants
Confitemini Domino 383

Liturgy of the Passion

Among us and before us 11
And can it be 12
An upper room did our Lord prepare 14
At the name of Jesus 418
Be still and know that I am God 24
Broken for me 34
Christ triumphant 43
Come and see 46
Come, now is the time to worship 51
Cross of Jesus 54
Forty days and forty nights in Judah's desert 81
From heaven you came 82
God is our strength from days of old 98
Great Son of God 114
Help us to help each other, Lord 126
Here hangs a man discarded 127
Holy, holy, holy is the Lord 131
How deep the Father's love 133
I do not know the man 144
I will offer up my life 167
Jesus, at your name 171
Jesus Christ, I think upon your sacrifice 173
Jesus, Name above all names 178
Jesus shall take the highest honour 181
Jesus took a piece of bread 184
Love is his word 214
Man of sorrows 222
May the mind of Christ my Saviour 225
Meekness and majesty 226
Name of all majesty 234
O Lord of our salvation 249
Onward, Christian pilgrims 260
Praise the Lord, rise up rejoicing 278
This is my body 330
Thy way, not mine, O Lord 336
We believe in God the Father 345
We bow down 346
You laid aside your majesty 375
Chants
Lord of creation 392
Stay with me 400

MONDAY OF HOLY WEEK - See YEAR A

TUESDAY OF HOLY WEEK - See YEAR A

WEDNESDAY OF HOLY WEEK - See YEAR A

MAUNDY THURSDAY - See YEAR A

GOOD FRIDAY - See YEAR A

EASTER EVE - See YEAR A
Services other than the Easter Vigil

EASTER

EASTER VIGIL - See YEAR A

EASTER DAY - B

A new commandment 13
Christians, lift up your hearts 40
From the very depths of darkness 85
I will enter his gates 166
Jesus, stand among us at the meeting of our lives 182
Led like a lamb 192
Lord, I lift your name on high 206
Morning has broken 227
On this day, the first of days 259
Shout for joy and sing 293
This is the day 332
Chants
Confitemini Domino 383

SECOND SUNDAY OF EASTER - B

Among us and before us 11
Blessed assurance 28
Crown him with many crowns 422
For ourselves no longer living 77
God is our strength from days of old 98
In an age of twisted values 153
Jesus calls us 172
Lamb of God, Holy One 191
Living God, your word has called us 203
On the bloodstained ground 258
The Spirit lives to set us free 326
We will lay our burden down 353

THIRD SUNDAY OF EASTER - B

From the very depths of darkness 85
How deep the Father's love 133
Jesus, Prince and Saviour 179
Chants
O Lord, hear my prayer 396

FOURTH SUNDAY OF EASTER - B

All hail the power of Jesus' name 417
At this time of giving 19
Faithful Shepherd, feed me 63
Forth in the peace of Christ we go 80
Hail, thou once despisèd Jesus 116
I cannot tell 142
I do not know the man 144
In heavenly love abiding 157
Loving shepherd of thy sheep 217
Praise him, praise him 274
Shout for joy and sing 293
The King of love my shepherd is 437
The Lord's my shepherd 438
Chants
Nada te turbe 395

FIFTH SUNDAY OF EASTER - B

Dance in your Spirit 57
God is love 94
If we only seek peace 146
Let us talents and tongues employ 197
O Love that wilt not let me go 251
O sacred King 262
This is my body 330
Chants
Ubi caritas 404

SIXTH SUNDAY OF EASTER - B

An upper room did our Lord prepare 14
If we only seek peace 146
Jesus calls us 172
Living God, your word has called us 203
Put thou thy trust in God 282
Shout for joy and sing 293
Sing to God new songs of worship 298
The ink is black 316
This is my will 331

ASCENSION DAY - see YEAR A

SEVENTH SUNDAY OF EASTER - B

I, the Lord of sea and sky 163
Soul of my Saviour 300
Will you come and follow me 368

PENTECOST (Whit Sunday) - B

All over the world	6
Breathe on me, Breath of God	419
Come, Holy Spirit, come	49
Father, Lord of all creation	68
Filled with the Spirit's power	71
If I were a butterfly	145
Lord, the light of your love	210
O Breath of Life	237
On this day, the first of days	259
Rejoice, the year upon its way	284
Send forth your spirit, Lord	290
Spirit of the living God (Armstrong)	302
Spirit of the living God (Iverson)	303
The King is among us	319
Chants	
You are the centre	408

ORDINARY TIME

TRINITY SUNDAY - B

Abba, Father, let me be	1
Breathe on me, Breath of God	419
Cross of Jesus	54
Father God, I wonder	65
From heaven you came	82
Hallelujah, my Father	118
Holy, holy, holy	130
Holy, holy, holy is the Lord	131
I cannot tell	142
Inspired by love and anger	158
I stand amazed in the presence	161
I, the Lord of sea and sky	163
Lord of our life, and God of our salvation	209
Lord, the light of your love	210
Name of all majesty	234
To God be the glory!	338
The kingdom of God	317
We want to see Jesus lifted high	352

DAY OF THANKSGIVING FOR HOLY COMMUNION
Thursday After Trinity Sunday (Corpus Christi) See YEAR A

PROPER 4 - B

God of grace and God of glory	101
Lord, the light of your love	210
You are beautiful	371

PROPER 5 - B

Only by grace	257
There's a wideness in God's mercy	324

PROPER 6 - B

For the fruits of his creation	78
I am a new creation	137
My Jesus, my Saviour	232
We want to see Jesus lifted high	352

PROPER 7 - B

Be still, my soul	26
Give thanks with a grateful heart	88
I cannot tell	142
Inspired by love and anger	158
Lead us, heavenly Father, lead us	429
Living God, your word has called us	203
Sweet sacrament divine	307
You are the light	374
Chants	
Calm me, Lord	382

PROPER 8 - B

Abba, Father, let me be	1
All that I am	7

PROPER 9 - B

Give thanks with a grateful heart	88
Great is the Lord and most worthy of praise	112
Inspired by love and anger	158
Wait for the Lord	407

PROPER 10 - B

Dance in your Spirit	57
Fill your hearts with joy and gladness	73
For ourselves no longer living	77
God is working his purpose out	99
King of glory, King of peace	427
Make way, make way	221
Praise God from whom all blessings flow	271

PROPER 11 - B

Faithful Shepherd, feed me	63
Forth in the peace of Christ we go	80
Gather around, for the table is spread	86
I'm not ashamed to own my Lord	152
In an age of twisted values	153
In heavenly love abiding	157
Put peace in each other's hands	281
The King of love my shepherd is	437
The Lord's my shepherd	438

PROPER 12 - B

Gather around, for the table is spread	86
I give you all the honour	147
In an age of twisted values	153
Just as I am, without one plea	426
Let us praise God together	196
Such love	306

PROPER 13 - B

Bread is blessed and broken	33
Come, build the Church	47
God is working his purpose out	99
Help us to help each other, Lord	126
My Lord, what love is this	233
Chants	
You are the centre	408

PROPER 14 - B

Bread is blessed and broken	33
Come on and celebrate	52
God forgave my sin	91
God is good	93
I am the bread of life	138
Let love be real	193
Lord, enthroned in heavenly splendour	430
Only by grace	257
Sing we of the blessèd Mother	299
Thee we adore, O hidden Saviour, thee	436
There's a wideness in God's mercy	324
Chants	
Eat this bread	384

PROPER 15 - B

Broken for me	34
Gather around, for the table is spread	86
Lord, enthroned in heavenly splendour	430
Thank you, Lord	312
Thee we adore, O hidden Saviour, thee	436
Chants	
Eat this bread	384

PROPER 16 - B

Alleluia, alleluia, give thanks to the risen Lord	4
God of grace and God of glory	101
Jesus lover of my soul	177
Lamb of God, Holy One	191
Lord, when I turn my back on you	212
Soldiers of Christ, arise	435
There is a Redeemer	323
You are the King of Glory	373

PROPER 17 - B

Be still, my soul	26
Great is thy faithfulness	113
In an age of twisted values	153

PROPER 18 - B

Take up your cross, he says	310
Thanks for the fellowship	311
The kingdom of God	317

PROPER 19 - B

All heaven declares	5
As the deer pants for the water	17
I love you, Lord, and I lift my voice	150
Jesus, Jesus	176
Lift high the cross	198
Take up your cross, he says	310
The ink is black	316

PROPER 20 - B

From heaven you came	82
Let there be love	194

PROPER 21 - B

As the deer pants for the water 17
Jesus, Jesus 176

PROPER 22 - B

All hail the power of Jesus' name 417
Be still, for the presence of the Lord 25
How deep the Father's love 133
It fell upon a summer day 162
Meekness and majesty 226
O Lord, my God 248

PROPER 23 - B

Blessed assurance 28
God is good 93

PROPER 24 - B

Cross of Jesus 54
From heaven you came 82
If I were a butterfly 145
Jesus is Lord! Creation's voice proclaims it 175
Meekness and majesty 226
Send forth your spirit, Lord 290
What a friend we have in Jesus 354

PROPER 25 - B

God is good 93
I know that my Redeemer lives 149
Chants
In the Lord I'll be ever thankful 387

Or: BIBLE SUNDAY - B

As the deer pants for the water 17
Jesus, Jesus 176
Put thou thy trust in God 282
Spirit of God 301

DEDICATION FESTIVAL - B

Beneath the cross of Jesus 23
Blessed assurance 28
Lord of our life, and God of our salvation 209
Loving Shepherd of thy sheep 217
Nearer, my God, to thee 235
Children's Hymns and Songs
As Jacob with travel was weary one day 16

ALL SAINTS' DAY - B

Be still, my soul 26
For ourselves no longer living 77
God is our strength from days of old 98
I'm not ashamed to own my Lord 152
O Lord, all the world belongs to you 247
The kingdom of heaven 317
Wake, O wake! with tidings thrilling 341

FOURTH SUNDAY BEFORE ADVENT - B

Father, Lord of all creation 68
Who sees it all 366

THIRD SUNDAY BEFORE ADVENT - B

Follow me 75
God is my great desire 96
O happy day 242
The kingdom of God 317
When God Almighty came to earth 356
Will you come and follow me 368

SECOND SUNDAY BEFORE ADVENT - B

Amazing grace 10
Lord, the light of your love 210

CHRIST THE KING - B

Crown him with many crowns 422
From the sun's rising 84
God is love, his the care 95
God is our strength from days of old 98
Jesus lover of my soul 177
Lord, enthroned in heavenly splendour 430

YEAR C

ADVENT

FIRST SUNDAY OF ADVENT - C

Be still and know that I am God 24
Lord of our life, and God of our salvation 209
Onward, Christian pilgrims 260
We shall stay awake 350
Chants
Wait for the Lord 407

SECOND SUNDAY OF ADVENT - C

I bind unto myself today 141
Purify my heart 280
Restore, O Lord 285
Chants
Wait for the Lord 407

THIRD SUNDAY OF ADVENT - C

All over the world 6
God is love 94
I'm accepted, I'm forgiven 151
Like a mighty river flowing 199
Rejoice in the Lord always 283
The kingdom of God 317
The Lord is my song 321
We shall stay awake 350
Chants
In the Lord I'll be ever thankful 387
Wait for the Lord 407

FOURTH SUNDAY OF ADVENT - C

Mary, blessèd teenage mother 224
The angel Gabriel from heaven came 313
When our God came to earth 361

Chants
Magnificat 393
Sanctum nomen Domini 398

CHRISTMAS

CHRISTMAS EVE - See YEAR A

CHRISTMAS DAY - See YEAR A

FIRST SUNDAY OF CHRISTMAS - C

All the nations of the earth 8
Bind us together, Lord 27
Forth in the peace of Christ we go 80
Let us praise God together 196
Lord, we come to ask your healing 211
My Father, for another night 230
New songs of celebration render 236
Praise the Lord of heaven 277

SECOND SUNDAY OF CHRISTMAS - See YEAR A

EPIPHANY

THE EPIPHANY - See YEAR A

THE BAPTISM OF CHRIST - C

All over the world 6
Come, Holy Spirit, come 49
Do not be afraid 59
God is our strength from days of old 98
Lord of our life, and God of our salvation 209
O let the Son of God enfold you 245
Spirit of the living God (Iverson) 303
Sweet sacrament divine 307

SECOND SUNDAY OF EPIPHANY - C

Come, Holy Spirit, come 49
Faithful God 62
Heaven shall not wait 123
Jesus is Lord! Creation's voice proclaims it 175
Lord Jesus Christ 207
Your love's greater 376

THIRD SUNDAY OF EPIPHANY - C

All heaven declares 5
As the deer pants for the water 17
Beauty for brokenness 22
Bind us together, Lord 27
Cry 'Freedom!' 55
God is working his purpose out 99
God of glory we exalt your name 100
I give you all the honour 147
I love you, Lord, and I lift my voice 150
Jesus, Jesus 176
Living God, your word has called us 203
Make way, make way 221
O for a thousand tongues to sing 238
The ink is black 316

The kingdom of God 317
Will you come and follow me 368

FOURTH SUNDAY OF EPIPHANY - C

By his grace 36
Come, Holy Spirit, come 49
Father, I place into your hands 67
Great is the Lord and most worthy of praise 112
Let love be real 193
Sing we of the blessèd Mother 299
Chants
Ubi caritas 404

THE PRESENTATION OF CHRIST IN THE TEMPLE - See YEAR A

ORDINARY TIME

PROPER 1 - C

A new commandment 13
Cross of Jesus 54
Holy, holy, holy 130
Holy, holy, holy is the Lord 131
Inspired by love and anger 158
I, the Lord of sea and sky 163
Lord, I lift your name on high 206
Lord, the light of your love 210
O happy day 242

PROPER 2 - C

Blessed assurance 28
I know that my Redeemer lives 149
Make way, make way 221
Think of a world without any flowers 329

PROPER 3 - C

Brother, sister, let me serve you 35
O Lord, all the world belongs to you 247

SECOND SUNDAY BEFORE LENT - C

Be still, my soul 26
Breathe on me, Breath of God 419
Holy, holy, holy 130
Holy, holy, holy is the Lord 131
I cannot tell 142
Inspired by love and anger 158
O Breath of Life 237
Sweet sacrament divine 307
Chants
Calm me, Lord 382

SUNDAY NEXT BEFORE LENT - C

Be still, for the presence of the Lord 25
He is exalted 124
Lord, the light of your love 210
The Lord is King! 320

LENT

ASH WEDNESDAY - See YEAR A

FIRST SUNDAY OF LENT - C

Forty days and forty nights in Judah's desert 81
I bind unto myself today 141
Lead us, heavenly Father, lead us 429
Soul of my Saviour 300
Chants
Wait for the Lord 407

SECOND SUNDAY OF LENT - C

God is our strength from days of old 98
Lord I come to you 205
Put thou thy trust in God 282
Spirit of God 301
To be in your presence 337
We bow down 346
Chants
The Lord is my light (Taizé) 402
The Lord is my light (Rizza) 403
Wait for the Lord 407

THIRD SUNDAY OF LENT - C

Faithful God 62
Praise him, praise him 274
Put thou thy trust in God 282
Rock of ages 434
Spirit of God 301

FOURTH SUNDAY OF LENT - C

Come and see 46
I am a new creation 137
I will sing the wondrous story 168
The kingdom of God 317

Or: MOTHERING SUNDAY - See YEAR A

FIFTH SUNDAY OF LENT - C

Come and see 46
Jesus put this song 180

PALM SUNDAY - C

Christians, lift up your hearts 40
I will enter his gates 166
You are the King of Glory 373
Chants
Confitemini Domino 383

Liturgy of the Passion

And can it be 12
At the name of Jesus 418
Be still and know that I am God 24
Broken for me 34
Christ triumphant 43
Come and see 46
Cross of Jesus 54
Forty days and forty nights in Judah's desert 81
From heaven you came 82
God is our strength from days of old 98
Great Son of God 114
Here hangs a man discarded 127
Jesus, at your name 171
Jesus, Name above all names 178
Jesus shall take the highest honour 181
Love is his word 214
Man of sorrows 222
May the mind of Christ my Saviour 225
Meekness and majesty 226
Name of all majesty 234
O Lord, all the world belongs to you 247
O Lord of our salvation 249
Thy way, not mine, O Lord 336
We believe in God the Father 345
Chants
Jesus, remember me 389
Stay with me 400

MONDAY OF HOLY WEEK - See YEAR A

TUESDAY OF HOLY WEEK - See YEAR A

WEDNESDAY OF HOLY WEEK - See YEAR A

MAUNDY THURSDAY - See YEAR A

GOOD FRIDAY - See YEAR A

EASTER EVE - See YEAR A Services other than the Easter Vigil

EASTER

EASTER VIGIL - See YEAR A

EASTER DAY - C

Christians, lift up your hearts 40
From the very depths of darkness 85
Hail the day that sees him rise 424
I will enter his gates 166
Led like a lamb 192
Morning has broken 227
On this day, the first of days 259
Shout for joy and sing 293
This is the day 332
Chants
Confitemini Domino 383
In the Lord is my joy 388

SECOND SUNDAY OF EASTER - C

Among us and before us 11
Bless the Lord, my soul 29
Christians, lift up your hearts 40
Crown him with many crowns 422
Dance and sing 56
From the sun's rising 84
God is our strength from days of old 98
I will enter his gates 166
Jesus lover of my soul 177
Lord, enthroned in heavenly splendour 430
New songs of celebration render 236

Praise him on the trumpet 273
Shout for joy and sing 293
This is the day 332
We will lay our burden down 353

THIRD SUNDAY OF EASTER - C

All heaven declares 5
Come and see 46
Father, we adore you 69
Hark, my soul, it is the Lord 119
I cannot tell 142
James and Andrew, Peter and John 169
Lamb of God, Holy One 191
Majesty, worship his majesty 219
Praise God from whom all blessings flow 271

FOURTH SUNDAY OF EASTER - C

All heaven declares 5
As we are gathered 18
At this time of giving 19
Blessed assurance 28
By his grace 36
Faithful Shepherd, feed me 63
Forth in the peace of Christ we go 80
In heavenly love abiding 157
Only by grace 257
The King of love my shepherd is 437
The Lord's my shepherd 438
Chants
Nada te turbe 395

FIFTH SUNDAY OF EASTER - C

All the nations of the earth 8
A new commandment 13
Be still, my soul 26
Christ's is the world 42
God is our strength from days of old 98
I'm not ashamed to own my Lord 152
Jesus lover of my soul 177
Let us praise God together 196
Living God, your word has called us 203
Love is his word 214
New songs of celebration render 236
O Lord, all the world belongs to you 247
Peace, perfect peace, is the gift 267
Praise the Lord of heaven 277
This is my will 331
Chants
Ubi caritas 404

SIXTH SUNDAY OF EASTER - C

Breathe on me, Breath of God 419
Crown him with many crowns 422
For the healing of the nations 79
Like a mighty river flowing 199
Peace, perfect peace, in this dark world of sin 266
Put peace into each other's hands 281
Shall we gather at the river 291
Spirit of the living God (Iverson) 303
This is my body 330

ASCENSION DAY - See YEAR A

SEVENTH SUNDAY OF EASTER - C

As we are gathered 18
Breathe on me, Breath of God 419
Forth in the peace of Christ we go 80
God forgave my sin 91
God is our strength from days of old 98
God is working his purpose out 99
Heaven is open wide 122
How good is the God we adore 135
I, the Lord of sea and sky 163
Jesus lover of my soul 177
Put thou thy trust in God 282
The Lord is King! 320
Will you come and follow me 368

PENTECOST (Whit Sunday) - C

Abba, Father, let me be 1
Alleluia (x8) 3
Breathe on me, Breath of God 419
Come, Holy Spirit, come 49
Father, Lord of all creation 68
Filled with the Spirit's power 71
Lord, the light of your love 210
O Breath of Life 237
Rejoice, the year upon its way 284
Send forth your spirit, Lord 290
Take up your cross, he says 310
The King is among us 319

ORDINARY TIME

TRINITY SUNDAY - C

All over the world 6
I am a new creation 137
I'm accepted, I'm forgiven 151
My Jesus, my Saviour 232
O let the Son of God enfold you 245
O Lord, my God 248
Put thou thy trust in God 282
The Lord is King! 320

DAY OF THANKSGIVING FOR HOLY COMMUNION
Thursday after Trinity Sunday (Corpus Christi) See YEAR A

PROPER 4 - C

Far and near 64
My Jesus, my Saviour 232
O sacred King 262
We cannot measure 347
When we walk with the Lord 362

PROPER 5 - C

Faithful God 62
Father, Lord of all creation 68
Thanks for the fellowship 311

PROPER 6 - C

Alleluia, alleluia, give thanks to the risen Lord 4
Come on and celebrate 52
God forgave my sin 91
I bind unto myself today 141
In full and glad surrender 156
I stand amazed in the presence 161
It's me, O Lord 164
Lord, for the years 204
My faith looks up to thee 229
My Father, for another night 230

PROPER 7 - C

As the deer pants for the water 17
In an age of twisted values 153
Listen, let your heart keep seeking 200
Living God, you word has called us 203
Spirit of God 301

PROPER 8 - C

Cry 'Freedom!' 55
Dance in your Spirit 57
Follow me 75
Moses, I know you're the man 228
When God Almighty came to earth 356
Will you come and follow me 368

PROPER 9 - C

Help us to help each other, Lord 126
In the cross of Christ I glory 159
Lord, for the years 204
Moses, I know you're the man 228
When I survey the wondrous cross 440

PROPER 10 - C

Be still and know that I am God 24
God is working his purpose out 99
Hark, my soul, it is the Lord 119
Lord of our life, and God of our Salvation 209
Meekness and majesty 226
When I needed a neighbour 359
Chants
Wait for the Lord 407

PROPER 11 - C

At the name of Jesus 418
Come, risen Lord 421
I am trusting thee, Lord Jesus 139
Jesus, stand among us at the meeting of our lives 182
Peace, perfect peace, in this dark world of sin 266

PROPER 12 - C

Fill your hearts with joy and gladness 73
God forgave my sin 91
I will offer up my life 167
Lord of our life, and God of our salvation 209
Make me a channel of your peace 220
O Lamb of God 244
Onward, Christian pilgrims 260
We have a dream 348

Who can sound the depths of sorrow 363

PROPER 13 - C

Dance in your Spirit 57
Now thank we all our God 431
Thanks for the fellowship 311
Thee we adore, O hidden Saviour, thee 436

PROPER 14 - C

Beauty for brokenness 22
One more step along the world I go 255

PROPER 15 - C

God of grace and God of glory 101
Onward, Christian pilgrims 260

PROPER 16 - C

Be still and know that I am God 24
I am trusting thee, Lord Jesus 139
I'm not ashamed to own my Lord 152
Jerusalem, my happy home 170
We pray thee, heavenly Father 439
Chants
Bless the Lord, my soul (Taizé) 381

PROPER 17 - C

I, the Lord of sea and sky 163

PROPER 18 - C

Onward, Christian pilgrims 260
Take my life, and let it be 309
You are beautiful 371

PROPER 19 - C

Amazing grace 10
Cross of Jesus 54
I will sing the wondrous story 168
Meekness and majesty 226
My Lord, what love is this 233
Name of all majesty 234
The kingdom of God 317
The King of love my shepherd is 437

PROPER 20 - C

Cry 'Freedom' 55
Inspired by love and anger 158
Stand up, stand up for Jesus 304

PROPER 21 - C

Beneath the cross of Jesus 23
I bind unto myself today 141
In an age of twisted values 153
King of kings and Lord of lords 189
Soul of my Saviour 300
Thanks for the fellowship 311

PROPER 22 - C

I'm not ashamed to own my Lord 152
Inspired by love and anger 158
Morning has broken 227
Name of all majesty 234
Spirit of God 301

PROPER 23 - C

Have faith in God, my heart 120

PROPER 24 - C

O God beyond all praising 240
Onward, Christian pilgrims 260

PROPER 25 - C

Alleluia, alleluia, give thanks to the risen Lord 4
All over the world 6
God is our strength from days of old 98
Praise God for the harvest 270
Soldiers of Christ, arise 435
The King is among us 319

Or: BIBLE SUNDAY - C

God is working his purpose out 99
God of glory we exalt your name 100
I give you all the honour 147
Make way, make way 221
O for a thousand tongues to sing 238
The kingdom of God 317
Will you come and follow me 368

DEDICATION FESTIVAL - C

For I'm building a people of power 76
Lord of our life, and God of our salvation 209

ALL SAINTS' DAY - C

Dance in your Spirit 57
God is working his purpose out 99
Make way, make way 221
New songs of celebration render 236
O Lord, all the world belongs to you 247
The kingdom of heaven 317

FOURTH SUNDAY BEFORE ADVENT - C

At the name of Jesus 418
Lord of all life and power 208
The Spirit lives to set us free 326

THIRD SUNDAY BEFORE ADVENT - C

I know that my Redeemer lives 149

SECOND SUNDAY BEFORE ADVENT - C

Judge eternal, throned in splendour 187
Shout for joy and sing 293
Sing to God new songs of worship 298
You are the King of Glory 373

CHRIST THE KING - C

At the name of Jesus 418
Come and see 46
Come, risen Lord 421
God is our strength and refuge 97
Great Son of God 114
Jesus, stand among us at the meeting of our lives 182
Meekness and majesty 226
My Jesus, my Saviour 232
Peace, perfect peace, in this dark world of sin 266
Your mercy flows 377
Chants
Jesus, remember me 389

Index of First Lines

This index is in four parts:

1. General Hymns and Songs
2. Chants
3. Music for the Eucharist
4. Additional Tunes

This index gives the first line of each hymn. If a hymn is known also by a title (e.g. Shine, Jesus, shine) this is given as well, but indented and in italics.

A

Abba, Father, let me be 1
Advent acclamations 350
Ah, holy Jesu, how hast thou offended 2
Alleluia (x 8) 3
Alleluia, alleluia, give thanks to the risen Lord 4
All heaven declares 5
All over the world 6
All that I am 7
All the nations of the earth 8
A man there lived in Galilee 9
Amazing grace 10
Amazing love 233
Among us and before us 11
And can it be 12
A new commandment 13
An upper room did our Lord prepare 14
Ascribe greatness 15
As Jacob with travel was weary one day 16
As the deer pants for the water 17
As we are gathered 18
A touching place 42
At this time of giving 19
At your feet we fall 20
Away in a manger 21

B

Beautiful world 335
Beauty for brokenness 22
Beneath the cross of Jesus 23
Be still and know that I am God 24
Be still, for the presence of the Lord 25
Be still, my soul 26
Bind us together, Lord 27
Black and white 316
Blessed assurance 28
Bless the Lord, my soul 29
Blest are you, Lord of creation 30
Blest Creator of the light 31
Born in the night, Mary's child 32
Bread is blessed and broken 33
Bridegroom and bride 92
Broken for me 34
Brother, sister, let me serve you 35
By his grace 36
By your side 37

C

Change my heart, O God 38
Child in the manger 39
Christians, lift up your hearts 40
Christ is alive! 41
Christ's is the world 42
Christ triumphant 43
Close to you 165
Cloth for the cradle 44
Colours of day 45
Come and see 46
Come, build the Church 47
Come, come, come to the manger 48
Come, Holy Spirit, come 49
Come, my Way, my Truth, my Life 50
Come, now is the time to worship 51
Come on and celebrate 52
Come, wounded Healer 53
Cross of Jesus 54
Cry 'Freedom!' 55

D

Dance and sing 56
Dance in your Spirit 57
Ding dong, merrily on high! 58
Do not be afraid 59
Doxology 272
Drop, drop, slow tears 60

E

Enfold me in your love 374

F

Fair waved the golden corn 61
Faithful God 62
Faithful Shepherd, feed me 63
Far and near 64
Father God, I wonder 65
Father God, we worship you 66
Father, I place into your hands 67
Father, Lord of all creation 68
Father, we adore you 69
Father, we love you 70
Father, who in Jesus found us see God whose love is all around us 105
Filled with the Spirit's power 71
Fill thou my life, O Lord my God 72
Fill your hearts with joy and gladness 73
Finished the strife 74
Follow me 75
For I'm building a people of power 76
For ourselves no longer living 77
For the fruits of his creation 78
For the healing of the nations 79
Forth in the peace of Christ we go 80
Forty days and forty nights in Judah's desert 81
Freely, freely 91
From heaven you came 82
From many grains 83
From the sun's rising 84
From the very depths of darkness 85

G

Gather around, for the table is spread 86
Give me joy in my heart 87
Give thanks with a grateful heart 88
Give to our God immortal praise 89
Glorify your name 70
Glory to thee, O God 90
God forgave my sin 91
God, in the planning 92
God is good 93
God is love 94
God is love: his the care 95
God is my great desire 96
God is our strength and refuge 97
God is our strength from days of old 98
God is working his purpose out 99
God knows me 322
God of glory we exalt your name 100
God of grace and God of glory 101
God of the Passover 102
God of the poor 22
God on earth 356
God rest you merry, gentlemen 103
God, whose farm is all creation 104
God whose love is all around us 105
Go forth and tell 106
Go forth in his name 343
Going home 107
Good Christians all, rejoice 108
Good King Wenceslas 109
Go, tell it on the mountain 110
Gracious God, in adoration 111
Great is the Lord and most worthy of praise 112
Great is thy faithfulness 113
Great love 231
Great Son of God 114

H

Hail, gladdening Light 115
Hail, thou once despisèd Jesus 116
Halle, halle, halle 117
Hallelujah, my Father 118
Hark, my soul, it is the Lord 119
Have faith in God, my heart 120
Have you heard the raindrops 121
Heal our nation 153
Heaven is open wide 122
Heaven shall not wait 123
He has made me glad 166
He is exalted 124
He is Lord 125
Help us to help each other, Lord 126
Here hangs a man discarded 127
Here I am, Lord 163
He's got the whole world in his hand 128
He was pierced 129
Holy and anointed one 176
Holy, holy, holy 130
Holy, holy, holy is the Lord 131
Hosanna, hosanna 132
Hosanna to the Son of David 373
How deep the Father's love 133
How firm a foundation 134
How good is the God we adore 135
How great thou art 248
How lovely on the mountains 136

I

I am a new creation 137
I am the bread of life 138
I am trusting thee, Lord Jesus 139
I believe in Jesus 140
I bind unto myself today 141

I cannot tell 142
I come with joy 143
I do not know the man 144
If I were a butterfly 145
If we only seek peace 146
I give you all the honour 147
I give you love 148
I kneel down 258
I know that my Redeemer lives 149
I love you, Lord, and I lift my voice 150
I'm accepted, I'm forgiven 151
I'm not ashamed to own my Lord 152
In an age of twisted values 153
I need thee every hour 154
I need you Lord 212
Infant holy, infant lowly 155
In full and glad surrender 156
In heavenly love abiding 157
In love for me 330
Inspired by love and anger 158
In the Cross of Christ I glory 159
In you, my God 160
I really want to worship you, my Lord 375
I stand amazed in the presence 161
I stand in awe 371
It fell upon a summer day 162
I, the Lord of sea and sky 163
It's all about you 177
It's me, O Lord 164
I watch the sunrise 165
I will enter his gates 166
I will offer up my life 167
I will sing the wondrous story 168
I will sing your praises 65
I worship you 147

J

James and Andrew, Peter and John 169
Jerusalem, my happy home 170
Jesus, at your name 171
Jesus calls us 172
Jesus Christ, I think upon your sacrifice 173
Jesus Christ is waiting 174
Jesus is Lord! Creation's voice proclaims it 175
Jesus is our joy 215
Jesus, Jesus 176
Jesus lover of my soul 177
Jesus, Name above all names 178
Jesus, Prince and Saviour 179
Jesus put this song 180
Jesus shall take the highest honour 181
Jesus, stand among us at the meeting of our lives 182
Jesus, the broken bread 183
Jesus took a piece of bread 184
Joy to the world 185
Jubilate, everybody 186
Judge eternal, throned in splendour 187
Just a closer walk with thee 188

K

King of kings and Lord of lords 189
Kum ba yah 190

L

Lamb of God, Holy One 191
Led like a lamb 192
Let love be real 193
Let the flame burn brighter 349
Let there be love 194
Let us break bread together 195
Let us praise God together 196
Let us talents and tongues employ 197
Lift high the cross 198
Light up the fire 45
Like a lamb 129
Like a mighty river flowing 199
Listen, let your heart keep seeking 200
Little Jesus, sleep away 201
Little Jesus, sweetly sleep 202
Living God, your word has called us 203
Living Lord 207
Lord, for the years 204
Lord I come to you 205
Lord, I lift your name on high 206
Lord Jesus Christ 207
Lord of all life and power 208
Lord of our life, and God of our salvation 209
Lord, the light of your love 210
Lord, we come to ask your healing 211
Lord, when I turn my back on you 212
Love came down at Christmas 213
Love is his word 214
Lovely in your littleness 215
Love songs from heaven 216
Loving Shepherd of thy sheep 217
Low in the grave he lay 218

M

Majesty, worship his majesty 219
Make me a channel of your peace 220
Make way, make way 221
Mallaig Sprinkling Song 301
Man of sorrows 222
Mary, blessèd grieving mother 223
Mary, blessèd teenage mother 224
May the mind of Christ my Saviour 225
Meekness and majesty 226
Morning has broken 227
Moses, I know you're the man 228
My desire 337
My faith looks up to thee 229
My Father, for another night 230
My heart will sing to you 231
My Jesus, my Saviour 232
My Lord, what love is this 233

N

Name of all majesty 234
Nearer, my God, to thee 235
New songs of celebration render 236
New Wine 256

O

O Breath of Life 237
O for a thousand tongues to sing 238
O give thanks 239
O God beyond all praising 240
O God of earth and altar 241
O happy day 242
O, how good is the Lord 243
O Lamb of God 244
O let the Son of God enfold you 245
O little one sweet, O little one mild 246
O Lord, all the world belongs to you 247
O Lord, my God 248
O Lord of our salvation 249
O Lord, your tenderness 250
O Love that wilt not let me go 251
O my Saviour, lifted from the earth 252
On a hill far away 253
Once again 173
On Christmas night all Christians sing 254
One more step along the world I go 255
One shall tell another 256
Only by grace 257
On the bloodstained ground 258
On this day, the first of days 259
Onward, Christian pilgrims 260
Open our eyes, Lord 261
O sacred King 262
Our Father (Caribbean) 263
Our Father (Wiener) 264
Our God reigns 136

P

Peace is flowing like a river 265
Peace, perfect peace, in this dark world of sin 266
Peace, perfect peace, is the gift 267
Peace to you 268
Peter and John went to pray 269
Power of your love 205
Praise God for the harvest 270
Praise God from whom all blessings flow 271
Praise God from whom all blessings flow 272
Praise him on the trumpet 273
Praise him, praise him 274
Praise him, praise him, praise him 275
Praise, O praise our God and King 276
Praise the Lord of heaven 277
Praise the Lord, rise up rejoicing 278
Praise to God for saints and martyrs 279
Purify my heart 280
Put peace into each other's hands 281
Put thou thy trust in God 282

R

Refiner's fire 280
Rejoice in the Lord always 283
Rejoice, the year upon its way 284
Reproaches 148
Restore, O Lord 285
Right where we are 312
Rise and shine 286

S

Say it loud 64
See amid the winter's snow 287
See him lying on a bed of straw 288
Seek ye first 289
Send forth your Spirit, Lord 290
Shall we gather at the river 291
Shall we not love thee, Mother dear 292
Shine, Jesus, shine 210
Shout for joy and sing 293
Shout to the Lord 232
Silent night 294
Silver and gold 269
Sing glory to God the Father 295
Sing hosanna 87

Sing it in the valleys 296
Sing lullaby 297
Sing to God new songs of worship 298
Sing we of the blessèd Mother 299
Soul of my Saviour 300
Spirit of God 301
Spirit of the living God (Armstrong) 302
Spirit of the living God (Iverson) 303
Spirit song 245
Stand up, stand up for Jesus (New text) 304
Steal away 305
Story of love 146
Such love 306
Sweet sacrament divine 307

T

Take me, Lord 308
Take my life, and let it be 309
Take up your cross, he says 310
Thanks for the fellowship 311
Thank you, Lord 312
The angel Gabriel from heaven came 313
The Beatitudes 318
The first Nowell 314
The giving song 19
The holly and the ivy 315
The ink is black 316
The kingdom of God 317
The kingdom of heaven 318
The King is among us 319
The Lord is King! 320
The Lord is my song 321
The old rugged cross 253
The people of God 228
There are hundreds of sparrows 322
There is a Redeemer 323
There's a wideness in God's mercy 324
The Saviour will come, resplendent in joy 325
The Servant King 82
The servant song 35
The Spirit lives to set us free 326
The Summons 368
The trees of the field 378
The universe was waiting 327
The Virgin Mary had a baby boy 328
Think of a world without any flowers 329
This is my body 330
This is my will 331
This is the day 332
This is your God 226
This joyful Eastertide 333
This little light of mine 334
This thankful heart 167
This world you have made 335
Thy way, not mine, O Lord 336
To be in your presence 337
To God be the glory! 338

U

Unto us a boy is born 339

W

Waken, O sleeper, wake and rise 340
Wake, O wake! with tidings thrilling 341
Wake up, O people 342
Walk in the light 326
Water of life 121
We are his children 343
We are marching 344
We believe in God the Father 345
We bow down 346
We cannot measure 347
We have a dream 348
We'll walk the land 349
We shall stay awake 350
We three kings of Orient are 351
We want to see Jesus lifted high 352
We will lay our burden down 353
We worship at your feet 46
What a friend we have in Jesus 354
What child is this 355
When God Almighty came to earth 356
When I feel the touch 357
When I look into your holiness 358
When I needed a neighbour 359
When, in our music, God is glorified 360
When our God came to earth 361
When we walk with the Lord 362
Who can sound the depths of sorrow 363
Who is this so weak and helpless 364
Who put the colours in the rainbow? 365
Who sees it all 366
Wide, wide as the ocean 367
Will you come and follow me 368
Will your anchor hold 369
Wonderful grace 370

Y

You are beautiful 372
You are beneath me 372
You are the Christ 171
You are the King of Glory 373
You are the light 374
You came from heaven to earth 206
You laid aside your majesty 375
You're alive 192
Your love's greater 376
Your mercy flows 377
You shall go out with joy 378

CHANTS

A Blessing 394
Adoramus te, Domine 379
Adoramus te, Domine Deus 380
Bless the Lord, my soul 381
Calm me, Lord 382
Come, light of our hearts 405
Confitemini Domino 383
Eat this bread 384
Exaudi nos, Domine 385
Holy God, we place ourselves 386
In the Lord I'll be ever thankful 387
In the Lord is my joy 388
Jesus, remember me 389
Kindle a flame 390
Laudate Dominum 391
Lord of creation 392
Magnificat 393
May the Lord bless you 394
Nada te turbe 395
Nothing can trouble 395
O Lord, hear my prayer 396
O Lord, my heart is not proud 397
Sanctum nomen Domini 398
Silent, surrendered 399
Sing Praise 391
Stay with me 400
Surrexit Christus 401
The Lord is my light (Taizé) 402
The Lord is my light (Rizza) 403
Ubi caritas 404
Veni, lumen cordium 405
Veni, Sancte Spiritus 406
Wait for the Lord 407
You are the centre 408

MUSIC FOR THE EUCHARIST

All hail the power of Jesus' name 417
Ash Grove Gloria 414
Clap Hands Gloria 412
Gloria (Anderson) 412
Gloria 3 411
Glory to God 413
Holy, most holy, all holy the Lord 415
Kyrie 1 409
Lord, have mercy (Filitz) 410
O Lamb of God 416
Peruvian Gloria 413
Sing glory to God 414
Slane Sanctus 415

ADDITIONAL TUNES

At the name of Jesus 418
Breathe on me, Breath of God 419
Brightest and best 420
Come, risen Lord 421
Crown him with many crowns 422
Firmly I believe and truly 423
Hail the day that sees him rise 424
I heard the voice of Jesus say 425
Just as I am, without one plea 426
King of glory, King of peace 427
Lead, kindly light 428
Lead us, heavenly Father, lead us 429
Lord, enthroned in heavenly splendour 430
Now thank we all our God 431
O Jesus, I have promised 432
O perfect love 433
Rock of ages 434
Soldiers of Christ, arise 435
Thee we adore, O hidden Saviour, thee 436
The King of love my shepherd is 437
The Lord's my shepherd 438
We pray thee, heavenly Father 439
When I survey the wondrous cross 440